MyEngineeringLab™

Right now, in your course, there are young men and women whose engineering achievements could revolutionize, improve, and sustain future generations.

Don't Let Them Get Away.

Thinking Like an Engineer, 2nd edition, together with MyEngineeringLab, is a complete solution for providing an engaging in-class experience that will inspire your students to stay in engineering, while also giving them the practice and scaffolding they need to keep up and be successful in the course.

Learn more at **www.myengineeringlab.com**

Elizabeth A. Stephan • David R. Bowman •
William J. Park • Benjamin L. Sill • Matthew W. Ohland

Thinking Like an Engineer: An Active Learning Approach

Custom Edition for Michigan State University

Taken from:
Thinking Like an Engineer: An Active Learning Approach, Second Edition
by Elizabeth A. Stephan, David R. Bowman, William J. Park,
Benjamin L. Sill, Matthew W. Ohland

Cover Image: Courtesy of Photodisc/Getty Images.

Taken from:

Thinking Like an Engineer: An Active Learning Approach, Second Edition
by Elizabeth A. Stephan, David R. Bowman, William J. Park, Benjamin L. Sill, Matthew W. Ohland
Copyright © 2013, 2011 by Pearson Education, Inc.
Upper Saddle River, New Jersey 07458

This special edition published in cooperation with Pearson Learning Solutions.

Pearson Learning Solutions, 501 Boylston Street, Suite 900, Boston, MA 02116
A Pearson Education Company
www.pearsoned.com

Printed in the United States of America

5 6 7 8 9 10 V092 16 15 14 13 12

000200010271676207

SR

PEARSON   ISBN 10: 1-256-80367-7
           ISBN 13: 978-1-256-80367-6

CONTENTS

PREFACE

At our university, all students who wish to major in engineering begin in the General Engineering Program, and after completing a core set of classes, they can declare a specific engineering major. Within this core set of classes, students are required to take math, physics, chemistry, and a two-semester engineering sequence. Over the past 12 years, our courses have evolved to address not only the changing qualities of our students, but also the changing needs of our customers. The material taught in our courses is the foundation upon which the upper level courses depend for the skills necessary to master more advanced material. It was for these freshman courses that this text was created.

We didn't set out to write a textbook: we simply set out to find a better way to teach our students. Our philosophy was to help students move from a mode of learning, where everything was neatly presented as lecture and handouts where the instructor was looking for the "right" answer, to a mode of learning driven by self-guided inquiry. We wanted students to advance beyond "plug-and-chug" and memorization of problem-solving methods—to ask themselves if their approaches and answers make sense in the physical world. We couldn't settle on any textbooks we liked without patching materials together—one chapter from this text, four chapters from another—so we wrote our own notes. Through them, we tried to convey that engineering isn't always about having the answer—sometimes it's about asking the right questions, and we want students to learn how to ask those sorts of questions. Real-world problems rarely come with all of the information required for their solutions. Problems presented to engineers typically can't be solved by looking at how someone else solved the exact same problem. Part of the fun of engineering is that every problem presents a unique challenge and requires a unique solution. Engineering is also about arriving at an answer and being able to justify the "why" behind your choice, and equally important, the "why not" of the other choices.

We realized quickly, however, that some students are not able to learn without sufficient scaffolding. Structure and flexibility must be managed carefully. Too much structure results in rigidity and unnecessary uniformity of solutions. On the other hand, too much flexibility provides insufficient guidance, and students flounder down many blind alleys, thus making it more difficult to acquire new knowledge. The tension between these two must be managed constantly. We are a large public institution, and our student body is very diverse. Our hope is to provide each student with the amount of scaffolding they need to be successful. Some students will require more background work than others. Some students will need to work five problems, and others may need to work 50. We talk a great deal to our students about how each learner is unique. Some students need to listen to a lecture; some need to read the text over three times, and others just need to try a skill and make mistakes to discover what they still don't understand. We have tried to provide enough variety for each type of learner throughout.

Over the years, we have made difficult decisions on exactly what topics, and how much of each topic, to teach. We have refined our current text to focus on mastering four areas, each of which is introduced below.

PART 1: ENGINEERING ESSENTIALS

There are three threads that bind the first six chapters in Engineering Essentials together. The first is expressed in the part title: all are essential for a successful career in engineering. The second is communications. Part 1 concludes with an introduction to a problem-solving methodology.

First, as an aspiring engineer, it is important that students attempt to verify that engineering is not only a career that suits their abilities but also one in which they will find personal reward and satisfaction.

Second, practicing engineers often make decisions that will affect not only the lives of people but also the viability of the planetary ecosystem that affects all life on Earth. Without a firm grounding in making decisions based on ethical principles, there is an increased probability that undesirable or even disastrous consequences may occur.

Third, most engineering projects are too large for one individual to accomplish alone; thus, practicing engineers must learn to function effectively as a team, putting aside their personal differences and combining their unique talents, perspectives, and ideas to achieve the goal.

Finally, communications bind it all together. Communication, whether written, graphical, or spoken, is essential to success in engineering.

This part ends off where all good problem solving should begin—with estimation and a methodology. It's always best to have a good guess at any problem before trying to solve it more precisely. SOLVEM provides a framework for solving problems that encourages creative observation as well as methodological rigor.

PART 2: UBIQUITOUS UNITS

The world can be described using relatively few dimensions. We need to know what these are and how to use them to analyze engineering situations. Dimensions, however, are worthless in allowing engineers to find the numeric solution to a problem. Understanding units is essential to determine the correct numeric answers to problems. Different disciplines use different units to describe phenomena (particularly with respect to the properties of materials such as viscosity, thermal conductivity, density and so on). Engineers must know how to convert from one unit system to another. Knowledge of dimensions allows engineers to improve their problem-solving abilities by revealing the interplay of various parameters.

PART 3: SCRUPULOUS WORKSHEETS

When choosing an analysis tool to teach students, our first pick is Excel™. Students enter college with varying levels of experience with Excel. To allow students who are novice users to learn the basics without hindering more advanced users, we have placed the basics of Excel in the Appendix material, which is available online. To help students determine if they need to review the Appendix material, an activity has been included in the introductions to Chapter 10 (Worksheets), Chapter 11 (Graphing), and Chapter 12 (Trendlines) to direct students to Appendices B, C, and D, respectively.

Once students have mastered the basics, each chapter in this part provides a deeper usage of Excel in each category. Some of this material extends beyond a simple introduction to Excel, and often, we teach the material in this unit by jumping around, covering half of each chapter in the first semester, and the rest of the material in the second semester course.

Chapter 12 introduces students to the idea of similarities among the disciplines, and how understanding a theory in one application can often aid in understanding a similar theory in a different application. We also emphasize the understanding of models (trendlines) as possessing physical meaning. Chapter 13 discusses a process for determining a mathematical model when presented with experimental data and some advanced material on dealing with limitations of Excel.

Univariate statistics and statistical process control wrap up this part of the book by providing a way for engineering students to describe both distributions and trends.

PART 4: PUNCTILIOUS PROGRAMMING

Part 4 (Punctilious Programming) covers a variety of topics common to any introductory programming textbook. In contrast to a traditional programming textbook, this part approaches each topic from the perspective of how each can be used in unison with the others as a powerful engineering problem-solving tool. The topics presented in Part 4 are introduced as if the student has no prior programming ability and are continually reiterated throughout the remaining chapters.

For this textbook we chose MATLAB™ as the programming language because it is commonly used in many engineering curricula. The topics covered provide a solid foundation of how computers can be used as a tool for problem solving and provide enough scaffolding for transfer of programming knowledge into other languages commonly used by engineers (such as C/C++/Java).

THE "OTHER" STUFF WE'VE INCLUDED...

Throughout the book, we have included sections on surviving engineering, time management, goal setting, and study skills. We did not group them into a single chapter, but have scattered them throughout the part introductions to assist students on a topic when they are most likely to need it. For example, we find students are much more open to discuss time management in the middle of the semester rather than the beginning.

In addition, we have called upon many practicing and aspiring engineers to help us explain the "why" and "what" behind engineering. They offer their "Wise Words" throughout this text. We have included our own set of "Wise Words" as the introduction to each topic here as a glimpse of what inspired us to include certain topics.

NEW TO THIS EDITION

The 2nd edition of *Thinking Like an Engineer: An Active Learning Approach* (TLAE) contains new material and revisions based off of the comments from faculty teaching with our textbook, the recommendations of the reviewers of our textbook, and most importantly, the feedback from our students. We have added approximately 30% new questions and six projects that intend to engage students to create meaningful learning experiences. In addition, we have added new material that reflects the constant changing face of engineering education because many of our upperclassman teaching assistants frequently comment to us "I wish I had ___ when I took this class."

New to This Edition, by chapter:

- Chapter 1: Everyday Engineering

  - New section on Engineering Grand Challenges.

- Chapter 2: Ethics

  - New sections on Plagiarism and Social Responsibility.

- Chapter 3: Design and Teamwork

  - New section on Sustainability.
  - Improved section on Teamwork by linking to CATME team evaluation system.

- Chapter 5: Estimation

  - New sections on Estimation by Analogy, Estimation by Aggregation, Establishing Upper and Lower Bounds, and Estimation Using Modeling.

- Chapter 11: Graphical Solutions

  - Combined material from Chapter 7: Graphing Guidelines in TLAE 1e.

- Chapter 14: Statistics

  - Combined material from Chapters 9 and 14 in TLAE 1e to make a single unified chapter on Statistics.

- Chapter 15: Algorithms

  - Selected material from Chapter 17 in TLAE 1e.
  - New material on algorithm variables, user interaction, calculations and conversions, referencing other algorithms (or functions), error checking and prevention, different types of errors to look for in algorithms, iteration, and testing algorithms.

- Chapter 16: Programs and Functions

  - Selected material from Chapter 17 in TLAE 1e. New separate section on programming basics.
  - New material on efficient creation of matrices and advanced matrix addressing techniques.

- Chapter 17: Input/Output in MATLAB

  - New material on creating error and warning messages.
  - New examples on creating proper plots in MATLAB using advanced graphing properties.
  - New section on use of POLYFIT for adding trendlines to graphs.

- Chapter 18: Logic and Conditionals
  - New sections on Applications of Loops: Cell Arrays and Cell Matrices, Applications of Loops: Excel I/O, and Applications of Loops: Graphical User Interfaces.
- Back materials:
  - New section, Umbrella Projects added to the end of the textbook.
  - New quick reference pages: MATLAB special characters and MATLAB graphing properties.
- Online Appendix Materials
  - New material in Appendix A: Interpolation (previously Chapter 8 in TLAE 1e). www.pearsonhighered.com/TLAE

HOW TO USE

As we have alluded to previously, this text contains many different types of instruction to address different types of learners. There are two main components to this text: hard copy and online.

In the hardcopy, the text is presented topically rather than sequentially, but hopefully with enough autonomy for each piece to stand alone. For example, we routinely discuss only part of the Excel material in our first semester course, and leave the rest to the second semester. We hope this will give you the flexibility to choose how deeply into any given topic you wish to dive, depending on the time you have, the starting abilities of your students, and the outcomes of your course. More information about topic sequence options can be found in the instructor's manual.

Within the text, there are several checkpoints for students to see if they understand the material. Within the reading are **Comprehension Checks**, with the answers provided in the back of the book. Our motivation for including Comprehension Checks within the text rather than include them as end of part questions is to maintain the active spirit of the classroom within the reading, allowing the students to self-evaluate their understanding of the material in preparation for class—to enable students to be self-directed learners, we must encourage them to self-evaluate regularly. At the end of each chapter, **In-Class Activities** are given to reinforce the material in each chapter. In-Class Activities exist to stimulate active conversation within pairs and groups of students working through the material. We generally keep the focus on student effort, and ask them to keep working the problem until they arrive at the right answer. This provides them with a set of worked out problems, using their own logic, before they are asked to tackle more difficult problems. The **Review** sections provide additional questions, often combining skills in the current chapter with previous concepts to help students climb to the next level of understanding. By providing these three types of practice, students are encouraged to reflect on their understanding in preparing for class, during class, and at the end of each chapter as they prepare to transfer their knowledge to other areas. Finally at the end of the text, we have provided a series of **Umbrella Projects** to allow students to apply skills that they have mastered to larger-scope problems. We have found the use of these problems extremely helpful in providing context for the skills that they learn throughout a unit.

Understanding that every student learns differently, we have included several media components in addition to traditional text. Each section within each chapter has an accompanying set of **video lecture slides** 📖. Within these slides, the examples presented are unique from those in the text to provide another set of sample solutions. The slides are presented with **voiceover**, which has allowed us to move away from traditional in-class lecture. We expect the students to listen to the slides outside of class, and then in class we typically spend time working problems, reviewing assigned problems, and providing **"wrap-up" lectures**, which are mini-versions of the full lectures to summarize what they should have gotten from the assignment. We expect the students to come to class with questions from the reading and lecture that we can then help clarify. We find with this method, the students pay more attention, as the terms and problems are already familiar to them, and they are more able to verbalize what they don't know. Furthermore, they can always go back and listen to the lectures again to reinforce their knowledge as many times as they need.

Some sections of this text are difficult to lecture, and students will learn this material best by **working through examples**. This is especially true with Excel and MATLAB, so you will notice that many of the lectures in these sections are shorter than previous material. The examples are scripted the first time a skill is presented, and students are expected to have their laptop open and work through the examples (not just read them). When students ask us questions in this section, we often start the answer by asking them to "show us your work from Chapter XX." If the student has not actually worked the examples in that chapter, we tell them to do so first; often, this will answer their questions.

After the first few basic problems, in many cases where we are discussing more advanced skills than data entry, we have **provided starting worksheets and code** 📖 in the online version by "hanging" the worksheets within the online text. Students can access the starting data through the online copy of the book. In some cases, though, it is difficult to explain a skill on paper, or even with slides, so for these instances we have included **videos** 📖.

Finally, for the communication section, we have provided **templates** 📄 📖 for several types of reports and presentations. These can also be accessed in the Pearson eText version, available with adoption of MyEngineeringLab™. Visit www.pearsonhighered.com/TLAE for more information.

MyEngineeringLab™

Thinking Like an Engineer, 2nd edition, together with MyEngineeringLab provides an engaging in-class experience that will inspire your students to stay in engineering, while also giving them the practice and scaffolding they need to keep up and be successful in the course. It's a complete digital solution featuring:

- A Customized Study Plan for each student with remediation activities provides an opportunity for self paced learning for students at all different levels of preparedness.
- Automatically graded Homework Review Problems from the book and Self Study Quizzes give immediate feedback to the student and provide comprehensive gradebook tracking for instructors.
- Interactive Tutorials with additional algorithmically generated exercises provide opportunity for point-of-use help and for more practice.
- "Show My Work" feature allows instructors to see the entire solution, not only the graded answer.
- Learning Objectives mapped to ABET outcomes provide comprehensive reporting tools.
- Available with or without the full eText.

If adopted, access to MyEngineeringLab can be bundled with the book or purchased separately. For a fully digital offering, learn more at www.myengineeringlab.com or www.pearsonhighered.com/TLAE.

ADDITIONAL RESOURCES FOR INSTRUCTORS

Instructor's Manual—Available to all adopters, this provides a complete set of solutions for all activities and review exercises. For the In-Class Activities, suggested guided inquiry questions along with time frame guidelines are included. Suggested content sequencing and descriptions of how to couple assignments to the umbrella projects are also provided.

PowerPoints—A complete set of lecture PowerPoint slides, available with voiceover or as standard slides, make course planning as easy as possible.

Sample Exams—Available to all adopters, these will assist in creating tests and quizzes for student assessment.

MyEngineeringLab—Provides web-based assessment, tutorial, homework and course management. www.myengineeringlab.com

All requests for instructor resources are verified against our customer database and/or through contacting the requestor's institution. Contact your local Pearson/Prentice Hall representative for additional information.

WHAT DOES THINKING LIKE AN ENGINEER MEAN?

We are often asked about the title of the book. We thought we'd take a minute and explain what this means, to each of us. Our responses are included in alphabetical order.

For me, thinking like an engineer is about creatively finding a solution to some problem. In my pre-college days, I was very excited about music. I began my musical pursuits by learning the fundamentals of music theory by playing in middle school band and eventually worked my way into different bands in high school (orchestra, marching and, jazz band) and branching off into teaching myself how to play guitar. I love playing and listening to music because it gives me an outlet to create and discover art. I pursued engineering for the same reason; as an engineer, you work in a field that creates or improves designs or processes. For me, thinking like an engineer is exactly like thinking like a musician—through my fundamentals, I'm able to be creative, yet methodical, in my solutions to problems.

D. Bowman, Computer Engineer

Thinking like an engineer is about solving problems with whatever resources are most available—or fixing something that has broken with materials that are just lying around. Sometimes, it's about thinking ahead and realizing what's going to happen before something breaks or someone gets hurt—particularly in thinking about what it means to fail safe—to design how something will fail when it fails. Thinking like an engineer is figuring out how to communicate technical issues in a way that anyone can understand. It's about developing an instinct to protect the public trust—an integrity that emerges automatically.

M. Ohland, Civil Engineer

To me, understanding the way things work is the foundation on which all engineering is based. Although most engineers focus on technical topics related to their specific discipline, this understanding is not restricted to any specific field, but applies to everything! One never knows when some seemingly random bit of knowledge, or some pattern discerned in a completely disparate field of inquiry, may prove critical in solving an engineering problem. Whether the field of investigation is Fourier analysis, orbital mechanics, Hebert boxes, personality types, the Chinese language, the life cycle of mycetozoans, or the evolution of the music of Western civilization, the more you understand about things, the more effective an engineer you can be. Thus, for me, thinking like an engineer is intimately, inextricably, and inexorably intertwined with the Quest for Knowledge. Besides, the world is a truly fascinating place if one bothers to take the time to investigate it.

W. Park, Electrical Engineer

Engineering is a bit like the game of golf. No two shots are ever exactly the same. In engineering, no two problems or designs are ever exactly the same. To be successful, engineers need a bag of clubs (math, chemistry, physics, English, social studies) and then need to have the training to be able to select the right combination of clubs to move from the tee to the green and make a par (or if we are lucky, a birdie). In short, engineers need to be taught to THINK.

B. Sill, Aerospace Engineer

I like to refer to engineering as the color grey. Many students enter engineering because they are "good at math and science." I like to refer to these disciplines as black and white—there is one way to integrate an equation and one way to balance a chemical reaction. Engineering is grey, a blend of math and science that does not necessarily have one clear answer. The answer can change depending on the criteria of the problem. Thinking like an engineer is about training your mind to conduct the methodical process of problem solving. It is examining a problem from many different angles, considering the good, the bad and the ugly in every process or product. It is thinking creatively to discover ways of solving problems, or preventing issues from becoming problems. It's about finding a solution in the grey and presenting it in black and white.

E. Stephan, Chemical Engineer

Lead author note: When writing this preface, I asked each of my co-authors to answer this question. As usual, I got a wide variety of interpretations and answers. This is typical of the way we approach everything we do, except that I usually try and mesh the responses into one voice. In this instance, I let each response remain unique. As you progress throughout this text, you will (hopefully) see glimpses of each of us interwoven with the one voice. We hope that through our uniqueness, we can each reach a different group of students and present a balanced approach to problem solving, and, hopefully, every student can identify with at least one of us.

—Beth Stephan
Clemson University
Clemson, SC

ACKNOWLEDGMENTS

When we set out to formalize our instructional work, we wanted to portray engineering as a reality, not the typical flashy fantasy portrayed by most media forums. We called on many of our professional and personal relationships to help us present engineering in everyday terms. During a lecture to our freshman, Dr. Ed Sutt [PopSci's 2006 Inventor of the Year for the HurriQuake Nail] gave the following advice: ***A good engineer can reach an answer in two calls: the first, to find out who the expert is; the second, to talk to the expert.*** Realizing we are not experts, we have called on many folks to contribute articles. To our experts who contributed articles for this text, we thank: Dr. Lisa Benson, Dr. Neil Burton, Jan Comfort, Jessica (Pelfrey) Creel, Solange Dao, Jason Huggins, Leidy Klotz, and Troy Nunmaker.

To Dr. Lisa Benson, thank you for allowing us to use "Science as Art" for the basis of many photos that we have chosen for this text. To explain "Science as Art": *Sometimes, science and art meet in the middle. For example, when a visual representation of science or technology has an unexpected aesthetic appeal, it becomes a connection for scientists, artists and the general public. In celebration of this connection, Clemson University faculty and students are challenged to share powerful and inspiring visual images produced in laboratories and workspaces for the "Science as Art" exhibit.* For more information, please visit www.scienceasart.org. To the creators of the art, thank you for letting us showcase your work in this text: Martin Beagley, Dr. Caye Drapcho, Eric Fenimore, Dr. Scott Husson, Dr. Jaishankar Kutty, Dr. Kathleen Richardson, and Dr. Ken Webb. A special thanks to Kautex Machines and Chuck Flammer, and to Russ Werneth for getting us the great Hubble teamwork photo.

To the Rutland Institute for Ethics at Clemson University: The four-step procedure outlined in Chapter 2 on Ethics is based on the toolbox approach presented in the Ethics Across the Curriculum Seminar. Our thanks to Dr. Daniel Wueste, Director, and the other Rutlanders (Kelly Smith, Stephen Satris and Charlie Starkey) for their input into this chapter.

To Jonathan Feinberg and all the contributors to the Wordle (http://www.wordle.net) project, thank you for the tools to create for the Wordle images in the introduction sections. We hope our readers enjoy this unique way of presenting information, and are inspired to create their own Wordle!

To our friends and former students who contributed their Wise Words: Tyler Andrews, Corey Balon, Ed Basta, Sergey Belous, Brittany Brubaker, Tim Burns, Ashley Childers, Jeremy Comardelle, Matt Cuica, Jeff Dabling, Christina Darling, Ed D'Avignon, Brian Dieringer, Lauren Edwards, Andrew Flowerday, Stacey Forkner, Victor Gallas Cervo, Lisa Gascoigne, Khadijah Glast, Tad Hardy, Colleen Hill, Tom Hill, Becky Holcomb, Beth Holloway, Selden Houghton, Allison Hu, Ryan Izard, Lindy Johnson, Darryl Jones, Maria Koon, Rob Kriener, Jim Kronberg, Rachel Lanoie, Mai Lauer, Jack Meena, Alan Passman, Mike Peterson, Candace Pringle, Derek Rollend,

Eric Roper, Jake Sadie, Janna Sandel, Ellen Styles, Adam Thompson, Kaycie (Smith) Timmons, Devin Walford, Russ Werneth, and Aynsley Zollinger.

To our fellow faculty members, for providing inspiration, ideas, and helping us find countless mistakes: Dr. Lisa Benson, Dr. Steve Brandon, Dr. Ashley Childers, Dr. Jonathan Maier, John Minor, and Dr. Julie Trenor. You guys are the other half of this team that makes this the best place on earth to work! We could not have done this without you.

To the staff of the GE program, we thank you for your support of us and our students: Kelli Blankenship, Lib Crockett, Chris Porter, and all of our terrific advising staff both past and present. To Chuck Heck, Linda Nilson, Barbara Weaver, and the rest of the Teaching with Technology group for helping us discover better ways to teach, spark our innovation, and create such wonderful classroom environments. To the administration at Clemson, we thank you for your continued support of our program: Associate Dean Dr. Randy Collins, Interim Director Dr. Don Beasley, Dean Dr. Esin Gulari, Provost Dr. Dori Helms, Former Dean Dr. Tom Keinath, and Former Dean Dr. Steve Melshimer. Special thanks to President Jim Barker for his inspirational leadership of staying the course and giving meaning to "One Clemson."

To the thousands of students who used this text in various forms over the years— thanks for your patience, your suggestions, and your criticism. You have each contributed not only to the book, but to our personal inspirations to keep doing what we do.

To all the reviewers who provided such valuable feedback to help us improve. We appreciate the time and energy needed to review this material, and your thoughtful comments have helped push us to become better.

To the great folks at Prentice Hall—this project would not be a reality without all your hard work. To Eric Hakanson, without that chance meeting this project would not have begun! Thanks to Holly Stark for her belief in this project and in us! Thanks to Scott Disanno for keeping us on track and having such a great vision to display our hard work. You make us look great! Thanks to Dan Sandin and his team for the work on the electronic text. Thanks to Tim Galligan and the fabulous Pearson sales team all over the country for promoting our book to other schools and helping us allow so many students to start "Thinking Like Engineers"! A special thanks to Clare Romeo for editing the text—both editions—about a zillion times and putting up with all of our seemingly endless questions! Your patience with us for the second edition has been amazing. We would not have made it through this without all of the Pearson team efforts and encouragement!

FINALLY, ON A PERSONAL NOTE

DRB: Thanks to my parents and sister for supporting my creative endeavors with nothing but encouragement and enthusiasm. To my grandparents, who value science, engineering, and education to be the most important fields of study. To my co-authors, who continue to teach me to think like an engineer. To Dana, you are the glue that keeps me from falling to pieces. Thank you for your support, love, laughter, inspiration, and determination, among many other things. You are entirely too rad. I love you.

MWO: My wife Emily has my love, admiration, and gratitude for all she does, including holding the family together. For my children, who share me with my students—Charlotte, whose "old soul" touches all who take the time to know her; Carson, who is quietly inspiring; and Anders, whose love of life and people endears him to all. I acknowledge my father Theodor, who inspired me to be an educator; my mother Nancy, who helped me understand people; my sister Karen, who lit a pathway in engineering; my brother Erik, who showed me that one doesn't need to be loud to be a leader; and my mother-in-law Nancy Winfrey, who shared the wisdom of a long career. I recognize those who helped me create an engineering education career path: Fred Orthlieb, Civil and Coastal Engineering at the University of Florida, Marc Hoit, Duane Ellifritt, Cliff Hays, Mary Grace Kantowski, and John Lybas, the NSF's SUCCEED Coalition, Tim Anderson, Clemson's College of Engineering and Science and General Engineering, Steve Melsheimer, Ben Sill, and Purdue's School of Engineering Education.

WJP: Choosing only a few folks to include in an acknowledgment is a seriously difficult task, but I have managed to reduce it to five. First, Beth Stephan has been the guiding force behind this project, without whom it would never have come to fruition. In addition, she has shown amazing patience in putting up with my shenanigans and my weird perspectives. Next, although we exist in totally different realities, my parents have always supported me, particularly when I was a newly married, destitute graduate student fresh off the farm. Third, my son Isaac, who has the admirable quality of being willing to confront me with the truth when I am behaving badly, and for this I am grateful. Finally, and certainly most importantly, to Lila, my partner of more than one-third century, I owe a debt beyond anything I could put into words. Although life with her has seldom been easy, her influence has made me a dramatically better person.

BLS: To my amazing family, who always picked up the slack when I was off doing "creative" things, goes all my gratitude. To Anna and Allison, you are wonderful daughters who both endured and "experienced" the development of many "in class, hands on" activities—know that I love you and thank you. To Lois who has always been there with her support and without whining for over 40 years, all my love. Finally, to my co-authors who have tolerated my eccentricities and occasional tardiness with only minimum grumbling, you make great teammates.

EAS: To my co-authors, for tolerating all my strange demands, my sleep-deprived ravings and the occasional "I need this now" hysteria—and it has gotten worse with the second edition—you guys are the best! I am beginning to understand that it does take a village, so to all those "villagers" who care for my family while this project consumes my every waking minute, I am eternally indebted. To my mom, Kay and Denny—thanks for your love and support. To Khadijah, wishes for you to continue to conquer the world! To Brock and Katie, I love you both a bushel and a peck. You are the best kids in the world, and the older you get the more you inspire me to be great at my job. Finally, to Sean . . . for all the times you held it all together, kept things running, and brought me a Diet Coke—I love you more than I can say—and know that even when I forget to say it, I still believe in us. I know this round has been rougher than the first . . . but I think we are finally finding our way. Thanks for continuing to remind me of what really matters most. "Show a little faith, there's magic in the night . . ."

Part 1

ENGINEERING ESSENTIALS

LEARNING OBJECTIVES

The overall learning objectives for this unit include the following:

- Communicate technical information effectively by composing clear and concise oral presentations and written descriptions of experiments and projects.
- Conduct research on ethical issues related to engineering; formulate and justify positions on these issues.
- Demonstrate an ability to design a system, component, or process to meet desired needs.
- Demonstrate an ability to function on multidisciplinary teams.
- Identify process variability and measurement uncertainty associated with an experimental procedure, and interpret the validity of experimental results.
- Use "practical" skills, such as visualizing common units and conducting simple measurements, calculations, and comparisons to make estimations.

As the reader of this text, you are no doubt in a situation where you have an idea you want to be an engineer. Someone or something put into your head this crazy notion—that you might have a happy and successful life working in the engineering profession. Maybe you are good at math or science, or you want a job where creativity is as important as technical skill. Maybe someone you admire works as an engineer. Maybe you are looking for a career that will challenge you intellectually, or maybe you like to solve problems.

You may recognize yourself in one of these statements from practicing engineers on why they chose to pursue an engineering degree.

"The National Academy of Engineering (NAE) is an independent, non-profit institution that serves as an adviser to government and the public on issues in engineering and technology. Its members consist of the nation's premier engineers, who are elected by their peers for their distinguished achievements. Established in 1964, NAE operates under the congressional charter granted to the National Academy of Sciences." http://www.nae.edu/About.aspx

I chose to pursue engineering because I enjoyed math and science in school, and always had a love for tinkering with electronic and mechanical gadgets since I was old enough to hold a screwdriver.

S. Houghton, Computer Engineer

I chose to pursue engineering because I always excelled in science and math and I really enjoy problem solving. I like doing hands-on activities and working on "tangible" projects.

M. Koon, Mechanical Engineer

I wanted to pursue engineering to make some kind of positive and (hopefully) enduring mark on the world.

J. Kronberg, Electrical Engineer

I was good at science and math, and I loved the environment; I didn't realize how much I liked stream and ground water movement until I look at BioSystems Engineering.

C. Darling, Biosystem

My parents instilled a responsibility to our community in us kids. As an engineer, I can serve my community through efficient and responsible construction while still satisfying my need to solve challenging problems.

J. Meena, Civil Engineer

I asked many different majors one common question: "What can I do with this degree?" The engineering department was the only one that could specifically answer my question. The other departments often had broad answers that did not satisfy my need for a secure job upon graduating.

L. Johnson, Civil Engineer

I am a first-generation college student and I wanted to have a strong foundation when I graduated from college.

C. Pringle, Industrial Engineer

Engineering is a highly regarded and often highly compensated profession that many skilled high-school students choose to enter for the challenge, engagement, and ultimately the reward of joining the ranks of the esteemed engineers of the world. But what, exactly, does an engineer do? This is one of the most difficult questions to answer because of the breadth and depth of the engineering field. So, how do the experts define engineering?

The National Academy of Engineering (NAE) says:

"Engineering has been defined in many ways. It is often referred to as the "application of science" because engineers take abstract ideas and build tangible products from them. Another definition is "design under constraint," because to "engineer" a product means to construct it in such a way that it will do exactly what you want it to, without any unexpected consequences."

Accc ng to the Merriam-Webster online dictionary:

gineering is the application of science and mathematics by which the properties f matter and the sources of energy in nature are made useful to people.

re or less, engineering is a broad, hard-to-define field requiring knowledge of sci-ce and mathematics and other fields to turn ideas into reality. The ideas and roblems posed to engineers often do not require a mastery-level knowledge of any particular scientific field, but instead require the ability to put together all of the pieces learned in those fields.

Because engineers solve real-life problems, their ultimate motivation is to work toward making life better for everyone. In "The Heroic Engineer" (*Journal of Engineering Education*, January 1997) by Taft H. Broome (Howard University), and Jeff Peirce (Duke University), those authors claimed:

Engineers who would deem it their professional responsibility to transcend self-interests to help non-experts advance their own interests may well prove indispensable to free societies in the twenty-first century.

Broome and Peirce go on to explain that the traits and behaviors of engineers can be compared to those of a hero. The motivation of any hero is to save someone's life; engineers create products, devices, and methods to help save lives. Heroes intervene to protect from danger; engineers devise procedures, create machines, and improve processes to protect people and the planet from danger. While learning an engineering discipline can be challenging, the everyday engineer does not see it as an obstacle: it is merely an opportunity to be a hero.

Scattered throughout this text, you will find quotes from practicing engineers. As a good engineering team would, we recognize we (the authors) are not experts at all things, and request input and advice when needed. We asked engineers we know who work at "everyday engineering" jobs to reflect on the choices they made in school and during their careers. We hope you benefit from their collective knowledge. When asked for advice to give to an incoming freshman, one gave the following reply, summing up this section better than we ever could have imagined.

[A career in engineering] is rewarding both financially and personally. It's nice to go to work and see some new piece of technology—to be on the cutting edge. It's also a great feeling to know that you are helping improve the lives of other people. Wherever there has been a great discovery, an engineer is to thank. That engineer can be you.

A. Thompson, Electrical Engineer

ENGINEERING IS AN . . . ITCH!

Contributed by: Dr. Lisa Benson, Assistant Professor of Engineering and Science Education, Clemson University

There are a lot of reasons why you are majoring in engineering. Maybe your goal is to impress someone, like your parents, or to defy all those who said you would never make it, or simply to prove to yourself that you have it in you. Maybe your goal is to work with your hands as well as your mind. Maybe you have no idea why you are here,

but you know you like cars. There are about as man
they serve to motivate students to learn. Some goals a

Lots of experts have studied goals and how they a
Not surprisingly, there are as many ideas and theories ab
But most experts agree on the idea that there are mastery

Students who are **mastery oriented** *try to do things we*
their best. They are not driven by external factors like gra
they seek to learn things because they want to really unders
get the correct answer.

Students who are **performance oriented** *seek to earn good grades*
they've worked. They study because they know it will get them som
ship, an above-average grade, or praise from their parents. Since grade
sense of achievement, students who are performance oriented tend to f
and anxious when they earn low grades. They tend to want to memorize
match to solve problems, rather than learn the underlying concepts and m

Most students have been performance oriented throughout high school. In co
will be more successful if you start thinking in terms of mastery. If you seek t
understand what you are learning in your classes, performance (i.e., good grade
follow. But performance (a grade, an award, or praise) is not everything, and it wil
be enough to keep you motivated when projects and coursework are challenging.

There is nothing like the feeling when you finally understand something that you d
not get before. Sometimes it is an "aha!" moment, and sometimes it is a gradual dawning.
The feeling is like an itch you can't scratch—you will want to keep at it once you get it.
When you are motivated to understand and master something, you're taking pride in your
achievement of conquering the material, not just getting a good grade on an exam. And
you are going to keep scratching that itch. Keep "scratching" at the material—working,
practicing, drilling skills if you need to, whatever it takes—to master that . . . itch!

WISE WORDS: WHAT WAS THE HARDEST ADJUSTMENT
FROM HIGH SCHOOL TO COLLEGE?

The biggest adjustment was the overwhelming amount of responsibility that I had to take on. There was no longer anybody there to tell me what to do or when to do it. I had to rely on myself to get everything done. All the things I took for granted when I was at home—not having to do my own laundry, not preparing all of my meals, not having to rely on my alarm clock to wake me up, etc.—quickly became quite apparent to me after coming to college. I had to start managing my time better so that I would have time to get all of those things done.

T. Andrews, CE

For me, the most difficult adjustment from high school to college has been unlearning some of the study habits adopted early on. In high school, you can easily get by one semester at a time and just forget what you "learned" when you move into a new semester or a new chapter of the text. College is just a little bit different. To succeed, you have to really make an effort to keep up with your studies—even the classes you have finished already. If you do not, chances are that a topic mentioned in a prerequisite course is going to reappear in a later class, which requires mastery of the previous material in order to excel.

R. Izard, CpE

The hardest adjustment was learning how to study. I could no longer feel prepared for tests by simply paying attention in class. I had to learn to form study groups and begin studying for tests well in advance. You can't cram for engineering tests.

M. Koon, ME

The hardest adjustment was taking full personal responsibility for everything from school work, to social life, and to finances. Life becomes a lot more focused when you realize that you are paying for your education and that your decisions will greatly impact your future. The key is to manage your time between classes, studying, having fun, and sleeping.

S. Belous, CpE

Studying, networking, talking to my professors about my strengths and weaknesses, taking responsibility for my actions, just the whole growing up into an adult was tough.

C. Pringle, IE

The hardest adjustment I had to make going from high school to college was realizing that I was on my own—and not just for academics, either. I was responsible for making sure I remembered to eat dinner, for not eating candy bars for lunch everyday, for balancing my social life with my studies, for managing my money . . . for everything.

J. Sandel, ME

The hardest adjustment from high school to college was changing my study habits. In high school, teachers coordinated their tests so we wouldn't have several on the same day or even in the same week. I had to learn how to manage my time more efficiently. Moreover, it was difficult to find a balance between both the social and academic aspects of college.

D. Walford, BioE

Since the tests cover more material and have more weight in college, I had to alter my study habits to make myself start studying more than a day in advance. It was overwhelming my first semester because there was always something that I could be studying for or working on.

A. Zollinger, CE

CHAPTER 1
EVERYDAY ENGINEERING

Most students who start off in a technical major know very little about their chosen field. This is particularly true in engineering, which is not generally present in the high-school curriculum. Students commonly choose engineering and science majors because someone suggested them. In this section, we help you ask the right questions about your interests, skills, and abilities; we then show you how to combine the answers with what you learn about engineering and science in order to make the right career decision.

1.1 CHOOSING A CAREER

In today's society, the careers available to you upon your graduation are numerous and diverse. It is often difficult as a young adult to determine exactly what occupation you want to work at for the rest of your life because you have so many options. As you move through the process, there are questions that are appropriate to ask. You cannot make a good decision without accurate information. No one can (or should) make the decision for you: not your relatives, professors, advisors, or friends. Only you know what feels right and what does not. You may not know all the answers to your questions right away. That means you will have to get them by gathering more information from outside resources and through your personal experience. Keep in mind that choosing your major and ultimately your career is a process. You constantly evaluate and reevaluate what you learn and experience. A key component is whether you feel challenged or overwhelmed. True success in a profession is not measured in monetary terms; it is measured in job satisfaction . . . enjoying what you do, doing what you enjoy. As you find the answers, you can choose a major that leads you into a successful career path that you enjoy.

Before you decide, answer the following questions about your tentative major choice. Start thinking about the questions you cannot answer and look for ways or resources to get the information you need. It may take a long time before you know, and that is okay!

- What do I already know about this major?
- What courses will I take to earn a degree in this major?
- Do I have the appropriate academic preparation to complete this major? If not, what will I have to do to acquire it?
- Am I enjoying my courses? Do I feel challenged or stressed?
- What time demands are involved? Am I willing to spend the time it takes to complete this major?
- What kinds of jobs will this major prepare me for? Which sounds most interesting?
- What kinds of skills will I need to do the job I want? Where can I get them?

This process will take time. Once you have the information, you can make a choice. Keep in mind, nothing is set in stone—you can always change your mind!

1.2 CHOOSING ENGINEERING AS A CAREER

In the previous section, we gave several examples of why practicing engineers wanted to pursue a career in engineering. Here are a few more:

- I was always into tinkering with things and I enjoyed working with computers from a young age. Math, science, and physics came very natural to me in high school. For me it was an easy choice.

  J. Comardelle, Computer Engineer

- My initial instinct for a career path was to become an engineer. I was the son of a mechanical engineer, performed well in science and mathematics during primary education, and was always "tinkering" with mechanical assemblies.

  M. Ciuca, Mechanical Engineer

- I chose engineering for a lot of the same reasons that the "typical" entering freshman does—I was good at math and science. I definitely did not know that there were so many types of engineering and to be honest, was a little overwhelmed by the decision I needed to make of what type of engineering was for me.

  L. Edwards, Civil Engineer

- I wasn't really sure what I wanted to do. My parents were not college graduates so there was not a lot of guidance from them, so my high school teachers influenced me a lot. I was taking advanced math and science classes and doing well in them. They suggested that I look into engineering, and I did.

  S. Forkner, Chemical Engineer

- I was a night time/part time student while I worked full time as a metallurgical technician. I was proficient in math and science and fortunate to have a mentor who stressed the need for a bachelor's degree.

  E. Basta, Materials Engineer

- Coming into college, I knew I wanted to pursue a career in medicine after graduation. I also knew that I did not want to major in chemistry, biology, etc. Therefore, bioengineering was a perfect fit. It provides a challenging curriculum while preparing me for medical school at the same time. In addition, if pursuing a career in medicine does not go according to plan, I know that I will also enjoy a career as a bioengineer.

  D. Walford, BioE

Table 1-1 describes the authors' perspective on how various engineering and science disciplines might contribute to different industries or innovations. This table is only an interpretation by a few engineers and does not handle every single possibility of how an engineer might contribute toward innovation. For example, an industrial engineer might be called into work on an energy to share a different perspective on energy efficiency. The broad goal of any engineering discipline is to solve problems, so there is often a need for a different perspective to possibly shed new light toward an innovative solution.

Table 1-1 Sample career paths and possible majors. Shaded boxes indicate a good starting point for further exploration

Careers	Engineering										Science				
	Aerospace	Biomedical	BioSystems	Civil	Chemical	Materials	Electric/computer	Environmental	Industrial	Mechanical	Chemistry	Computer Science	Geology	Mathematics	Physics
GENERAL															
Energy industry				■	■			■		■	■		■		
Machines		■					■		■	■					
Manufacturing					■				■	■					
Materials	■				■	■					■				
Structures	■			■		■				■			■		
Technical sales		■		■	■		■					■			■
SPECIFIC															
Rocket/airplane	■			■						■					
Coastal engineering			■										■		
Computing							■					■		■	
Cryptography												■		■	
Defense	■						■		■		■	■			
Environment								■					■		■
Fiber optics						■							■		
Forensics					■						■				
Groundwater				■				■					■		
Healthcare		■								■	■				
Human factors	■								■			■			
Industrial sensors	■				■		■								
Intelligent systems		■										■		■	
Management	■	■	■	■	■	■	■	■	■	■					
Operations research									■			■		■	
Outdoor work			■					■					■		
Pharmaceutical		■			■						■				
Plastics					■	■				■					
Robotics	■						■			■					
Semiconductors						■	■								■
Telecommunications							■					■			
Transportation				■									■		
Waste management			■	■				■							

MORE WISE WORDS: HOW DID YOU CHOOSE A MAJOR IN COLLEGE?

Since I knew I wanted to design computers, I had a choice between electrical and computer engineering. I chose computer engineering, so I could learn about both the hardware and software. It was my interests in computers and my high school teachers that were the biggest influence in my decision.

E. D'Avignon, CpE

My first choice in majors was Mechanical Engineering. I changed majors after taking a drafting class in which I did well enough to get a job teaching the lab portion, but I did not enjoy the work. After changing to Electrical and Computer Engineering, I took a Statics and Dynamics course as part of my required coursework and that further confirmed my move as I struggled with that material.

A. Flowerday, EE

Some people come into college, knowing exactly what they want their major and career to be. I, on the other hand, was not one of those people. I realized that I had a wide spectrum of interests, and college allows you to explore all those options. I wanted a major that was innovative and would literally change the future of how we live. After looking through what I loved and wanted to do, my choice was Computer Engineering.

S. Belous, CpE

1.3 NAE GRAND CHALLENGES FOR ENGINEERING

History (and prehistory) is replete with examples of technological innovations that forever changed the course of human society: the mastery of fire, the development of agriculture, the wheel, metallurgy, mathematics of many flavors, the printing press, the harnessing of electricity, powered flight, nuclear power, and many others. The NAE has established a list of 14 challenges for the twenty-first century, each of which has the potential to transform the way we live, work, and play. Your interest in one or more of the Grand Challenges for Engineering may help you select your engineering major. For more information, visit the NAE website at http://www.engineeringchallenges.org/. In case this address changes after we go to press, you can also type "NAE Grand Challenges for Engineering" into your favorite search engine.

A burgeoning planetary population and the technological advances of the last century are exacerbating many current problems as well as engendering a variety of new ones, for example:

- Relatively inexpensive and rapid global travel make it possible for diseases to quickly span the globe whereas a century ago, they could spread, but much more slowly.
- The reliance of the developed world on computers and the Internet makes the fabric of commerce and government vulnerable to cyber terrorism.
- Increased demand for limited resources not only drives up prices for those commodities, but also fosters strain among the nations competing for them.

These same factors can also be a force for positive change in the world.

- Relatively inexpensive and rapid global travel allows even people of modest means to experience different cultures and hopefully promote a more tolerant attitude toward those who live by different sets of social norms.

■ Modern communications systems—cell phones, the Internet, etc.—make it essentially impossible for a government to control the flow of information to isolate the members of a population or to isolate that population from the political realities in other parts of the world. An excellent example was the rapid spread of rebellion in the Middle East and Africa in early 2011 against autocratic leaders who had been in power for decades.

■ Increased demand for, and rising prices of limited resources is driving increased innovation in alternatives, particularly in meeting the world's energy needs.

As should be obvious from these few examples, technology not only solves problems, but also creates them. A significant portion of the difficulty in the challenges put forth by the NAE to solve critical problems in the world lies in finding solutions that do not create other problems. Let us consider a couple of the stated challenges in a little more detail. You probably already have some familiarity with several of them, such as "make solar energy economical," "provide energy from fusion," "secure cyberspace," and "enhance virtual reality," so we will begin with one of the NAE Grand Challenges for Engineering that is perhaps less well known.

The Nitrogen Cycle

Nitrogen is an element required for all known forms of life, being part of every one of the 20 amino acids that are combined in various ways to form proteins, all five bases used to construct RNA and DNA, and numerous other common biological molecules such as chlorophyll and hemoglobin. Fortunately, the supply of nitrogen is—for all practical purposes—inexhaustible, constituting over 75% of the Earth's atmosphere. However, nitrogen is mostly in the molecular form N_2, which is chemically unavailable for uptake in biological systems since the two nitrogen atoms are held together by a very strong triple bond.

For atmospheric nitrogen to be available to biological organisms, it must be converted, or "fixed," by the addition of hydrogen, into ammonia, NH_3, that may then be used directly or converted by other microorganisms into other reactive nitrogen compounds for uptake by microorganisms and plants. The term nitrogen fixation includes conversion of N_2 into both ammonia and these other reactive compounds, such as the many oxides of nitrogen. Eventually the cycle is completed when these more readily available forms of nitrogen are converted back to N_2 by microorganisms, a process called denitrification.

Prior to the development of human technology, essentially all nitrogen fixation was performed by bacteria possessing an enzyme capable of splitting N_2 and adding hydrogen to form ammonia, although small amounts of fixed nitrogen are produced by lightning and other high-energy processes. In the early twentieth century, a process called the Haber-Bosch process was developed that would allow conversion of atmospheric nitrogen into ammonia and related compounds on an industrial scale. Today, slightly more than a century later, approximately one-third of all fixed nitrogen is produced using this process.

The ready availability of relatively inexpensive nitrogen fertilizers has revolutionized agriculture, allowing people to increase yields dramatically and to grow crops on previously unproductive lands. However, the widespread use of synthetic nitrogen has caused numerous problems, including water pollution, air pollution, numerous human health problems, and disruption of marine and terrestrial ecosystems to the extent that entire populations of some organisms have died off.

Deliberate nitrogen fixation is only one part of the nitrogen cycle problem, however. Many human activities, especially those involving the combustion of fossil fuels, pump huge quantities of various nitrogen compounds into the atmosphere. Nitrous oxide (N_2O), also of some notoriety as the dissociative anesthetic commonly known as "laughing gas," is particularly problematic since it is about 200 times more effective than carbon dioxide as a greenhouse gas, and persists in the atmosphere for over a century.

Altogether, human-caused conversion of nitrogen into more reactive forms now accounts for about half of all nitrogen fixation, meaning that there is twice as much nitrogen fixed today than there was a little more than a century ago. However, we have done little to augment the natural denitrification process, so the deleterious effects of excessive fixed nitrogen continue to increase. We have overwhelmed the natural nitrogen cycle. If we are to continue along this path, we must learn to manage the use of these products more efficiently and plan strategies for denitrification to bring the cycle back into balance.

Reverse-Engineering the Brain

The development of true artificial intelligence (AI) holds possibly the most overall potential for positive change in the human race as well as the most horrendous possible negative effects. This is reflected in science fiction, where the concept of thinking machines is a common plot device, ranging from Isaac Asimov's benevolent R. Daneel Olivaw to the malevolent Skynet in the Terminator movies. If history is any guide, however, the potential for disastrous consequences seldom deters technological advances, so let us consider what is involved in the development of AI.

Although great strides have been made in creating machines that seem to possess "intelligence," almost all such systems that have come to the public notice either rely on brute-force calculations, such as the chess-playing computer, Deep Blue, that defeated world champion Garry Kasparov in 1997, or reliance on incredibly fast access to massive databases, such as the Jeopardy-playing computer, Watson, that defeated both the highest money winner, Brad Rutter, and the record holder for longest winning streak, Ken Jennings, in 2011. Perhaps needless to say, these are oversimplifications, and there are many more aspects to both of these systems. However, one would be hard-pressed to argue that these computers are truly intelligent—that they are self-aware and contain the unexplainable spark of creativity, which is the hallmark of humans, and arguably other highly intelligent creatures on Earth.

Today's robots perform many routine tasks, from welding and painting vehicles to vacuuming our homes and cutting our grass. However, all of these systems are programmed to perform within certain restrictions and have serious limitations when confronted with unexpected situations. For example, if your school utilized vacuuming robots to clean the floors in the classrooms, it would probably be unable to handle the situation effectively if someone became nauseous and regurgitated on the carpet. If we could endow such robots with more human-like intelligence, the range of tasks that they could successfully accomplish would increase by orders of magnitude, thus increasing their utility tremendously.

To date, we have almost exclusively attempted merely to construct intelligent systems that mimic behavior and thought, not design systems that actually store and process information in a manner analogous to that of a biologically based computer (a brain). The human brain utilizes a network of interconnections between specialized subsections that makes even the most advanced computers look like a set of children's building blocks. Although some understanding has been gained, the means of encoding information and its transfer in the brain is almost completely a mystery.

Gaining even a basic understanding of brain function might allow us to develop prosthetic limbs that actually function as well as the originals, restore sight to the blind, repair brain damage, or even enhance human intelligence.

1.4 CHOOSING A SPECIFIC ENGINEERING FIELD

The following paragraphs briefly introduce several different types of engineering majors. By no means is this list completely inclusive.

Bioengineering or Biomedical Engineering

Bioengineering (BioE) and biomedical engineering (BME) apply engineering principles to the understanding and solution of medical problems. Bioengineers are involved in research and development in all areas of medicine, from investigating the physiological behavior of single cells to designing implants for the replacement of diseased or traumatized body tissues. Bioengineers design new instruments, devices, and software, assemble knowledge from many scientific sources to develop new procedures, and conduct research to solve medical problems.

Typical bioengineers work in such areas as artificial organs, automated patient monitoring, blood chemistry sensors, advanced therapeutic and surgical devices, clinical laboratory design, medical imaging systems, biomaterials, and sports medicine.

Bioengineers are employed in universities, industry, hospitals, research facilities, and government. In industry, they may be part of a team serving as a liaison between engineers and clinicians. In hospitals, they select appropriate equipment and supervise equipment performance, testing, and maintenance. In government agencies, they are involved in safety standards and testing.

Biosystems Engineering

Biosystems engineering (BE) is the field of engineering most closely allied with advances in biology. BE emphasizes two main areas: (1) bioprocess engineering, with its basis in microbiology, and (2) ecological engineering, with its basis in ecology. The field focuses on the sustainable production of biorefinery compounds (biofuels, bioactive molecules, and biomaterials) using metabolic pathways found in nature and green processing technologies. Further, BE encompasses the design of sustainable communities utilizing low-impact development strategies (bioretention basins, rainwater harvesting) for stormwater retention and treatment—and ecologically sound food and energy-crop production. Scientific emphasis is shifting toward the biosciences. Biosystems engineers apply engineering design and analysis to biological systems and incorporate fundamental biological principles to engineering designs to achieve ecological balance.

Here are some activities of biosystems engineers:

- Design bioprocesses and systems for biofuels (biodiesel, hydrogen, ethanol), biopharmaceutical, bioplastics, and food processing industries
- Develop ecological designs (permeable pavement, bioswales, green infrastructure) to integrate water management into the landscape
- Integrate biological sustainability concepts into energy, water, and food systems
- Provide engineering expertise for agriculture, food processing, and manufacturing
- Pursue medical or veterinary school or graduate school in the fields of BE, BME, or ecological engineering

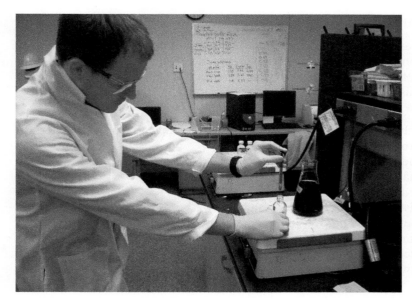

My research is part of a Water Research Foundation project, which is investigating the formation of emerging disinfection byproducts (DBPs) in drinking water treatment.

DBPs are undesirable, toxic compounds that are formed when water is chlorinated. I am investigating the effects of pH, bromide and iodide concentrations, and preoxidants on the formation of a specific family of DBPs.

D. Jones, BE

I am a project manager for new product development.

I oversee and coordinate the various activities that need to be completed in order to get a new product approved and manufactured, and ultimately in the hands of our consumers.

S. Forkner, ChE

Chemical Engineering

Chemical engineering (ChE) incorporates strong emphasis on three sciences: chemistry, physics, and mathematics. Chemical engineers are involved in the research and development, manufacture, sales, and use of chemicals, pharmaceuticals, electronic components, food and consumer goods, petroleum products, synthetic fibers and films, pulp and paper, and many other products. They work on environmental remediation and pollution prevention, as well as in medical and health-related fields. Chemical engineers:

- Conduct research and develop new products
- Develop and design new manufacturing processes
- Earn additional degrees to practice medicine or patent, environmental, or corporate law
- Sell and provide technical support for sophisticated chemical products to customers
- Solve environmental problems; work in biotechnology
- Troubleshoot and solve problems in chemical manufacturing facilities

My team is responsible for implementing the engineered design in the field.

We install, tune, test, and accept into operations all of the electronics that allow customers to use our state of the art fiber optic network to run voice, video, and data for their residential needs.

L. Gascoigne, CE

Civil Engineering

CE involves the planning, design, construction, maintenance, and operation of facilities and systems to control and improve the environment for modern civilizations. This includes projects of major importance such as bridges, transportation systems, buildings, ports, water distribution systems, and disaster planning.

Here are just a few of many opportunities available for civil engineers:

- Design and analyze structures ranging from small buildings to skyscrapers to offshore oil platforms
- Design dams and building foundations
- Develop new materials for pavements, buildings, and bridges
- Design improved transportation systems
- Design water distribution and removal systems
- Develop new methods to improve safety, reduce cost, speed construction, and reduce environmental impact
- Provide construction and project management services for large engineered projects throughout the world

I am responsible for assisting in the management of commercial and healthcare projects for Brasfield & Gorrie. Working closely with the owner and architect, I maintain open lines of communication and aim to provide exceptional service to the entire project team from the preconstruction phase of the project through construction. I assist in establishing and monitoring procedures for controlling the cost, schedule, and quality of the work in accordance with the construction contract.

L. Edwards, CE

Computer Engineering

Computer engineering (CpE) spans the fields of computer science and engineering, giving a balanced view of hardware, software, hardware-software trade-offs, and basic modeling techniques that represent the computing process involving the following technologies:

- Communication system design
- Computer interface design
- Computer networking
- Digital signal processing applications
- Digital system design
- Embedded computer design
- Process instrumentation and control
- Software design

As a Radiation Effects Engineer I test the performance of electronic components in a specific application exposed to different types of radiation. Responsibilities include interfacing with design and system engineers, creating test plans, performing testing and data analysis, and authoring test reports.

A. Passman, EE

I manage global programs that help develop leadership capabilities and skills of our current and future leaders. I am a consultant, a coach, a mentor, and a guide. If leaders are interested in improving how they lead and the impact they have on their employees and on company results, we work with them to identify the best ways for them to continue their development.

A. Hu, EE

Electrical Engineering

Electrical engineering (EE) ranges from the generation and delivery of electrical power to the use of electricity in integrated circuits. The rapid development of technology, based on integrated circuit devices, has enabled the pervasive use of computers in command, control, communication, and computer-aided design. Some systems electrical engineers work on include the following:

- Communication system design
- Control systems—from aircraft to automotive
- Electrical power generation and distribution
- Electromagnetic waves
- Integrated circuit design
- Process instrumentation and control
- Robotic systems design
- Telecommunications

My group supports [a major automotive manufacturer's] decisions pertaining to where to put new plants around the world, what products to build in them, and at what volumes.

In particular, my work involves understanding what the other auto manufacturers are planning for the future (footprint, capacity, technology, processes, etc.), so that information can be used to affect decisions about how to compete around the globe.

M. Peterson, EE

Environmental Engineering

Environmental engineering (EnvE) is an interdisciplinary field of engineering that is focused on cleaning up environmental contamination, as well as designing sustainable approaches to prevent future contamination. Environmental engineers apply concepts from basic sciences (including chemistry, biology, mathematics, and physics) to develop engineered solutions to complex environmental problems.

Environmental engineers design, operate, and manage both engineered and natural systems to protect the public from exposure to environmental contamination and to develop a more sustainable use of our natural resources. These activities include the following:

■ Production of safe, potable drinking water
■ Treatment of wastewater so that it is safe to discharge to surface water or reuse in applications such as landscape irrigation
■ Treatment of air pollutants from mobile (e.g., automobiles) and stationary (e.g., power plants) sources
■ Characterization and remediation of sites contaminated with hazardous wastes (e.g., polychlorinated biphenyls, or PCBs)
■ Disposal of municipal solid wastes
■ Management of radioactive wastes, including characterization of how radioactive materials move through the environment and the risks they pose to human health
■ Evaluation of methods to minimize or prevent waste production and inefficient use of energy by manufacturing facilities
■ Reduce human health risks by tracking contaminants as they move through the environment
■ Design a more sustainable future by understanding our use of resources

With a BS degree in EnvE, students will find employment with consulting engineering firms, government agencies involved in environmental protection, and manufacturing industries.

Industrial Engineering

Industrial engineering (IE) deals with the design and improvement of systems, rather than with the objects and artifacts that other engineers design. A second aspect of IE is the involvement of people in these systems—from the people involved in the design and production to the people who are ultimate end users. A common theme is the testing and evaluation of alternatives that may depend on random events. Industrial engineers use mathematical, physical, social sciences, and engineering combined with the analytical and design methods to design, install, and improve complex systems that provide goods and services to our society. Industrial engineers are called upon to:

■ Analyze and model complex work processes to evaluate potential system improvements
■ Analyze how combinations of people and machines work together
■ Analyze how the surroundings affect the worker, and design to reduce the negative effects of this environment
■ Develop mathematical and computer models of how systems operate and interact
■ Improve production and service processes from the perspectives of quality, productivity, and cost
■ Work on teams with other professionals in manufacturing, service industries, government agencies

My primary job responsibilities include maintaining, upgrading, and designing all the computer systems and IT infrastructure for the Vermont Railroad. I handle all the servers and take care of network equipment. When needed, I also program customized applications and websites for customers or our own internal use. I also serve as a spare conductor and locomotive engineer when business needs demand.

S. Houghton, CpE

As the Business Leader for Central Florida at a major power company, I develop and manage a $42 million budget. I ensure that our engineering project schedule and budget match, and report on variances monthly. I also conduct internal audits and coach employees on Sarbanes-Oxley compliance requirements.

R. Holcomb, IE

Currently I am working on a project to determine patient priorities for evacuations from healthcare facilities during emergencies. The assumption of an evacuation is that there will be enough time to transfer all of the patients, but in the event of limited resources, there may not be enough time to move all of the patients to safety. Further—and depending on the emergency type—it may be an increased risk to transport some patient types. Based on certain objectives, we are developing guidelines to most ethically determine a schedule for choosing patients for emergency evacuations.

A. Childers, IE

Material Science and Engineering

Material science and engineering (MSE) focuses on the properties and production of materials. Nature supplied only 92 naturally occurring elements to serve as building blocks to construct all modern conveniences. A materials engineer works to unlock the relationship between atomic, molecular, and larger-scale structures and the resultant properties. This category includes majors such as ceramic engineering, metallurgical engineering, and polymer science and engineering.

Here is a partial list of products designed and manufactured by MSE:

- Brick, tile, and whitewares research and manufacturing for the home and workplace
- Ceramic spark plugs, oxygen sensors, and catalytic converters that optimize engine performance
- Metal and ceramic materials that enable biomedical implants and prosthetics
- Microwave responsive ceramics that stabilize and filter cellular phone reception
- Nanotechnology, including silver nanoparticles used as antibacterial agents in socks and t-shirts and carbon nanotubes used to reinforce the fork of racing bicycles
- Plastics found in bulletproof vests, replacement heart valves, and high tension wires on bridges

- Superconducting metals that are used in medical imaging devices like magnetic resonance imaging (MRI)
- Ultrapure glass optical fibers that carry telephone conversations and Internet communications

As a Metallurgical Engineer, my duties include

- Consulting firm management/administration
- Failure analysis
- Subcontracted metals testing services
- Metallurgical quality systems design/auditing
- Metallurgical expert in litigation cases
- Materials selection and design consultant, in-process and final inspection and testing services

E. Basta,
Metallurgical Engineer

Mechanical Engineering

I implement technology to protect national assets against adversaries.

J. Dabling, ME

Mechanical engineering (ME) involves areas related to machine design, manufacturing, energy production and control, materials, and transportation. Areas supported by mechanical engineers include:

- Construction
- Energy production and control
- Environmental systems
- Food production
- Management
- Materials processing
- Medicine
- Military service
- Propulsion and transportation systems
- Technical sales

In my job as a management consultant, I address CEO-level management decisions as part of a project team by helping clients identify, analyze, and solve business-related problems. My responsibilities include generating hypotheses, gathering, and analyzing data, conducting benchmarking and best practices assessments, recommending actions, and working with clients to develop implementation plans.

M. Ciuca, ME

As Plant Engineering Manager I report directly to the Plant Manager. My primary responsibilities are managing all the capital investments; providing technical support and expertise to the plant leadership team; and mentoring and developing the plant's engineering staff and technical resources.

J. Huggins, ME

I am a salesman, so at the end of the day I'm looking to grow my market share while trying to protect the market share I already have. I help companies maintain a safe, reliable, and efficient steam and condensate system by utilizing the many products and services that we have to offer. This is mostly done by designing and installing upgrades and improving my customer's existing steam systems.

T. Burns, ME

I am an aerospace engineering manager responsible for developing unique astronaut tools and spacewalk procedures and for testing and training for NASA's Hubble Space Telescope servicing missions. My job ranges from tool and procedure design and development to underwater scuba testing to real-time, on-console support of Space Shuttle missions.

R. Werneth, ME

WISE WORDS: WHAT DID YOU DO YESTERDAY MORNING AT WORK?

I worked on completing a failure analysis report for an industrial client.

E. Basta, CME

I reviewed the results of the overnight simulation runs. There were several failures, so I analyzed the failures and devised fixes for the problems.

E. D'Avignon, CpE

On any given day, my morning might be spent this way: in meetings, at my computer (e-mail, drafting documents/reports), making phone calls, talking to other project members, running a test on the manufacturing lines. Not glamorous, but necessary to solve problems and keep the project moving forward.

S. Forkner, ChE

I continued to design a warehouse/office building on a nuclear expansion project.

T. Hill, CE

Yesterday I designed a spreadsheet to assist in more precisely forecasting monthly expenditures.

R. Holcomb, IE

I attended the Plant Morning Meeting and the Boardmill Leadership Team Meeting, followed by the Plant Budget Meeting. In between meetings I returned e-mails and project-related phone calls. Typically I spend about 50% of my time in meetings. I use the information I receive at these meetings to direct and focus the efforts of the engineering staff.

J. Huggins, ME

Testing some failed prototype biostimulators returned by a trial user, to determine why and how they failed and how to prevent it from happening in coming production versions.

J. Kronberg, EE

Yesterday, I worked on a patent infringement opinion involving agricultural seeding implements, a Chinese patent office response for a component placement and inspection machine used in circuit board manufacturing, and a U.S. patent office response for database navigation software.

M. Lauer, EnvE

In my current position, I spend much of my time reading technical manuals and interface control documents. I attended a meeting detailing lightning protection for the Ares rocket.

E. Styles, EE

1.5   GATHERING INFORMATION

You will need to gather a lot of information in order to answer your questions about engineering or any other major. Many resources are available on your campus and through the Internet.

The Career Center

Most universities have a centralized campus career center. The staff specializes in helping students explore various occupations and make decisions. They offer testing and up-to-date information on many career fields. Professional counselors are available by appointment to assist students with job and major selection decisions.

Career Websites

To learn more about engineering and the various engineering fields, you can find a wealth of information from engineering professional societies. Each engineering field has a professional society dedicated to promoting and disseminating knowledge about that particular discipline. Table 1-2 provides a list of most major engineering fields and the professional society in the United States with which it is associated. In some cases, more than one society is connected with different subdisciplines. Other regions of the world may have their own professional societies.

Perusing the various societies' websites can provide you with information invaluable in helping you decide on a future career. We have not given URLs for the societies, since these sometimes change. To find the current address, simply use an online search engine with the name of the society.

In addition, a few engineering societies are not specific to a discipline, but to their membership;

- National Society of Black Engineers (NSBE)
- Society of Hispanic Professional Engineers (SHPE)
- Society of Women Engineers (SWE)
- Tau Beta Pi, The Engineering Honor Society (TBP).

Most engineering schools have student chapters of the relevant organizations on campus. These organizations provide an excellent opportunity for you to learn more about your chosen discipline or the ones you are considering, and they also help you meet other students with similar interests. Student membership fees are usually nominal, and the benefits of membership far outweigh the small cost.

Active participation in these societies while in school not only gives you valuable information and experience, but also helps you begin networking with professionals in your field and enhances your résumé.

Table 1-2 **Website research starting points**

Society	Abbreviation
American Ceramic Society	ACerS
American Institute of Aeronautics and Astronautics	AIAA
American Institute of Chemical Engineers	AIChE
American Nuclear Society	ANS
American Society of Agricultural and Biological Engineers	ASABE
American Society of Civil Engineers	ASCE
American Society for Engineering Education	ASEE
American Society of Mechanical Engineers	ASME
American Society of Metals International	ASM Int'l.
Association for Computing Machinery	ACM
Audio Engineering Society	AES
Biomedical Engineering Society	BMES
Engineers Without Borders	EWB
Institute of Biological Engineering	IBE
Institute of Electrical and Electronics Engineers	IEEE
Institute of Industrial Engineers	IIE
Institute of Transportation Engineers	ITE
Materials Research Society	MRS
National Academy of Engineering	NAE
National Society of Black Engineers	NSBE
National Society of Professional Engineers	NSPE
Society of Automotive Engineers International	SAE Int'l.
Society of Hispanic Professional Engineers	SHPE
Society of Petroleum Engineers	SPE Int'l.
Society of Plastics Engineers	SPE
Society of Women Engineers	SWE
Tau Beta Pi, The Engineering Honor Society	TBP

WISE WORDS: ADVICE ABOUT SOCIETY PARTICIPATION

Get involved! It is so much fun! Plus, you're going to meet a ton of cool people doing it!

T. Andrews, CE

I am a very involved person, and I love it. I definitely recommend participating in professional societies because not only do they look good on a résumé but they also provide you with useful information for your professional life. It also allows you to network with others in your field which can be helpful down road. Also, do something fun as it is a nice stress relief and distraction when life seems to become really busy.

C. Darling, Biosystem

My advice to students willing to participate on student activities is for them to not be shy when going to a student organization for the first couple of times. It takes time to get well known and feel comfortable around new people, but don't let that prevent you from being part of a student organization that can bring many benefits to you. Always have a positive attitude, be humble, and learn to listen to others; these last advices are traits which you will use in your professional life.

V. Gallas Cervo, ME

My advice to first-year students is to not get involved with too many organizations all at once. It is easy to get distracted from your class work with all the activities on campus. Focus on a couple and be a dedicated officer in one of them. This way you have something to talk about when employers see it on your résumé. I would recommend that you are involved with one organization that you enjoy as a hobby and one organization that is a professional organization.

D. Jones, BE

The most important thing to do when joining any group is to make sure you like the people in it. This is probably even more important than anything the group even does. Also make sure that if the group you're joining has a lot of events they expect you to be at, you have the time to be at those events.

R. Kriener, EE

The field of engineering is a collaborative project; therefore, it is important to develop friendships within your major.

S. Belous, CpE

Make the time to participate in student activities. If possible, try to get a leadership position in one of the activities because it will be useful in interviews to talk about your involvement. While employers and grad schools may not be impressed with how you attended meetings occasionally as a general member, they will be interested to hear about the projects that you worked on and the challenges that you faced in a leadership position.

K. Smith, ChE

Get involved! College is about more than just academics. Participating in student activities is a lot of fun and makes your college experience more memorable. I've made so many friends not just at my school, but all over the country by getting involved. It is also a great way to develop leadership and interpersonal skills that will become beneficial in any career.

A. Zollinger, CE

1.6 PURSUING STUDENT OPPORTUNITIES

In addition to the traditional educational experience, many students seek experience outside of the classroom. Many engineering colleges and universities have special departments that help place students in programs to gain real engineering work experience or provide them with a culturally rich study environment. Ask a professor or advisor if your university provides experiences similar to those described in this section.

Cooperative Education

Contributed by: Dr. Neil Burton, Director of
Cooperative Education Program, Clemson University

People learn things in many different ways. Some people learn best by reading; others by listening to others; and still others by participating in a group discussion. One very effective form of learning is called **experiential learning**, also referred to as engaged learning in some places. As the name suggests, experiential learning means learning through experience, and there is a very good chance you used this method to learn how to ride a bike, bake a cake, change a flat tire, or perform any other complex process that took some practice to perfect. The basic assumption behind experiential learning is that you learn more by doing than by simply listening or watching.

Becoming a good engineer is a pretty challenging process, so it seems only natural that experiential learning would be especially useful to an engineering student. In 1906, Herman Schneider, the Dean of Engineering at the University of Cincinnati, developed an experiential learning program for engineering students because he felt students would understand the material in their engineering classes much better if they had a chance to put that classroom knowledge into practice in the workplace. Schneider called this program **Cooperative Education**, and more than 100 years later, colleges and universities all over the world offer cooperative (co-op) education assignments to students in just about every major, although engineering students remain the primary focus of most co-op programs.

There are many different kinds of co-op programs, but all of them offer engineering students the chance to tackle real-world projects with the help and guidance of experienced engineers. One common model of cooperative education allows students to alternate semesters of co-op with semesters of school. In this model, students who accept co-op assignments spend a semester working full-time with a company, return

On my co-op, I worked on the hazard analysis for the new Ares I launch vehicle that NASA is designing to replace the Space Shuttles when they retire in 2010.

Basically, we looked at the design and asked: what happens if this part breaks, how likely is it that this part will break, and how can we either make it less likely for the part to break or give it fault tolerance so the system can withstand a failure?

J. Sandel, on co-op

to school for the following academic term, go back out for a second co-op **rotation**, return to school the following term, and continue this pattern until they have spent enough time on assignment to complete the co-op program.

Students learn a lot about engineering during their co-op assignments, but there are many other benefits as well. Engineering is a tough discipline, and a co-op assignment can often help a student determine if he or she is in the right major. It is a lot better to figure out that you do not want to be an engineer before you have to take thermodynamics or heat transfer! Students who participate in co-op also have a chance to develop some great professional contacts, and these contacts are very handy when it comes time to find a permanent job at graduation. The experience students receive while on a co-op assignment is also highly valued by employers who want to know if a student can handle the challenges and responsibilities of a certain position. In fact, many students receive full-time job offers from their co-op employers upon graduation.

Perhaps the most important benefit a co-op assignment can provide is improved performance in the classroom. By putting into practice the theories you learn about in class, you gain a much better understanding of those theories. You may also see something on your co-op assignment that you will cover in class the following semester, putting you a step ahead of everyone else in the class. You will also develop time management skills while on a co-op assignment, and these skills should help you complete your school assignments more efficiently and effectively when you return from your assignment.

Companies that employ engineers often have cooperative education programs because co-op provides a number of benefits to employers as well as students. While the money companies pay co-op students may be double or even triple than what those students would earn from a typical summer job, it is still much less than companies would pay full-time engineers to perform similar work. Many employers also view cooperative education as a recruiting tool—what better way to identify really good employees than to bring aboard promising students and see how they perform on co-op assignments!

WISE WORDS: WHAT DID YOU GAIN FROM YOUR CO-OP OR INTERNSHIP EXPERIENCE?

I was able to learn how to practically apply the knowledge I was gaining from college. Also, the pay allowed me to fund my schooling.

B. Dieringer, ME

The best part about that experience was how well it meshed with my courses at the time. My ability to apply what I was learning in school every day as well as to take skills and techniques I was learning from experienced engineers and use them toward the projects I was working on in school was invaluable.

A. Flowerday, CpE

My internships were a great introduction to the professional work place—the skills and responsibilities that are expected; the relationships and networks that are needed.

S. Forkner, ChE

I decided to pursue a co-op because I had trouble adapting to the school environment in my first years and taking some time off to work at a company seemed a good way to rethink and reorganize myself. I made a good decision taking some time off, since it allowed me to learn a lot more about myself, how I work, how I learn, and how I operate. I learned that the biggest challenges were only in my mind and believing in me was, and still is, the hardest thing.

V. Gallas Cervo, ME

My internship taught me that I could be an engineer—and a good one too. I had a lot of self-doubt before that experience, and I learned that I was better than I thought I was.

B. Holloway, ME

Being able to immediately apply the things I learned in school to real-world applications helped reinforce a lot of the concepts and theories. It also resulted in two job offers after graduation, one of which I accepted.

J. Huggins, ME

This was an amazing opportunity to get a real taste for what I was going to be doing once I graduated. I began to realize all the different types of jobs I could have when I graduated, all working in the same field. In addition, my work experience made my résumé look 100 times more appealing to potential employers. The experience proved that I could be a team player and that I could hit the ground running without excessive training.

L. Johnson, CE

It gave me a chance to see how people work together in the "real world" so that I could learn how to interact with other people with confidence, and also so that I could learn what kind of worker or manager I wanted to be when I "grew up."

M. Peterson, ME

Without a doubt, the best professional decision of my life. After my co-op rotation finished, I approached school as more like a job. Furthermore, cooping makes school easier! Imagine approaching something in class that you have already seen at work!

A. Thompson, EE

Internship

Contributed by: Mr. Troy Nunamaker, Director of Graduate and Internship Programs, Michelin Career Center, Clemson University

Internships offer the unique opportunity to gain career-related experience in a variety of settings. Now, more than ever, employers look to hire college graduates with internship experience in their field.

WHY CHOOSE AN INTERNSHIP?

- Bridge classroom applications to the professional world
- Build a better résumé
- Possibly receive higher full-time salary offers upon graduation
- Gain experience and exposure to an occupation or industry
- Network and increase marketability
- Potentially fulfill academic requirements and earn money

Employers indicate that good grades and participation in student activities are not always enough to help students land a good, full-time job. In today's competitive job market, the students with career-related work experience are the students getting the best interviews and job offers. As an added bonus, many companies report that over 70% of full-time hires come directly from their internship program.

Searching for an Internship

Although a number of students will engage in an internship experience during their freshman and sophomore years, most students pursue an internship during their junior and senior years. Some students might participate in more than one internship during their college career. Allow plenty of time for the search process to take place and be sure to keep good records of all your applications and correspondences.

- **Figure out what you are looking for.** You should not start looking for an internship before you have answered the following questions:
  - What are my interests, abilities, and values?
  - What type of organization or work environment am I looking for?
  - Are there any geographical constraints, or am I willing to travel anywhere?
- **Start researching internship opportunities.** Start looking one to two semesters before your desired start date. Many students find that the search process can take anywhere from 3 to 4 weeks up to 5 to 6 months before securing an internship. You should utilize as many resources as possible in order to have the broadest range of options.

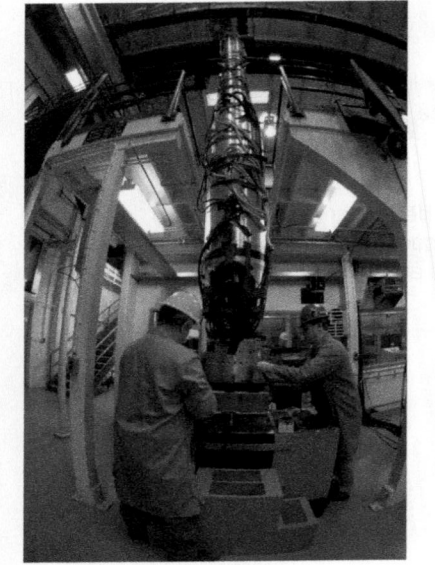

The biggest project I worked on was the Athena model. The Athena is one of NASA's launch platforms.

Before I came here to the contract, several other interns had taken and made Solid Works parts measured from the actual Athena. My task was to take their parts, make them dimensionally correct and put it together in a large assembly.

I took each individual part (~ 300 of them!) and made them dimensionally correct, then put them together into an assembly. After I finished the assembly I animated the launcher and made it move and articulate.

E. Roper, ME

- Visit your campus's career center office to do the following: meet with a career counselor; attend a workshop on internships; find out what positions and resources are available; and look for internship postings through the career center's recruiting system and website resources.
- Attend a career fair on your campus or in your area. Career fairs typically are not just for full-time jobs, but are open to internship applicants as well. In addition, if there are specific companies where you would like to work, contact them directly and find out if they offer internships.
- Network. Network. Network. Only about a quarter of internship opportunities are actually posted. Talk to friends, family, and professors and let them know that you are interested in an internship. Networking sites like LinkedIn and Facebook are also beginning to see more use by employers and students. However, be conscious what images and text are associated with your profile.

- **Narrow down the results and apply for internships.** Look for resources on your campus to help with developing a résumé and cover letter. *Each résumé and cover letter should then be tailored for specific applications.* As part of the application process, do not be surprised if a company requests additional documents such as references, transcripts, writing samples, and formal application packets.
- **Wait for responses.** It may take up to a month to receive any responses to your applications. One to 2 weeks after you have submitted your application, call the organization to make sure they received all the required documents from you.
- **Interview for positions.** Once you have your interviews scheduled, stop by the career center to see what resources they have available to help you prepare for the interview. Do not forget to send a thank-you note within 24 hours of the interview, restating your interest in the position.

Accepting an Internship

Once you have secured an internship, look to see if academic internship coursework is available on your campus so that the experience shows up on your transcripts. If you were rejected from any organizations, take it as a learning experience and try to determine what might have made your application stronger.

POINTS TO PONDER

Am I eligible for an internship?
Most companies look to hire rising juniors and seniors, but a rising sophomore or even a freshman with relevant experience and good grades can be a strong candidate.

Will I be paid for my internship?
The pay rate will depend on your experience, position, and the individual company. However, most engineering interns receive competitive compensation; averages are $14–$20 per hour.

When should I complete an internship?
Contrary to some popular myths, an internship can be completed not only during summers, but also during fall and spring semesters. Be sure to check with your campus on how to maintain your student enrollment status while interning.

Will I be provided housing for an internship?
Do not let the location of a company deter you. Some employers will provide housing, while others will help connect you with resources and fellow interns to find an apartment in the area.

I think that first year-students in engineering should do a co-op or internship. It was extremely valuable to my education. Now that I am back in the classroom, I know what to focus on and why what I am learning is important.

Before the experience I did not know what I wanted to do with my major, and I didn't fully understand word problems that were presented in a manner that applied to manufacturing or real life. Being in industry and working in a number of different departments, I figured out that I liked one area more than any other area, and that is where I am focusing my emphasis area studies during my senior year.

K. Glast, IE

WISE WORDS: DESCRIBE A PROJECT YOU WORKED ON DURING YOUR CO-OP OR INTERNSHIP

The large project I worked on was an upgrade of an insulin production facility. A small project I worked on for 2 weeks was the design of a pressure relief valve for a heat exchanger in the plant.

D. Jones, BE

I have been working on a series of projects, all designed to make the production of electric power meters more efficient. I am rewriting all the machine vision programs to make the process more efficient and to provide a more sophisticated graphical user interface for the operators. These projects have challenged me by requiring that I master a new "machine vision" programming language, as well as think in terms of efficiency rather than simply getting the job done.

R. Izard, ME

A transmission fluid additive was not working correctly and producing harmful emissions, so I conducted series of reactions adding different amounts of materials in a bioreactor. I determined the best fluid composition by assessing the activation energy and how clean it burned.

C. Darling, Biosystem

At Boeing, I worked with Liaison Engineering. Liaison engineers provide engineering solutions to discrepancies on the aircraft that have deviated from original engineering plans. As one example, I worked closely with other engineers to determine how grain properties in titanium provide a sound margin or safety in the seat tracks.

J. Compton, ME

The site I worked at designs and manufactures radar systems (among others). During my internship I wrote C code that tests the computer systems in a certain radar model. The code will eventually be run by an operator on the production floor before the new radars are sent out to customers.

D. Rollend, EE

One of my last projects I worked on during my first term was building a new encoder generator box used to test the generator encoder on a wind turbine. The goal was to make a sturdier box that was organized inside so that if something had broken, somebody who has no electrical skills could fix it. I enjoyed this project because it allowed me to use my skills I have learned both from school and my last internship.

C. Balon, EE

Study Abroad

Contributed by: Mrs. J. P. Creel, International Programs
Coordinator, College of Engineering and Science, Clemson University

In today's global economy, it is important for engineering students to recognize the importance of studying abroad. A few reasons to study abroad include the following:

- Taking undergraduate courses abroad is an exciting way to set your résumé apart from those of your peers. Prospective employers will generally inquire about your international experiences during the interview process, giving you the chance to make a lasting impression that could be beneficial.
- Studying abroad will give you a deeper, more meaningful understanding of a different culture. These types of learning experiences are not created in traditional classrooms in the United States, and cannot be duplicated by traveling abroad on vacation.
- Students who study abroad generally experience milestones in their personal development as a result of stepping outside of their comfort zone.
- There is no better time to study abroad than now! Students often think that they will have the opportunity to spend significant amounts of time traveling the world after graduation. In reality, entering the workforce typically becomes top priority.
- Large engineering companies tend to operate on a global scale. For instance, a company's headquarters may be in the United States, but that company may also control factories in Sweden, and have parts shipped to them from Taiwan. Having an international experience under your belt will give you a competitive edge in your career because you will have global knowledge that your co-workers may not possess.

While programs differ between universities, many offer a variety of choices:

- **Exchange Programs:** Several institutions are part of the Global Engineering Education Exchange, or GE^3. This consortium connects students from top engineering schools in the United States with foreign institutions in any of 18 countries. In an ideal situation, the number of international students on exchange in the United States would be equal to the number of U.S. students studying abroad during the same time frame.

   Generally, students participating in these types of exchange programs will continue to pay tuition at their home institution; however, you should check your university's website for more information. Also, by entering "Global E3" into a web browser, you will be able to access the website to determine if your institution currently participates, which foreign institutions offer courses taught in English, and which schools offer courses applicable to your particular major. If your institution is not a member of GE^3, consult with someone in the international, or study abroad, office at your institution to find out about other exchange opportunities.

- **Faculty-Led Programs:** It is not unusual for faculty members to connect with institutions or other professionals abroad to establish discipline-specific study-abroad programs. These programs typically allow students to enroll in summer classes at their home institution, then travel abroad to complete the coursework. Faculty-led programs offer organized travel, lodging, administration, and excursions, making the overall experience hassle-free. Consult with professors in your department to find out if they are aware of any programs that are already in place at your institution.

- **Third-Party Providers:** Many universities screen and recommend providers of programs for students. If there's a place you want to go for study and your university does not have an established program at that particular location, you will probably

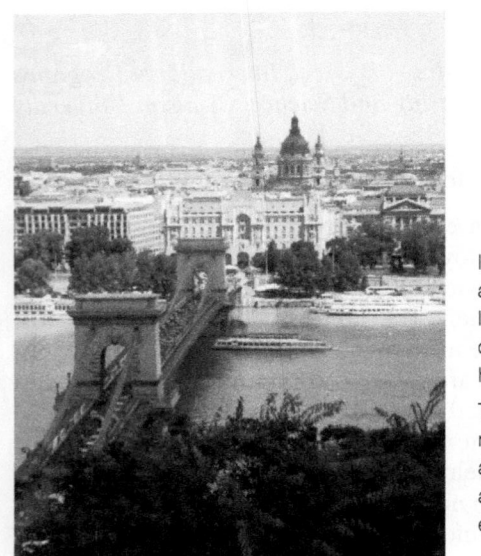

I studied abroad twice. The first time I spent a semester in the Netherlands, experiencing a full immersion in the Dutch culture and exploring my own heritage, and the second time I spent a summer in Austria taking one of my core chemical engineering classes. Both countries are beautiful and unique places and they will always hold a special place in my heart.

Through studying abroad, I was able to expand my own comfort zone by encountering novel situations and become a more confident individual. Although the experiences were amazing and the memories are truly priceless, the biggest thing I gained from studying abroad was that I was able to abandon many perceptions about other cultures and embrace new perspectives.

R. Lanoie, studying abroad in the Netherlands and Austria

find a study program of interest to you by discussing these options with the study-abroad office at your university.

- **Direct Enrollment:** If you are interested in a particular overseas institution with which your home university does not have an established program, there is always the option of direct enrollment. This process is basically the same as applying to a university in the United States. The school will likely require an admissions application, a purpose statement, transcripts, and a letter of reference. Be cautious if you choose this route for study abroad, as it can be difficult to get credits transferred back to your home institution. It is a good idea to get your international courses preapproved prior to your departure. On a positive note, it can be cheaper to directly enroll in a foreign institution than it is to attend at your home university. This option is best suited for students who want to go abroad for a semester or full year.

I think study abroad is a wonderful learning experience everyone should have. In going abroad you get to meet people you would never meet otherwise, and experience things you never thought you would see.

I learned about independently navigating a new country, as well as adjusting to foreign ways of doing things. It is interesting to take classes that you would have taken at home and experience them a completely different way.

Studying abroad teaches you how to easily adjust to new situations and allows you to learn about cultures you had no idea of before.

B. Brubaker, studying abroad in Scotland

Typically, students go abroad during their junior year, though recently there has been an increase in the number of second-year students participating. The timing of your experience should be agreed upon by you and your academic advisor. Each program offers different international incentives, and some are geared for better opportunities later in your academic career, whereas others may be better toward the beginning.

If you would like to go abroad for a semester or year but do not feel entirely comfortable with the idea, why not get your feet wet by enrolling in a summer program first? This will give you a better idea of what it is that you are looking for without overwhelming you. Then, you can plan for a semester or year abroad later in your academic career. In fact, more students are electing to spend a semester or year of study abroad, and increasingly more opt for an academic semester plus a semester internship combination.

There are three basic principles to follow when deciding on a location:

- **Personal Preference:** Some people are more interested in Asia than Europe, or maybe Australia instead of Latin America. There are excellent opportunities worldwide, regardless of the location.
- **Program Opportunities:** Certain countries may be stronger or have more options in certain fields. For example, Germany is well known for innovations in mechanical engineering, while the Japanese tend to be more widely recognized for their efforts in computer engineering. Listen to your professors and weigh your options.
- **Language:** You may not feel like you are ready to study in a foreign country, speaking and reading in a foreign language. There are numerous institutions that offer courses taught in English. However, if you have taken at least 2 years of the same foreign language, you should be knowledgeable enough to succeed in courses taught in that language. Do not let your fears restrict you!

India is quite an eye-opening country. All of your senses work on overload just so you can take everything in at once. My time studying in India was simply phenomenal. I had an excellent opportunity placed before me to travel to India to earn credit for Electrical Engineering courses and I would have been a fool to pass up that chance. I regret nothing, I would do it again, and I would urge everyone with the slightest inkling of studying abroad to put their worries aside and have the experience of a lifetime.

J. Sadie, studying abroad in India

Writing Assignments

For each question, write a response according to the directions given by your instructor. Each response should contain correct grammar, spelling, and punctuation. Be sure to answer the question completely, but choose your words carefully so as to not exceed the word limit if one is given. There is no right or wrong answer; your score will be based upon the strength of the argument you make to defend your position.

1. On a separate sheet, write a one-page résumé for one person from the following list. Include information such as education, job experience, primary accomplishments (inventions, publications, etc.), and references. If you want, you can include a photo or likeness no larger than 2 inches by 3 inches. You can add some "made up" material such as current address and references, but do not overdo this.

- Ammann, Othmar
- Ampere, Andre Marie
- Arafat, Yasser
- Archimedes
- Avogadro, Armedeo
- Bernoulli, Daniel
- Bessemer, Henry
- Bezos, Jeffrey P.
- Birdseye, William
- Bloomberg, Michael
- Bohr, Niels
- Boyle, Robert
- Brezhnev, Leonid
- Brown, Robert
- Brunel, Isambard
- Calder, Alexander
- Capra, Frank
- Carnot, Nicolas
- Carrier, Willis Haviland
- Carter, Jimmy
- Cauchy, Augustin Louis
- Cavendish, Henry
- Celsius, Anders
- Clausius, Rudolf
- Coulomb, Charles
- Cray, Seymour
- Crosby, Philip
- Curie, Marie
- Dalton, John
- Darcy, Henri
- de Coriolis, Gaspard
- de Mestral, George
- Deming, W. Edwards

- Diesel, Rudolf
- Dunbar, Bonnie
- Eiffel, Gustave
- Euler, Leonhard
- Fahrenheit, Gabriel
- Faraday, Michael
- Fleming, Sandford
- Ford, Henry
- Fourier, Joseph
- Fung, Yuan-Cheng
- Gantt, Henry
- Gauss, Carl Friedrich
- Gibbs, Josiah Willard
- Gilbert, William
- Gilbreth, Lillian
- Goizueta, Robert
- Grove, Andrew
- Hancock, Herbie
- Henry, Beulah
- Hertz, Heinrich Rudolf
- Hitchcock, Alfred
- Hooke, Robert
- Hoover, Herbert
- Hopper, Grace
- Iacocca, Lee
- Joule, James Prescott
- Juran, Joseph Moses
- Kelvin, Lord
- Kraft, Christopher, Jr.
- Kwolek, Stephanie
- Landry, Tom
- Laplace, Pierre-Simon
- Leibniz, Gottfried

- LeMessurier, William
- MacCready, Paul
- Mach, Ernst
- McDonald, Capers
- Midgley, Thomas Jr.
- Millikan, Robert
- Navier, Claude-Louis
- Newton, Isaac
- Nielsen, Arthur
- Ochoa, Ellen
- Ohm, Georg
- Pascal, Blaise
- Poiseuille, Jean Loius
- Porsche, Ferdinand
- Prandtl, Ludwig
- Rankine, William
- Rayleigh, Lord
- Resnik, Judith

- Reynolds, Osborne
- Rømer, Ole
- Sikorsky, Igor Ivanovich
- Stinson, Katherine
- Stokes, George
- Sununu, John
- Taguchi, Gen'ichi
- Taylor, Fredrick
- Teller, Edward
- van der Waals, Johannes
- Venturi, Giovanni
- Volta, Count Alessandro
- von Braun, Wernher
- von Kármán, Theodore
- Watt, James
- Welch, Jack
- Wyeth, Nathaniel
- Yeltsin, Boris

Personal Reflections

2. Please address the following questions in approximately one page. You may write, type, draw, sketch your answers . . . whatever form you would like to use.

   (a) Where are you from?
   (b) What type of engineering are you interested in? Why?
   (c) Are there any engineers in the circle of your friends and family?
   (d) How would you classify yourself as a student (new freshman, transfer, or upperclassman)?
   (e) What are your activities and hobbies?
   (f) What are you most proud of?
   (g) What are you fantastic at?
   (h) What are you passionate about?
   (i) What has been the most difficult aspect of college so far?
   (j) What do you expect to be your biggest challenge this term?
   (k) Do you have any concerns about this class?
   (l) Anything else you would like to add?

3. In 2008, experts convened by the National Academy of Engineering (NAE) met and proposed a set of Grand Challenges for Engineering, a list of the 14 key goals for engineers to work toward during the 21st century. For any aspiring engineer, reading this list should feel like reading a description of the challenges you will face throughout your career. To read a description of each Challenge, as well as a description of some connected areas within each, visit the NAE's Grand Challenges for Engineering website at http://www.engineeringchallenges.org.

After reading through the list, write a job description of your dream job. The job description should include the standard components of a job description: title, responsibilities (overall and specific), a description of the work hierarchy (whom you report to, whom you work with), as well as any necessary qualifications. Do not include any salary requirements, as this is a completely fictional position.

After writing the description of your dream job, identify which of the 14 Grand Challenges for Engineering this position is instrumental in working toward solving. Cite specific examples of the types of projects your fictional job would require you to do, and discuss the impact of those projects on the Grand Challenges you have identified.

4. Choose and explain your choice of major, and the type of job you envision yourself doing in 15 years. Consider the following:

    (a) What skills or talents do you possess that will help you succeed in your field of interest?
    (b) How passionate are you about pursuing a career in engineering? If you do not plan on being an engineer, what changed your mind?
    (c) How confident are you in your choice of major?
    (d) How long will it take you to complete your degree?
    (e) Will you obtain a minor?
    (f) Will you pursue study abroad, co-op, or internship?
    (g) Do you plan to pursue an advanced degree, or become a professional engineer (PE)?
    (h) What type of work (industry, research, academic, medical, etc.) will you pursue?

5. In 2008, the University of Memphis made national headlines when the Memphis Tigers played in the NCAA basketball national championship game. When interviewed by a local newspaper about how he helped his team "own" the tournament, Coach Calipari revealed that before each game, he had his star player write an essay about how the game would play out. This particular player was prone to nervousness, so to help him focus, the coach told him to mentally envision the type of plays and how he himself would react to them.

    In this assignment, write a short essay on how you will prepare for and take the final exam. Consider the following:

    (a) What will you do to study? What materials will you gather, and how will you use them? Where will you study? Will it be quiet? Will you play music?
    (b) What kinds of things could go wrong on the day of the exam, and how would you avoid them? (List at least three.)
    (c) What will the exam look like, and how will you work through it?

    Thank you to Dr. Lisa Benson for contributing this assignment.

6. Read the essay "Engineering is an . . . itch!" in the Engineering Essentials introduction. Reflect on what it means to have performance-focused versus mastery-focused learning goals.

    (a) Describe in your own words what it means to be a performance-based learner compared with a mastery-based learner.
    (b) What learning goals do you have? Are these goals performance based or mastery based?
    (c) Is it important to you to become more mastery focused?
    (d) Do you have different kinds of learning goals than you had in the past, and do you think you will have different learning goals in the future?

7. An article in *Science News* addressed the topics of nature and technology. In our electronic world, we are in constant contact with others, through our cell phones, iPods, Facebook, e-mail, etc. Researchers at the University of Washington have determined that this effect may create long-term problems in our stress levels and in our creativity.

Scenes of Nature Trump Technology in Reducing Low-Level Stress

Technology can send a man to the moon, help unlock the secrets of DNA, and let people around the world easily communicate through the Internet. But can it substitute for nature?

"Technology is good and it can help our lives, but let's not be fooled into thinking we can live without nature," said Peter Kahn, a University of Washington associate professor of psychology who led the research team.

We are losing direct experiences with nature. Instead, more and more we're experiencing nature represented technologically through television and other media. Children grow up watching Discovery Channel and Animal Planet. That's probably better than nothing. But as a species we need interaction with actual nature for our physical and psychological well-being.

Part of this loss comes from what the researchers call environmental generational amnesia. This is the idea that across generations the amount of environmental degradation increases, but each generation views conditions it grew up with as largely non-degraded and normal. Children growing up today in the cities with the worst air pollution often, for example, don't believe that their communities are particularly polluted.

"This problem of environmental generational amnesia is particularly important for children coming of age with current technologies," said Rachel Severson, a co-author of the study and a University of Washington psychology doctoral student. "Children may not realize they are not getting the benefits of actual nature when interacting with what we're calling technological nature."

[University of Washington (2008, June 16). "Scenes of Nature Trump Technology in Reducing Low-level Stress." Science Daily]

Go someplace quiet and spend at least 10 minutes clearing your head. Only after these 10 minutes, get out a piece of paper and sketch something you see; are thinking of; want to create or invent or imagine, etc. On the same sheet of paper, write a poem about your sketch; something you are thinking of; or quiet, wonder of the universe, lack of technology, etc.

Rules:

- Must be done all by hand.
- Must be original work (no copied poems or artwork).
- Ability does not count—draw like you are 5 years old!
- Draw in any medium you want: use pencil, pen, colored pencils, markers, crayons, watercolors.
- Poetic form does not matter: use rhyme, no rhyme, haiku, whatever you want it to be.
- It does not need to be elaborate; simple is fine.

CHAPTER 2
ETHICS

Every day, we make numerous ethical decisions, although most are so minor that we do not even view them as such.

- When you drive your car, do you knowingly violate the posted speed limit?
- When you unload the supermarket cart at your car, do you leave it in the middle of the parking lot, or spend the extra time to return it to the cart corral?
- You know that another student has plagiarized an assignment; do you rat him or her out?
- A person with a mental disability tries to converse with you while waiting in a public queue. Do you treat him or her with respect or pretend he or she does not exist?
- In the grocery, a teenager's mother tells her to put back the package of ice cream she brought to the cart. The teenager walks around the corner and places the ice cream on the shelf with the soft drinks and returns to the buggy. Do you ignore this or approach the teenager and politely explain that leaving a package of ice cream in that location will cause it to melt thus increasing the cost of groceries for everyone else, or do you replace it in the freezer yourself?
- When going through a public door, do you make a habit of looking back to see if releasing the door will cause it to slam in someone's face?
- You notice a highway patrolman lying in wait for speeders. Do you flash your lights at other cars to warn them?
- A cashier gives you too much change for a purchase. Do you correct the cashier?
- You are on the lake in your boat and notice a person on a JetSki chasing a great blue heron across the lake. The skier stops at a nearby pier. Do you pilot your craft over to the dock and reprimand him for harassing the wildlife?

> Good people do not need laws to tell them to act responsibly, while bad people will find a way around the laws.
>
> *Plato*

On a grand scale, none of these decisions is particularly important, although some might lead to undesirable consequences. However, as an aspiring engineer, you may face numerous decisions in your career that could affect the lives and well-being of thousands of people. Just like almost everything else, practice makes perfect, or at least better. The more you practice analyzing day-to-day decisions from an ethical stand-point, the easier it will be for you to make good decisions when the results of a poor choice may be catastrophic.

In very general terms, there are two reasons people try to make ethical decisions.

- They wish to make the world a better place for everyone—in a single word, altruism.
- They wish to avoid unpleasant consequences, such as fines, incarceration, or loss of job.

In an ideal society, the second reason would not exist. However, history is replete with examples of people, and even nations, who do not base their decisions solely on whether or not they are acting ethically. Because of the common occurrence of

- If a man commits a murder, he must be killed.
- If a man commits a robbery, he will be killed.
- If a man commits a kidnapping, he is to be imprisoned and pay 15 shekels of silver.
- If a man knocks out the eye of another man, he shall weigh out half a mina of silver.
- If a man has cut off another man's foot, he is to pay 10 shekels of silver.
- If someone severed the nose of another man with a copper knife, he must pay two-thirds of a mina of silver.
- If a man knocks out a tooth of another man, he shall pay 2 shekels of silver.

unethical behavior and the negative impact it has on others, almost all societies have developed rules, codes, and laws to specify what is and is not acceptable behavior, and the punishments that will be meted out when violations occur.

The major religions all have fairly brief codes summarizing how one should conduct their life. Some examples are given below; other examples exist as well.

- Judaism, Christianity, and derivatives thereof have the Decalogue, or Ten Commandments.
- Islam has the Five Pillars in addition to a slightly modified and reorganized form of the Decalogue.
- Buddhism has the Noble Eightfold Path.
- Bahá'í has 12 social principles.
- In Hinduism, Grihastha dharma has four goals.

Secular codes of conduct go back more than four millennia to the Code of Ur-Nammu. Although by today's standards, some of the punishments in the earliest codes seem harsh or even barbaric, it was one of the earliest known attempts to codify crimes and corresponding punishments.

Admittedly, although not specifically religious in nature, these codes are usually firmly rooted in the prevailing religious thought of the time and location. Through the centuries, such codes and laws have been expanded, modified, and refined so that most forms of serious antisocial behavior are addressed and consequences for violations specified. These codes exist from a local to a global level. Several examples are given below.

- Most countries purport to abide by the Geneva Conventions, which govern certain types of conduct on an international scale.
- Most countries have national laws concerning murder, rape, theft, etc.
- In the United States, it is illegal to purchase alcohol unless you are 21 years of age. In England, the legal age is 18.
- In North and South Dakota, you can obtain a driver's license at age $14\frac{1}{2}$. In most other states, the legal age is 16.
- It is illegal to say "Oh boy!" in Jonesboro, Georgia.
- Many cities, such as Santa Fe, New Mexico, have ordinances prohibiting use of cell phones while driving.

2.1 ETHICAL DECISION MAKING

Some ethical decisions are clear-cut. For example, essentially everyone (excluding psychopaths) would agree that it is unethical to kill someone because you do not like his or her hat. Unfortunately, many real-world decisions that we must make are far from "black and white" issues, instead having many subtle nuances that must be considered to arrive at what one believes is the "best" decision.

There is no proven algorithm or set of rules that one can follow to guarantee that the most ethical decision possible is being made in any particular situation. However, numerous people have developed procedures that can guide us in considering questions with ethical ramifications. A four-step procedure is discussed here, although there are various other approaches.

Step 1: Determine *What* the issues are and *Who* might be affected by the various alternative courses of action that might be implemented.

We will refer to the *Who* as **stakeholders**. Note that at this point, we are not trying to determine how the stakeholders will be affected by any particular plan of action.

- The issues (What) can refer to a wide variety of things, including, for example, personal freedom, national security, quality of life, economic issues, fairness, and equality.
- The term stakeholders (Who) does not necessarily refer to people, but might be an individual, a group of people, an institution, or a natural system, among other things.

● **EXAMPLE 2-1**

Consider the question of whether to allow further drilling for oil in the Alaska National Wildlife Refuge (ANWR). List several issues and stakeholders.

Issues:

- *Oil independence*
- *The price of gasoline*
- *Possible impacts on the ecosystem*

Stakeholders:

- *Oil companies*
- *The general population of the United States*
- *Other countries from whom we purchase oil*
- *The flora and fauna in ANWR*
- *The native people in Alaska*

Step 2: Consider the effects of alternative courses of action from different perspectives.

Here, we look at three perspectives: consequences, intent, and character.

Perspective 1: Consequences

When considering this perspective, ask how the various stakeholders will be affected by each alternative plan being contemplated. In addition, attempt to assign a relative level of importance (weight) to each effect on each stakeholder. For instance, an action that might affect millions of people adversely is almost always more important than an action that would cause an equivalent level of harm to a dozen people.

● **EXAMPLE 2-2**

Should all U.S. children be fingerprinted when entering kindergarten and again each third year of grade school (3, 6, 9, 12)? Identify the stakeholders and consequences.

Stakeholders:

- *All U.S. children*
- *All U.S. citizens*
- *Law enforcement*
- *The judicial system*
- *The U.S. Constitution*

Consequences:

- *Provides a record to help identify or trace missing children (not common, but possibly very important in some cases)*
- *Affords an opportunity for malicious use of the fingerprint records for false accusation of crime or for identity theft (probability unknown, but potentially devastating to affected individuals)*
- *Could help identify perpetrators of crimes, thus improving the safety of law-abiding citizens (importance varies with type of crime)*
- *Raises serious questions concerning personal freedoms, possibly unconstitutional (importance, as well as constitutionality, largely dependent on the philosophy of the person doing the analysis)*

This list could easily be continued.

Fingerprint technology has advanced in recent years with the implementation of computer recognition for identification. Originally in the United States, the Henry Classification System was used to manually match fingerprints based on three main patterns: arches, loops, and whorls (shown below from left to right).

Today, the Automated Fingerprint Identification System (AFIS) uses algorithmic matching to compare images. Future work of AFIS systems is in the adoption and creation of secure multitouch devices like mobile computers and tablets, which can identify different security levels for the operator of the device. For example, a multitouch computer owner might be able to issue permissions to an administrator that might not be available to a 5-year old, all without providing a single password!

Perspective 2: Intent

The intentions of the person doing the acting or deciding are considered in this perspective, sometimes called the "rights" perspective. Since actions based on good intentions can sometimes yield bad results, and vice versa, the intent perspective avoids this possible pitfall by not considering the outcome at all, only the intentions.

It may be helpful when considering this perspective to recall Immanuel Kant's Categorical Imperative: "Act only according to that maxim whereby you can at the same time will that it should become a universal law." To pull this out of the eighteenth century, ask yourself the following questions:

(a) Is the action I am taking something that I believe everyone should do?
(b) Do I believe that this sort of behavior should be codified in law?
(c) Would I like to be on the receiving end (the victim) of this action?

● **EXAMPLE 2-3**

Should you download music illegally over the Internet?

Rephrasing this question using the suggestions above yields:

(a) *Should everyone illegally download the music they want if it is there for the taking?*
(b) *Should the laws be changed so that anyone who obtains a song by any means can post it on the web for everyone to get for free?*
(c) *If you were a struggling musician trying to pay the bills, would you like your revenue stream to dry up because everyone who wanted your music got it for free?*

Perspective 3: Character

Character is the inherent complex of attributes that determines a person's moral and ethical actions and reactions. This perspective considers the character of a person who takes the action under consideration. There are different ways of thinking about this. One is to simply ask: Would a person of good character do this? Another is to ask: If I do this, does it enhance or degrade my character? Yet another way is to ask yourself if a person you revere as a person of unimpeachable character (whoever that might be) would take this action.

● **EXAMPLE 2-4**

Your friends are deriding another student behind her back because she comes from a poor family and does not have good clothes.

Do you:

(a) *Join in the criticism?*
(b) *Ignore it, pretend it is not happening, or simply walk away?*
(c) *Tell your friends that they are behaving badly and insist that they desist?*

- ■ *Which of these actions would a person of good character take?*
- ■ *Which of these actions would enhance your character and which would damage it?*
- ■ *What would the founder of your religion do? (Moses or Jesus or Buddha or Mohammed or Bahá'u'lláh or Vishnu or whoever.) If you are not religious, what would the person who, in your opinion, has the highest moral character do?*

Step 3: **Correlate perspectives.**

Now look back at the results of considering the issues from the three perspectives. In many cases, all three perspectives will lead to the same or a similar conclusion. When this occurs, you have a high level of confidence that the indicated action is the best choice from an ethical standpoint.

If the three perspectives do not agree, you may wish to reconsider the question. It may be helpful to discuss the issue with people whom you have not previously consulted in this matter. Did you omit any factors? For complicated issues, it is difficult to make sure you have included all possible stakeholders and consequences. Did you properly assign weights to the various aspects? Upon reconsideration, all three perspectives may converge.

If you cannot obtain convergence of all three perspectives, no matter how hard you try to make sure you left nothing out, then go with two out of three.

Step 4: **Act.**

This is often the hardest step of all to take, since ethical action often requires courage. The whistle-blower who risks losing his or her job, Harriet Tubman repeatedly risking her life to lead slaves to freedom via the Underground Railroad, the elected official standing up for what she knows to be right even though it will probably cost her the next election, or even something as mundane as risking the ridicule of your friends because you refuse to go along with whatever questionable activities they are engaging in for "fun." Ask yourself the question: "Do *I* have the courage to do what I know is right?"

● EXAMPLE 2-5

NOTE

In the interest of brevity, this is not an exhaustive analysis but shows the general procedure.

Your company has been granted a contract to develop the next generation of electronic cigarette, also known as a "nicotine delivery system," and you have been assigned to the design team. Can you in good conscience contribute your expertise to this project?

Step 1: *Identify the issues (What) and the stakeholders (Who).*

Issues:

- *Nicotine is poisonous and addictive*
- *These devices eliminate many of the harmful components of tobacco smoke*
- *Laws concerning these devices range from completely legal, to classification as a medical device, to banned, depending on country*
- *There are claims that such devices can help wean tobacco addicts off nicotine*
- *The World Health Organization does not consider this an effective means to stop smoking*
- *Whether an individual chooses to use nicotine should be a personal decision, since its use does not generally degrade a person's function in society*
- *The carrier of the nicotine (80–90% of the total inhaled product) is propylene glycol, which is relatively safe, but can cause skin and eye irritation, as well as other adverse effects in doses much larger than would be obtained from this device*
- *A profit can be made from nicotine products or anti-smoking devices*

Stakeholders:

- *You (your job and promotions)*
- *Your company and stockholders (profit)*
- *Cigarette manufacturers and their employees and stockholders (lost revenue)*
- *Tobacco farmers (less demand)*
- *The public (less second-hand smoke)*
- *The user (various health effects, possibly positive or negative)*

Step 2: *Analyze alternative courses of action from different perspectives.*

1. *Consequences*

   - *You may lose your job or promotion if you refuse*
   - *If you convince management to abandon the project, the company may lose money*
   - *If you succeed brilliantly, your company may make money hand over fist, and you receive a promotion*
   - *If the project goes ahead, the possibility of future lawsuits exists*
   - *Users' health may be damaged*
   - *Users' dependence on nicotine may either increase or decrease*

2. *Intent*

- *Should everyone use electronic cigarettes, or at least condone their use?*
- *Should use of electronic cigarettes be unrestricted by law?*
- *Would I like to risk nicotine addiction because of using these devices?*
- *Would I be able to kick my tobacco habit by using these devices?*

3. *Character*

- *Would a person of good character develop this device, use it, or condone its use?*
- *Would work on this project (thus implicitly condoning its use) or use of the device itself enhance or degrade my character?*
- *Would my personal spiritual leader, or other person I revere, condone development or use of this product?*

Step 3: *Correlate perspectives.*

Here we enter the realm of subjective judgment. The individual author responsible for this example has a definite personal answer, but it is in the nature of ethical decision making that different people will often arrive at different results in good conscience. You would have to weigh the various factors (including any that have been overlooked or knowingly omitted) to arrive at your own conclusion. We refuse to dictate a decision to you.

Step 4: *Act on your decision.*

If your decision was that working on this project poses no threat to your soul (if you happen to believe in such), probably little courage is required to follow through, since your career may blossom, or at least not be curtailed.

On the other hand, if you believe that the project is unethical, you need to have the intestinal fortitude to either attempt to change the minds of management or refuse to work on the project, both of which may put your career at risk.

2.2 PLAGIARISM

> **Did you know?** There are Internet services available that will accept a document and search the web for exact or similar content. Also, there are programs that will scan multiple documents and search for exact or similar content.
>
> ---
>
> **Did you know?** Prior to the romantic movement of the eighteenth century, European writers were encouraged not to be inventive without good reason and to carefully imitate the work of the great masters of previous centuries.

You probably know what plagiarism is—claiming someone else's work as your own. This is most often used in reference to written words, but may be extended to other media as well. From a legal standpoint, plagiarism per se is not illegal, although it is widely considered unethical. However, if the plagiarism also involves copyright infringement, then this would be a violation of the law. Certainly, in the context of your role as a student, plagiarism is almost universally regarded as academic dishonesty, and subject to whatever punitive actions your school deems appropriate.

In some cases, plagiarism is obvious, as when an essay submitted by a student is almost identical to one found on the Internet, or is the same as that submitted by another student. It is amazing how frequently students are caught cheating because they copied verbatim from another student's work, complete with strange mistakes and bizarre phrasing that grab the grader's attention like an 18-wheeler loaded with live pigs locking its brakes at 80 miles per hour. (*Thanks to Gilbert Shelton for that image.*)

In other cases, things are far less clear. For example, if you were writing a short story for your English class and used the simile "her lips were like faded tulips, dull and wrinkled," can you (or the professor) really be sure whether that was an original phrase or if you had read it at some time in the past, and your brain dragged it up from your subconscious memory as though it were your own?

We all hear or read things during our lives that hang around in our brains whether we are consciously aware of them or not. We cannot go through life in fear of being accused of plagiarism because our brain might drag up old data masquerading as our own original thought, or even worrying about whether our own original thoughts have ever been concocted by another person completely independently.

Any reasonable person (although admittedly, there is a surfeit of unreasonable people) will take the work as a whole into account. If there is simply a single phrase or a couple of instances of wordings that are similar to another source, this is most likely an innocent coincidence. On the other hand, if a work has many such occurrences, the probability that the infractions are innocent is quite low.

We arrive here at intent. Did you knowingly copy part of someone else's work and submit it as your own without giving proper credit? If you did not, stop worrying about it. If you did, Big Brother, also known as your professor, is watching, possibly with the assistance of high-tech plagiarism detection tools. (*A tip of the hat to George Orwell.*)

2.3 ENGINEERING CREED

Ethical decisions in engineering have, in general, a narrow focus specific to the problems that arise when designing and producing products or services of a technical nature. Engineers and scientists have, by the very nature of their profession, a body of specialized knowledge that is understood only vaguely, if at all, by most of the population. This knowledge can be used for tremendous good in society, but can also cause untold mischief when used by unscrupulous practitioners. Various engineering organizations have thus developed codes of conduct specific to the profession. Perhaps the most well known is the Code of Ethics for Engineers developed by the National Society of Professional Engineers (NSPE). The entire NSPE Code of Ethics is rather long, so we list only the Engineer's Creed and the Fundamental Canons of the Code here.

Engineer's Creed

As a Professional Engineer, I dedicate my professional knowledge and skill to the advancement and betterment of human welfare. I pledge:

- To give the utmost of performance
- To participate in none but honest enterprise
- To live and work according to the laws of man and the highest standards of professional conduct
- To place service before profit, the honor and standing of the profession before personal advantage, and the public welfare above all other considerations

In humility and with need for Divine Guidance, I make this pledge.

Fundamental Canons

Engineers, in the fulfillment of their professional duties, shall

- Hold paramount the safety, health, and welfare of the public
- Perform services only in areas of their competence
- Issue public statements only in an objective and truthful manner
- Act for each employer or client as faithful agents or trustees
- Avoid deceptive acts
- Conduct themselves honorably, responsibly, ethically, and lawfully so as to enhance the honor, reputation, and usefulness of the profession

The complete code can easily be found online at a variety of sites. When this book went to press, the URL for the Code of Ethics on the NSPE site was http://www.nspe.org/Ethics/CodeofEthics/index.html.

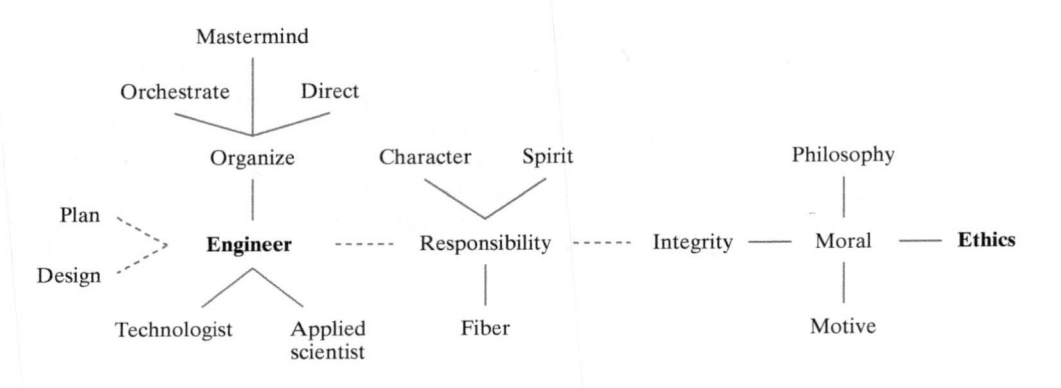

2.4 SOCIAL RESPONSIBILITY

Contributed by: Jason Huggins, P.E., Executive Councilor for Tau Beta Pi, the National Engineering Honor Society, 2006–2014.

NOTE

Social responsibility is the ideology that an individual has an obligation to act to benefit society at large.

As a freshman engineering student, you are just beginning your journey to join the Engineering Profession. Have you thought about what it will mean to be a part of a profession? Being a professional means we hold the public's trust and confidence in our training, skills, and knowledge of engineering. As a profession, we recognize the importance of this trust in the Engineering Canons and the Engineering Creed that define our standards for ethics, integrity, and regard for public welfare. So, does adherence to the Engineering Canons and the Engineering Creed fulfill our social responsibilities as engineers?

Traditionally, professions have always been held in very high regard by society, largely due to the extensive amount of training, education, and dedication required for membership. With this come high expectations of how the members of a profession conduct themselves both in their professional and private lives: doctors save lives, lawyers protect people's rights, and engineers make people's lives better. I did not really make this connection or understand what it meant until I was initiated into Tau Beta Pi, the National Engineering Honor Society. The Tau Beta Pi initiation ceremony has remained largely unchanged for over 100 years, and emphasizes the obligation as rs and members of Tau Beta Pi to society that extends beyond the services we en our employers and our clients.

over the years, I have taken these obligations to mean that as a profession we are levated above anyone else in society. We are affected by the same problems as the ral public and we must have an equal part in addressing them. In your lifetime, you be impacted by issues such as the strength of the economy, the effectiveness of the olic educational system, unemployment, the increasing national debt, national secu-ty, and environmental sustainability. You cannot focus your talents as an engineer on olving only technical issues and assume the rest of society will address the nontechni-cal issues. The same skill sets you are currently developing to solve technical issues can be applied to solve issues outside the field of engineering. Your ability as an engineer to effectively examine and organize facts and information in a logical manner and then present our conclusions in an unbiased fashion allows others to more fully understand complex issues and in turn help develop better solutions.

This does not mean that as an engineering profession, we are going to solve all of the world's problems. It simply means that it is our responsibility to use our skills and talents as engineers in helping to solve them. It is our obligation to actively use our skills and talents to act upon issues impacting our local, national, and global communi-ties, not merely watching as passive observers.

I challenge you to pick one issue or problem facing society that you feel passionate about and get involved. Once you do, you will be surprised at the impact you can have, even if on a small scale. By adhering to the Engineering Canon and Creed in your professional life and getting actively involved trying to solve societal issues in your personal life, you will be fulfilling your social responsibility.

In-Class Activities

ICA 2-1

For each of the following situations, indicate whether you think the a
or you are unsure. Do not read ahead; do not go back and change you

Situation	Ethical	Unethical	unethical
1. Not leaving a tip after a meal because your steak was not cooked to your liking			
2. Speeding 5 miles per hour over the limit			
3. Killing a roach			
4. Speeding 15 miles per hour over the limit			
5. Having plastic surgery after an accident			
6. Killing a mouse			
7. Driving 90 miles per hour			
8. Using Botox			
9. Not leaving a tip after a meal because the waiter was inattentive			
10. Killing a healthy cat			
11. Driving 90 miles per hour taking an injured child to the hospital			
12. Killing a healthy horse			
13. Dyeing your hair			
14. Killing a person			
15. Having liposuction			

2-2

each of the following situations, indicate whether you think the action is ethical or unethical
you are unsure. Do not read ahead; do not go back and change your answers.

Situation	Ethical	Unethical	Unsure
1. Using time at work to IM your roommate			
2. Accepting a pen and pad of paper from a company trying to sell a new computer system to your company			
3. Obtaining a fake ID to purchase alcohol			
4. Using time at work to plan your friend's surprise party			
5. Accepting a wedge of cheese from a company trying to sell a new computer system to your company			
6. Taking a company pen home from work			
7. Taking extra time at lunch once a month to run a personal errand			
8. Accepting a set of golf clubs from a company trying to sell a new computer system to your company			
9. Drinking a beer while underage at a party in your dorm			
10. Using the company copier to copy your tax return			
11. Drinking a beer when underage at a party, knowing you will need to drive yourself and your roommate home			
12. Taking extra time at lunch once a week to run a personal errand			
13. Borrowing company tools			
14. Going to an NC-17 rated movie when underage			
15. Accepting a Hawaiian vacation from a company trying to sell a new computer system to your company			

ICA 2-3

For each of the following situations, indicate whether you think th[...] is ethical or unethical or you are unsure. Do not read ahead; do not go back and change y[...]rs.

Situation	Ethical	Unethical	Unsure
1. Acting happy to see an acquaintance who is spreading rumors about you			
2. Letting a friend who has been sick copy your homework			
3. Shortcutting by walking across the grass on campus			
4. "Mooning" your friends as you drive by their apartment			
5. Registering as a Democrat even though you are a Republican			
6. Cheating on a test			
7. Shortcutting by walking across the grass behind a house			
8. Saying that you lunched with a coworker, rather than your high school sweetheart, when your spouse asks who you ate lunch with			
9. Helping people with their homework			
10. Shortcutting by walking through a building on campus			
11. Not telling your professor that you accidentally saw several of the final exam problems when you visited his or her office			
12. Suppressing derogatory comments about the college because the dean has asked you not to say anything negative when he or she invited you [to] meet with an external board [eval]uating the college			
[13. Letting] somebody copy your [homewo]rk			
[14. Shortcutting] by walking through a [building on campus]			
[15. Telling your] professor that your [exam] was incorrectly totaled [as X inst]ead of the correct 58			

ICA 2-4

For each of the following situations, indicate how great you feel the need is in the world to solve the problem listed. Do not read ahead; do not go back and change your answers.

Situation	Urgent	Great	Somewhat	Little	None
1. Teaching those who cannot read or write					
2. Helping starving children in poor nations					
3. Helping people locked in prisons					
4. Helping to slow population growth					
5. Helping to reduce dependence on foreign oil					
6. Helping to reduce greenhouse gas emissions					
7. Helping people persecuted for sexual orientation					
8. Helping to reduce gun ownership					
9. Helping those who are mentally disabled					
10. Helping to supply laptops to poor children					
11. Helping prevent prosecution of "victimless" crimes					
12. Helping to end bigotry					
13. Helping to prevent development of WMD (weapons of mass destruction)					
14. Helping prosecute "hate" crimes					
15. Helping to eliminate violence in movies					
16. Helping homeless people in your community					
17. Helping people with AIDS					
18. Helping people in warring countries					
19. Helping endangered species					

ICA 2-5

Discuss the possible actions, if any, that you would take in each of the following situations. In each case, use the four-step analysis procedure presented in Section 2.1 to help determine an appropriate answer.

(a) Your roommate purchased a theme over the Internet and submitted it as his or her own work in English class.

(b) Your project team has been trying to get your design to work reliably for 2 weeks, but it still fails about 20% of the time. Your teammate notices another team's design that is much simpler, that is easy to build, and that works almost every time. Your teammate wants your group to build a replica of the other team's project at the last minute.

(c) You notice that your professor forgot to log off the computer in lab. You are the only person left in the room.

(d) The best student in the class, who consistently wrecks the "curve" by making 15–20 points higher than anyone else on every test, accidentally left her notes for the course in the classroom.

(e) You have already accepted and signed the paperwork for a position as an intern at ENGR-R-US. You then get an invitation to interview for an intern position (all expenses paid) at another company in a city you have always wanted to visit. What would you do? Would you behave differently if the agreement was verbal, but the papers had not been signed?

(f) One of your professors has posted a political cartoon with which both you and your friend vehemently disagree. The friend removes the cartoon from the bulletin board and tears it up.

ICA 2-6

Discuss the possible actions, if any, that you would take in each of the following situations. In each case, use the four-step analysis procedure presented in Section 2.1 to help determine an appropriate answer.

(a) You witness several students eating lunch on a bench on campus. When they finish, they leave their trash on the ground.

(b) You see a student carving his initials in one of the largest beech trees on campus.

(c) You see a student writing graffiti on a trash dumpster.

(d) There is a squirrel in the road ahead of a car you are driving. You know that a squirrel's instinct is to dart back and forth rather than run in a straight line away from a predator (in this case a vehicle) making it quite likely it will dart back into the road at the last instant.

(e) You find a wallet containing twenty-three $100 bills. The owner's contact information is quite clear. Does your answer change if the wallet contained three $1 bills?

ICA 2-7

Read the Engineer's Creed section of this chapter.

If you are planning to pursue a career in engineering: Type the creed word for word, then write a paragraph (100–200 words) on what the creed means to you, in your own words, and how the creed make you feel about your chosen profession (engineering).

If you are planning to pursue a career other than engineering, does your future discipline have such a creed? If so, look this up and type it, then write a paragraph (100–200 words) on what the creed means to you, in your own words, and how the creed makes you feel about your chosen profession. If not, write a paragraph (100–200 words) on what items should be included in a creed if your profession had one and how the lack of a creed makes you feel about your chosen profession.

ICA 2-8

Engineers often face workplace situations in which the ethical aspects of the job should be considered.

Table 2-1 lists a variety of types of organizations that hire engineers, and one or more possibly ethical issues that might arise.

Pick several of the organizations from the table that interest you (or those assigned by your professor) and answer the following:

(a) Can you think of other ethical problems that might arise at each of these organizations?

(b) Apply the four-step ethical decision-making procedure to gain insight into the nature of the decision to be made. In some cases, you may decide that an ethical issue is not really involved, but you should be able to justify why it is not.

(c) List 10 other types of organizations at which engineers would confront ethical problems, and explain the nature of the ethical decisions to be made.

(d) How does one find a balance between profit and environmental concerns?

(e) Under what circumstances should an engineer be held liable for personal injury or property damage caused by the products of his or her labor?

(f) Under what situations would you blow the whistle on your superior or your company?

(g) Should attorneys specializing in personal injury and property damage litigation be allowed to advertise, and if so, in what venues?

Table 2-1 **Industries and issues for ICA 2-8**

Organization/Occupation	Possible Issues
Alternative energy providers	Use of heavy metals in photovoltaic systems Effect of wind generators on bird populations Aesthetic considerations (e.g., NIMBY) Environmental concerns (e.g., Three Gorges project)
Environmental projects	Fertile floodplains inundated by dams/lakes Safety compromised for cost (e.g., New Orleans levees) Habitat destruction by projects Habitat renovation versus cost (e.g., Everglades)
Chemical engineers	Toxic effluents from manufacturing process Pesticide effect on ecosystem (e.g., artificial estrogens) Insufficient longitudinal studies of pharmaceuticals Non-biodegradable products (e.g., plastics)
Civil engineers	Runoff/erosion at large projects Disruption of migration routes (freeways) Quality of urban environments Failure modes of structures
Computer engineers	Vulnerability of software to malware Intellectual property rights (e.g., illegal downloads) Safety issues (e.g., programmed medical devices, computer-controlled transportation)
Electrical engineers	Toxic materials in batteries Cell phone safety concerns Power grid safety and quick restoration in crises Possible use to break the law (e.g., radar detectors)
Electric power industry	Shipment of high sulfur coal to China Disposal of nuclear waste Environmental issues (e.g., spraying power-line corridors)
Food processing industry	Health possibly compromised by high fat/sugar/salt products Use of genetically engineered organisms Sanitation (e.g., *Escherichia coli*, *Salmonella*) Use of artificial preservatives
Manufacturing companies	Manufacturing in countries with poor labor practices Lax safety standards in some countries Domestic jobs lost Environmental pollution due to shipping distances Trade imbalance
Industrial engineers	Quality/safety compromised by cost Efficiency versus quality of working environment Management of dangerous tools and materials
Mechanical engineers	Automotive safety versus cost Environmental impact of fossil fuels Robot failsafe mechanisms

CHAPTER 3
DESIGN AND TEAMWORK

Regardless of your selected engineering discipline or career path, communication is critical for survival as an engineer. Due to the complexity of many analysis and design projects, it is necessary for all engineers to operate effectively on a team. For a project to be completed successfully, there needs to be a synergy of all entities engaged, including design and teamwork. This chapter introduces the two together to emphasize the importance of teamwork in the design process.

3.1 THE DESIGN PROCESS

Design is a creative process that requires problem definition, idea searches, solutions development, and solutions sharing. Design is inherently multiobjective, so one expects that any problem addressed will have multiple solutions. While a particular solution might address some objectives very well, other objectives might not be well suited at all. The goal is to identify the design that meets the most important objectives. To evaluate ideas and communicate them to others, engineers commonly sketch possible solutions and even build models of their work.

There are many different versions of "the design process," but they have a lot of similarities. Recognizing that design is a creative process, it is more important to think about "a design process." The process we will use is the one used to design engineering education itself. ABET (pronounced with a long "A") was once the Accreditation Board for Engineering and Technology but is known now by just the acronym because it accredits computing and applied science programs as well. In 1932 ABET was established as the Engineers' Council for Professional Development (ECPD). ECPD was formed to fill the apparent need for a "joint program for upbuilding engineering as a profession." Currently, ABET accredits some 2,700 programs at more than 550 colleges and universities nationwide. Accreditation is a non-governmental, peer-review process. ABET accreditation is assurance that a college or university program meets the quality standards established by the profession for which it prepares its students.

The engineering profession is self-governing; the Engineering Accreditation Commission of ABET is made up of member engineering societies, and the Commission operates under a philosophy of outcomes assessment. This approach focuses on determining the outcomes we desire in engineering graduates and allowing the engineering degree program the flexibility of determining how to achieve those outcomes and demonstrating how they have been achieved.

The design process for engineering programs is made up of two iterative processes, shown in Figure 3-1. The iterative loop on the left comes first because a new program would begin there; it includes getting input from constituencies, determining educational objectives, and evaluating or assessing how well those objectives are being

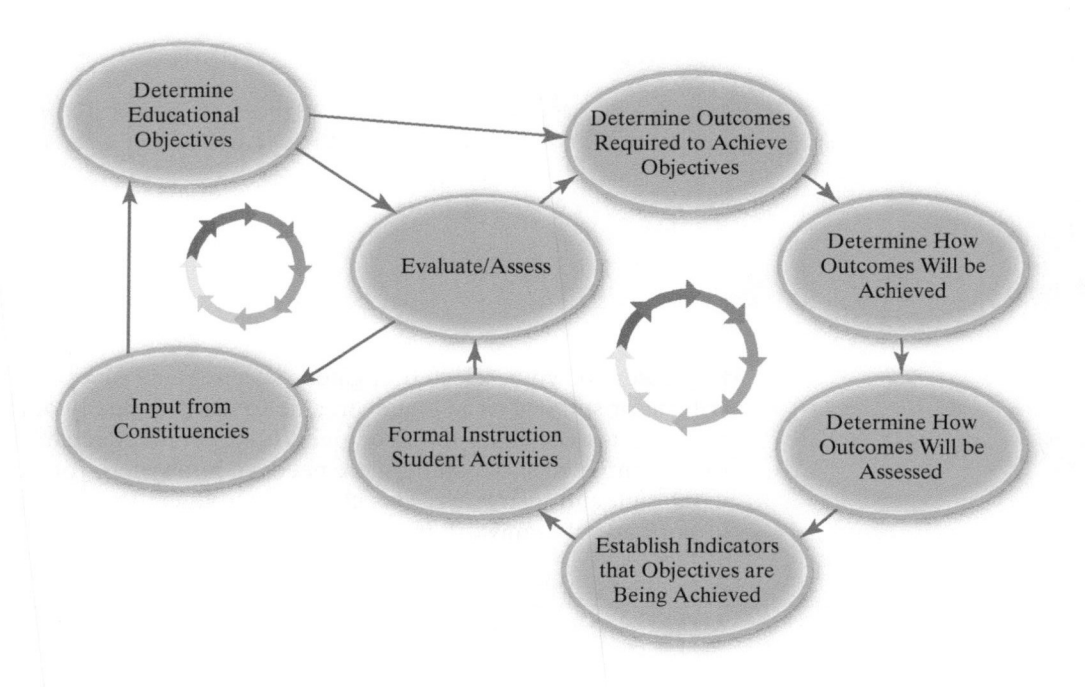

Figure 3-1 The ABET design approach.

achieved. In other engineering processes, these steps might be called something like "problem definition." "Constituencies" may also be called users, clients, stakeholders, or other terms. The process is iterative because it is important to confirm that the constituencies are pleased with the results, to adapt to changing needs, and to achieve the continuous improvement expected by the engineering profession.

With the problem identified (knowing our educational objectives), the iterative process on the right side of Figure 3-1 begins. This process occurs primarily in the designer's workspace, whatever that is. In the case of designing engineering curriculum, the process takes place within the walls of the university or college. Knowing the objectives, the design team determines the outcomes that will accomplish those objectives, how those outcomes will be achieved, how they will be assessed, and what indicators will demonstrate success before any students are actually taught. Once students have had learning experiences (including extracurricular experiences), evaluation and assessment guide both processes into another cycle.

The step "determine outcomes required to achieve objectives" is called "problem definition" or "specification" in many other design processes. This step is critical because it shapes all the others. "Determine how the outcomes will be achieved" is a particularly creative step in the process and is commonly referred to as "generating ideas," "innovating," "developing possible solutions," or something similar, and might include "research." "Determine how the outcomes will be assessed" is a step that might not be mentioned if most agree on how to measure the success of a design, but in designs with more complex objectives, designers must think carefully about what will be measured and how, finishing up with determining indicators of success. These steps are commonly called "analysis" in a more general design process, breaking down the design to examine its assumptions, benefits, and risks. The remaining part of the process is one of "prototyping," "implementation," and "testing."

What follows in this chapter describes the tools engineers use in this process.

3.2 BRAINSTORMING IN THE DESIGN PROCESS

Most high-school graduates have heard the term **brainstorming**, and many have participated in a process called by that name. This term refers to one particular process by which ideas are generated. Idea generation follows three common rules: encourage a lot of ideas, encourage a wide variety of ideas, and do not criticize. The third rule is important if the first two are to be achieved. It has been said: "The best way to get a good idea is to get lots of ideas!"

Where is quality in this process? We have often been encouraged on "quality, not quantity." While some idea-generation methods facilitate the identification of a small number of quality solutions, in brainstorming, "quality *is* quantity." The nature of generating and evaluating ideas is that the greater the number of ideas generated, the more likely that several high-quality ideas are found.

The following story is taken from Alex Osborn's *Applied Imagination* (out of print), illustrating the importance of generating ideas before evaluating them.

> *In November 1952, in Washington State, the local telephone company had to clear the frost from 700 miles of telephone lines to restore long distance service. The company believed strongly enough in the importance of variety in the process that ALL the company's employees were asked to participate in a brainstorming session, executives and secretaries, engineers and linemen.*
>
> *After some time of idea generation, it was clear that the participants needed a break. One of the sessions overheard one lineman say to another at the water fountain, "Ever had a bear chase you up one of the poles? That would sure shake the ice off the lines!" The facilitator encouraged the lineman to repeat himself when the session reconvened.*
>
> *The facilitator hoped that the unusual suggestion would encourage new ideas, and the lineman sheepishly offered his suggestion. "How should we encourage the bears to climb all the poles?" asked the facilitator. "We could put honey pots at the tops of all the poles!" shouted someone else in the room. "How should we put honey pots on the tops of all the poles?" asked the facilitator. "Use the company helicopters that the executives use!" piped in another participant. "Hmm," said one of the company secretaries calmly. "When I served in the Korean War, I was impressed by the force of the downdraft off helicopter blades. I wonder if that would be enough to shake the ice off the power lines."*

The idea was so intriguing that it was tested immediately—it provided a successful and economically viable solution. This story clearly illustrates the benefit of variety and the value of avoiding criticism in a brainstorming session. The rest of the story illustrates how essential quantity is to the process.

A problem-solving group composed of five veteran air force helicopter pilots was convened to address this same problem. Each was unfamiliar with the solution that had already been implemented. It was hoped that because of their background, they would eventually arrive at the same solution. In fact, they did, but it was the 36th idea on their list. If they had stopped after generating 35 ideas, they may very well have had an acceptable solution, but it might not have been as elegant or as successful as the proven solution.

NOTE

Brainstorming Rules:

- More is better.
- Variety is better.
- Do not criticize.

NOTE

Another great example of brainstorming is baking soda. Originally marketed for culinary use, today it is found in hundreds of products. How do you sell more product? Find more ways to use it!

3.3 EXPERIMENTAL DESIGN: PERIOD ANALYSIS

Experiments enable engineers to come up with a creative solution to a problem and test the validity of the proposed idea. An experiment is a test of a proposed explanation of a problem. A good design of an experiment is a critical part of the scientific method.

What Constitutes the Scientific Method?

1. Observation: Observe the problem and note items of interest.
2. Hypothesis: Search for a known explanation of the phenomenon or attempt to formulate a new explanation.
3. Prediction: Create a model or prediction of behavior based on that hypothesis.
4. Experiment: Test your predictions. If necessary, modify your hypothesis and retest.

Why Is Experimental Design Important?

As you move through your college career, you will be inundated with many equations and theories. These are useful in solving a wide variety of problems. However, as you will see, often the equations are only really useful in solving the most basic type of problems.

As an example, suppose you are interested in the speed of a ball as it rolls across the floor after rolling down a ramp. In physics, you will learn the equations of motion for bodies moving under the influence of gravity. If you are good, you can use these to examine rolling balls. What you will quickly find, however, is that numerous complicating factors make it difficult to apply the basic equations to obtain an adequate answer. Let us suppose you are interested in smooth balls (such as racquetballs), rough balls (tennis balls), heavy balls (bowling balls), and lightweight balls (ping-pong balls). The simplified equations of motion predict that all these will behave in essentially the same way. You will discover, however, that the drag of the air affects the ping-pong ball, the fuzz affects the tennis ball, and the flexible nature of the racquetball will allow it to bounce at steep ramp angles. It is difficult to predict the behavior analytically. Often, one of the quickest ways to learn about the performance of such complex situations is to conduct experiments.

What Are Experimental Measurements?

NOTE

Do you know what these unique measurement instruments do?

- Durometer
- Dynamometer
- Euidometer
- Galvanometer
- Gyroscope
- Manometer
- Opisometer
- Pycnometer
- Tachymeter
- Thiele tube

Most scientific experiments involve measuring the effect of variability of an attribute of an object. In an experiment, the **independent variable** is the variable that is controlled. The **dependent variable** is a variable that reacts to a change in the independent variable. A **control variable** is part of the experiment that can vary but is held constant to let the experimenter observe the influence of the independent variable on the dependent variable. Keeping control variables constant throughout an experiment eliminates any confounding effects resulting from excess variability.

Any measurement acquired in an experiment contains two important pieces of information. First, the measurement contains the actual value measured from the instrument. In general, a measurement is some physical dimension that is acquired with some man-made data-collection instrument. As with any man-made device, there may be some imperfection that can cause adverse effects during data collection. Thus, the second piece of information that goes along with any measurement is the level of uncertainty.

Any uncertainty in measurement is not strictly by instrumentation error. Systematic error is any error resulting from human or instrumentation malfunction. Random error is caused by the limits of the precision of the data-collection device. It is possible to minimize the systematic error in an experiment, but random error cannot be completely eliminated.

What Measurements Do You Need to Make?

You need to develop a coherent experimental program. You should make enough measurements to answer any anticipated questions, but you do not usually have the time or money to test every possible condition. Points to consider:

- What are the parameters of interest?
- What is the range of these parameters—minimum values, maximum values?
- What increments are reasonable for testing (every 10 degrees, every 30 seconds, etc.)?
- What order is best to vary the parameters? Which should be tested first, next, etc.?

Here is an acronym (PERIOD) that can help you remember these important steps. As an example, it is applied to the problem of the ramp and rolling balls, described above.

P – Parameters of interest determined

- Parameter 1 is the ramp angle.
- Parameter 2 is the distance up the ramp that we release the ball.
- Parameter 3 is the type of ball.

E – Establish the range of parameters

- Ramp angle can vary between 0 and 90 degrees in theory, but in reality can only vary between 10 degrees (if too shallow, ball would not move) and 45 degrees (if too steep, ball will bounce).
- The distance we release the ball up the ramp can vary between 0 and 3 feet in theory, assuming that the ramp is 3 feet long. We cannot release the ball too close to the bottom of the ramp or it would not move. In reality, we can only vary between 0.5 and 3 feet.
- We will test as many types of balls as we have interest in.

R – Repetition of each test specified

- The ramp angle will be set according to the height of the ramp from the floor, so there is not much room for error in this measurement; only one measurement is needed for such geometry.
- Each placement of the ball before release will vary slightly and may cause the ball to roll slightly differently down the ramp; this is probably the most important factor in determining the speed, so three measurements at each location are needed.
- We will assume that every ball is the same, and the actual ball used will not change the outcome of the experiment; only one ball of each type is needed.

I – Increments of each parameter specified

- We will test every 10 degrees of ramp angle, starting at 10 degrees and ending at 40 degrees.
- We will release the balls at a height of 0.5, 1, 1.5, 2, 2.5, and 3 feet up the ramp.
- We will test five types of balls: racquetball, baseball, tennis ball, ping-pong ball, and bowling ball.

O – Order to vary the parameters determined

- We will set the ramp angle and then test one ball type by releasing it at each of the four different distances up the ramp.
- We will repeat this process three times for each ball.
- We will then repeat this process for each type of ball.
- We will then change the ramp angle by 10 degrees and repeat the process.
- This process is repeated until all conditions have been tested.

D - Determine number of measurements needed and Do the experiment

It is always important to determine before you start how many measurements you need to make. Sometimes you can be too ambitious and end up developing an experimental program that will take too much effort or cost too much money. If this is the case, then you need to decide which increments can be relaxed, to reduce the number of overall measurements.

The number of measurements (N) you will need to make can be easily calculated by the following equation for a total of n parameters:

N = (# increments parameter 1 * number of repetitions for parameter 1) *

(# increments parameter 2 * number of repetitions for parameter 2) *. . .

(# increments parameter n * number of repetitions for parameter n) * . . .

Continuing the examples given above, the number of actual measurements that we need to make is calculated as

N = (4 angles) * (6 distances * 3 repetitions) * (5 types of balls) = 360 measurements

In this example, 360 measurements may be extreme. If we examine our plan, we can probably make the following changes without losing experimental information:

- We decide to test every 10 degrees of ramp angle, starting at 20 degrees and ending at 40 degrees. This will lower the angle testing from four to three angles.
- We will release the balls at a height of 1, 2, 2.5, and 3 ft up the ramp. This will lower the distances from six to four.
- We will test three types of balls: racquetball, ping-pong ball, and bowling ball. This will lower the type of balls from five to three.

The number of actual measurements that we now need to make is calculated as

N = (3 angles) * (4 distances * 3 repetitions) * (3 types of balls) = 108 measurements

This result seems much more manageable to complete than 360!

3.4 CRITERIA AND EVALUATION

We can generate and evaluate problem definitions, implementation strategies, and even the methods we use to evaluate our implementations. Brainstorming problem definitions stresses how the way we define a problem affects the solutions we consider. Is the problem that there is ice on the electrical lines, that there is water on the lines that can freeze, or that the lines and surrounding air are too cold? Looking at the problem these three different ways suggests different solution approaches. The second might suggest covering the lines to keep them dry or coating them with a material with special hydrophobic properties. The third might suggest heating the lines or moving them to somewhere warmer (maybe underground).

There are countless examples of how redefining a problem has been commercially profitable. When Dum Dum Pops® are made, the process is continuous, which causes the manufacture of some lollipops that combine two of the flavors. This might have been considered a problem, and some companies would have designed their manufacturing process so as to stop and clean the machinery between flavor runs. Instead, the Dum Dum company wraps these "combination" flavor lollipops and labels them "Mystery" flavor. By their defining the problem a different way, a creative solution emerged, saving money and providing a market attraction. In all designs, the way in which the problem is defined will affect the set of solutions explored. Once a particular solution approach is selected, it might be appropriate to generate and evaluate ideas for how to implement that solution.

Criteria: Deciding What Is Important

First, the problem definition must be clear so that we can generate an appropriate set of criteria. Then, when we stop generating solutions and begin evaluating the various solutions, we use those **criteria** to narrow our choices objectively. We might be particularly concerned about cost, so certain approaches become less attractive. Other proposed solutions might be hazardous, thus further narrowing our options. The criteria for evaluating potential solutions must be well defined before evaluation begins so that all ideas can be considered fairly—this helps avoid arguments based on hidden criteria.

Defining criteria before brainstorming solutions seems as if it might threaten the "do not criticize" objective—proposed solutions could be steered to match the expectations established by the criteria. Unfortunately, while defining criteria first might constrain idea generation, generating solutions first might cause participants to develop an opinion of a "best solution" and then force their criteria choices to fit their preferred idea. In this way, the process of generating solutions and the process of generating criteria to evaluate those solutions are linked. The second interaction is more damaging to the design process, so we will focus on identifying constraints and criteria first.

COMPREHENSION CHECK 3-1

We frequently express criteria in terms that are not clear and measurable. Write a clear criterion to replace each of these vague criteria for the products.

Product	Computer	Automobile	Bookshelf
Inexpensive	Less than $300		
Small			
Easy to assemble			Requires only a screwdriver
Aesthetically pleasing			
Lightweight			
Safe			
Durable			
Environmentally friendly		Has an estimated MPG of at least 50	

In general, using fewer criteria keeps things simple. A rule of thumb is that if you can think of 10 criteria that are meaningful, you should consider only the two most important criteria to compare solutions. In this way, you can be sure that the important criteria maintain their importance in your decision-making. Seek consensus on what the most important criteria are. Experts, specialists, managers, customers, research, etc., can help you focus on the most important criteria. In certain situations, many criteria are used—for example, when a magazine rates consumer products, extra criteria should be included to be sure that all the criteria important to the magazine's readers have been considered.

Another situation, in which a large number of criteria are included, occurs when very complex decisions are being evaluated. The U.S. Green Building Council has long lists of criteria used for certifying various types of projects according to the Leadership in Energy and Environmental Design (LEED) Green Building Rating System. A subset of items from the LEED for Homes project checklist is shown below.

LEED is an internationally recognized green building certification system, providing third-party verification that a building or community was designed and built using strategies aimed at improving performance across all the metrics that matter most: energy savings, water efficiency, CO_2 emissions reduction, improved indoor environmental quality, and stewardship of resources and sensitivity to their impacts.

From the U.S. Green Building Council website: www.usgbc.org

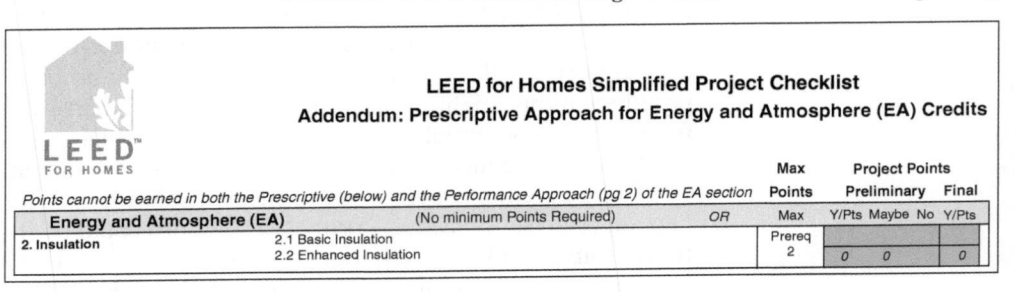

These checklist items are neither clear nor measurable, however, as shown above. The full LEED for Homes rating system and the reference guide associated with the rating system provide the additional detail needed to make the insulation criteria both clear and measurable. Note that these criteria build from existing standards, meaning that even greater levels of detail can be found elsewhere (e.g., Chapter 4 of the 2004 International Energy Conservation Code and The National Home Energy Rating Standards).

Prerequisites

2.1 Basic Insulation. Meet all the following requirements:

(a) Install insulation that meets or exceeds the R-value requirements listed in Chapter 4 of the 2004 International Energy Conservation Code. Alternative wall and insulation systems, such as structural insulated panels (SIPs) and insulated concrete forms (ICFs), must demonstrate a comparable R-value, but thermal mass or infiltration effects cannot be included in the R-value calculation.

(b) Install insulation to meet the Grade II specifications set by the National Home Energy Rating Standards (Table 16). Installation must be verified by an energy rater or Green Rater conducting a predrywall thermal bypass inspection, as summarized in Figure 3.

Note: For any portion of the home constructed with SIPs or ICFs, the rater must conduct a modified visual inspection using the ENERGY STAR Structural Insulated Panel Visual Inspection Form.

Note that the LEED criteria specify only those characteristics that are important to the overall goal of green building. This leaves the choice of the type of insulation (fiberglass, cellulose) up to the designer and the consumer. Because homes, outdoor facilities, and factories face different challenges, different LEED criteria apply. It is important to recognize which choices are "options" rather than criteria—even the most energy efficient factory cannot substitute for a house. Further, the LEED criteria allow different thresholds for different size houses, so as not to penalize multifamily households—even though multifamily households will require more material to build and more energy to operate, the marginal cost is not as high as building another home.

When designing a product or a process, you must first listen to what a client wants and needs. The "client" might be from a department such as manufacturing, marketing, or accounting; a customer; your boss; the government; etc. Subsequently, you will need to translate those wants and needs into engineering specifications. Pay particular attention to separating the wants (criteria) from the needs (requirements). Requirements can be imposed legally (e.g., Corporate Average Fuel Economy regulations, building codes), they can be from within your company (e.g., the finished product must not cost more than $50 to manufacture), or they may come from your client (e.g., the product must be made from at least 90% recycled material).

COMPREHENSION CHECK 3-2	You have been asked to improve the fuel efficiency of an automobile by 20%. Convert this request into engineering criteria. What changes might be made to the automobile to achieve this objective?

Evaluation: Deciding on Options

Simply identifying criteria is not enough information for a decision—each proposed solution must be evaluated against the criteria. The first step will be to eliminate any solutions that do not meet the minimum requirements—those solutions are out-of-bounds and need not be considered further.

Once the minimum requirements have been satisfied, there are many ways of applying the remaining criteria to select a solution. One approach is to make **pairwise comparisons**. In this approach, you use a table for each criterion to summarize how each of the solutions compares with others. An example is shown in Table 3-1 for the criterion "safety." Among the table entries, 0 indicates that that option in that column is worse than the option in that row; 1 indicates that both options rank equally; and 2 indicates that that option in that column is better than the option in that row.

Table 3-1 **Comparing options**

Safety	Option 1	Option 2	Option 3
Option 1		0	1
Option 2	0		0
Option 3	1	2	
Total	1	2	1

Since a high level of safety is preferred, "better" means "safer." In the example, the first column indicates that option 1 is less safe than option 2, but the same as option 3. The resulting totals indicate that option 2 ranks best in terms of safety. To complete the process, generate similar tables for each of the criteria being considered and then sum the totals to identify the best solution.

A disadvantage of the pairwise comparisons approach is that all criteria have equal weight, whereas some criteria are likely to be more important than others. An alternative approach is to use **weighted benefit analysis**, shown in Table 3-2. In this approach, each option is scored against each of the criteria.

Table 3-2 Options with a weighted benefit analysis

	Weights	Option 1	Option 2	Option 3
Cost	2	2	6	10
Safety	8	10	4	6
Weight	10	7	7	2
Wow	5	2	4	6
Totals		$4 + 80 + 70 + 10 = 164$	$12 + 32 + 70 + 20 = 134$	$20 + 48 + 20 + 30 = 118$

Table 3-3 Sample scoring rubric

Score	Meaning
0	Not satisfactory
1	Barely applicable
2	Fairly good
3	Good
4	Very good; ideal

In Table 3-2, the weights are in the first column and each option has been assigned a score from 0 to 10, indicating how well that option meets each criterion. This approach may be inconsistent in that a "7" for one rater may be different from a "7" for another rater, so it can help to better define the scale. For example, the options may be scored on the scale shown in Table 3-3 as to how well the option fits each criterion.

Reality: Checking It Out

When a solution has been identified as the best fit to the criteria, it is best to stop for a reality check before moving forward. After the evaluation process, some ideas will be left on the cutting room floor. Do any of these merit further consideration? Are there important elements of those ideas that can be incorporated into the chosen design? If the reality check reveals that an idea really should not have been eliminated, then a change in the selection criteria may be appropriate.

After deciding, you will implement your chosen solution. Undoubtedly, both carrying out the design and using the design once it is complete will provide new information about how the design might be improved. In this way, design tends to be iterative—design, build, test, redesign, and so on. Even when a design performs as expected, it may be important to test a model extensively or even build multiple models to be sure that the design is reliable.

WISE WORDS: IN YOUR JOB, DO YOU WORK ALONE OR ON A TEAM?

I often work alone on projects and analyses, but I do need to interact with client company teams, sometimes leading the team as an outside expert, but still a "member" of the company I am trying to help. Some of the teams I will work with also have mechanical, chemical, industrial, and process engineers involved.

E. Basta, MSE

I work on a team made up of all electrical and computer engineers.

E. D'Avignon, CpE

Team: chemist, package engineer, process development engineer (chemical engineer), industrial designer, line engineer (mechanical engineer or chemical engineer), process engineer (chemical engineer), planner, quality engineer, marketing, and market research.

S. Forkner, ChE

I work mostly alone on my assignments. I am given tasks and I have to find solutions for my problems on my own. Only when needed I consult someone for questions and guidance on my task.

V. Gallas Cervo, ME

I worked the first 5 years of my career as a "sole contributor" in an engineering role. Since then, I have worked in a team setting managing technical employees.

L. Gascoigne, CE

I work with a chemical engineer, an instrumentation engineer, a mechanical engineer, and a piping engineer.

D. Jones, BE

Every project involves a team. My typical team includes surveyors, structural engineers, environmental scientists (wetlands, endangered species), permit specialists, electrical engineers, land appraisers, archaeologists, and architects.

J. Meena, CE

I work alone, but seek advice from my management team.

C. Pringle, IE

I work on a team including mechanical, electrical, aeronautical and systems hardware designers, software designers, integrators, power engineers, and other liaisons like myself.

E. Styles, EE

The Hubble Space Telescope servicing mission project is made up of a team of mechanical design engineers, human factors engineers, environmental test engineers, thermal engineers, underwater test engineers, safety engineers, mechanical technicians, documentation specialists, space scientists, and systems engineers.

R. Werneth, ME

3.5 SUSTAINABILITY

Contributed by: Dr. Leidy Klotz, Associate Professor,
Civil Engineering, Clemson University

The most common definition of sustainability is "meeting the needs of the present without compromising the ability of future generations to do the same."[1] Notice that this definition is fundamentally about people. There is no mention of hippies or saving trees just for the sake of saving trees (of course, we are dependent on the ecosystem services trees provide). Notice also that the definition includes future generations as well as present ones. Sustainability is not just an issue for our children and grandchildren, it is an issue that is affecting all of us right now.

"Environmental" and sustainability are often used interchangeably; however, sustainability also has social and economic dimensions. All three of these dimensions must be balanced for truly sustainable engineering solutions. The figures show the relationships between these dimensions. Our society would not exist if our environment did not support human life. Our economy would not exist if we did not have a stable society (most people do not want to start businesses in failed states). These relationships seem quite obvious, but can be overlooked if we just focus on one dimension of sustainability. As business leader Peter Senge points out: "the economy is the wholly owned subsidiary of nature, not the other way around."

You can apply a basic understanding of sustainability to your own engineering solutions. Sustainability is not a stand-alone topic. It cannot be bolted onto an engineering design at the end of the project. For example, in a new building project, one of the first sustainability considerations should be whether this project is even necessary. Perhaps similar goals could be achieved by more efficient use of existing facilities. This is quite an ethical dilemma! Imagine telling a potential client they do not need to hire and pay your engineering firm to design a new building. Assuming the building project is necessary, some of the best sustainability opportunities occur early on in the project, during project planning and design. This is where engineers play a key role. Teamwork and communication in the process are vital because sustainable solutions require consideration of multiple issues. We must be able to work with engineers from different disciplines and with non-engineers such as architects, contractors, and lawmakers. We must be able to communicate with the end users who will occupy and operate the building. After all, the end user is the recipient of your design. These basic ideas apply across disciplines, whether you are designing a building, an engine, or a new material.

You may be wondering how much humanity currently considers sustainability. Maybe we are already on a sustainable path? Unfortunately, this is not the case. Our use of critical resources, such as energy and water, and less critical resources, such as tequila and chocolate, cannot be sustained at current rates. Increasing population and affluence will stress these resources even more. Allocation of resources for the present and future is a huge ethical question engineers must consider. Should you build a reservoir that will provide water for an impoverished area, but restrict availability downstream? Do the risks associated with nuclear energy outweigh the fact that it is a carbon-free source of energy?

Creating solutions for sustainability issues requires expanding the boundaries of single-discipline thinking, being able to recognize relationships between systems and the associated problems and opportunities. For example, our fossil-fuel based energy system has increased standards of living all over the world but this same system also contributes to climate change, which is already having significant negative impacts, with more predicted for the future. In addition, the system contributes to inequalities between those who

---

[1]From the UN's Brundtland report.

have energy and those who do not, which is a major source of poverty and conflict. These complex relationships can make problems seem overwhelming; however, these relationships also offer opportunities. Engineers creating sustainable energy solutions will have positive impacts in multiple areas, such as helping to curb climate changing emissions, while reducing energy poverty and resource conflict. You can make a conscious effort to build your skills in the broad, systems-thinking needed to identify these opportunities.

PERSONAL REFLECTION ON SUSTAINABILITY

Dr. Leidy Klotz

I see sustainability issues as challenges, but also as incredible opportunities for engineers. Is your goal to save the world? Here is your chance. Is your goal to make as much money as possible? Engineering solutions that address sustainability issues offer huge opportunities for profit. Those who figure out ways to make solar energy more economical or provide greater access to clean water will be the Bill Gates and Steve Jobs of their time.

In particular, young engineers must play a key role. It is unlikely that an engineer who graduated before 2005 was exposed to sustainability topics during college. This is an area where older engineers need your help, where you can be a leader right away. History shows us that groundbreaking advances, like those needed in engineering for sustainability, are often made by young people. Albert Einstein had his most groundbreaking year at age 26, the same age at which Martin Luther King Jr. led the Montgomery bus boycott. Thomas Jefferson wrote the declaration of independence at 33, and Harriet Tubman started the Underground Railroad at 28. We need similar innovative ideas and bold actions in all areas of engineering for sustainability. I think young people are our best shot.

Please work hard to learn more about sustainability in engineering. In your area of engineering, learn as much as possible about the fundamentals and how they are related to sustainability. Develop your broad, systems-thinking skills. Take classes that provide additional information on engineering for sustainability. Pursue opportunities for hands-on practice with engineering for sustainability on your campus and beyond. I think you will truly enjoy the collaborative process and unique design challenges associated with creating sustainable solutions!

3.6 WORKING IN TEAMS

> The ability to work in a team is one of the most critical traits an engineer needs. Even if you're the greatest engineer in the world, you will not know all of the answers or have all of the right ideas. We can always learn something from our peers.
>
> *A. Thompson, EE*

Group: *A number of people who come together at the same place, at the same time.*

Team: *Individuals cooperating to accomplish a common goal.*

As a student and in the workplace, you will complete some assignments individually and complete some as part of a team. When you work independently, you are mostly free to choose when and how you will work. When you work as part of a team, make sure the team has ground rules for how it will operate. Any time several people are asked to work closely together, there is a potential for much good from a diversity of ideas and skills but there is also a potential for conflict. Because conflict can be both productive and unproductive, you need to manage it.

Team Behavior

The most critical task for a team, particularly a new team, is to establish its purpose, process (its way of doing things), and a means of measuring team progress. Here are several topics regarding team behavior that you may wish to consider.

- **Ground rules:** Each team needs to come to a consensus about acceptable and unacceptable individuals as well as team behavior.

We trained hard but it seemed that every time we were beginning to form teams we would be reorganized. I was to learn later in life that we tend to meet every situation by reorganizing, and a wonderful method it can be for creating the illusion of progress while producing confusion, inefficiency, and demoralization.

Petronius

- **Decision making:** Teams by necessity make decisions. Each team needs to decide how these decisions will be made. For example, will they be done through consensus, majority vote (either secret or show of hands), or by other methods?
- **Communication:** This is often one of the hardest parts of working effectively as a team. Team members need to recognize the value of real listening and constructive feedback. During the course of team meetings, *every* team member needs to participate *and* listen.
- **Roles:** You may adopt various roles on your team. In a long-term project, roles should rotate so that everyone has a chance to learn each role.
- **Participation:** Decide as a team how work will be distributed. Your team should also consider how to handle shifts in workload when a team member is sick or otherwise unavailable.
- **Values:** The team as a whole needs to acknowledge and accept the unique insights that each team member can contribute to their work.
- **Outcomes:** Discuss and agree on what types of measures will be used to determine that the team has reached its final goal.

Underwater Training for a Hubble Space Telescope Servicing Mission. NASA engineers (on SCUBA) and astronauts (in modified space suits) take advantage of the effects of neutral buoyancy to practice replacing a Wide Field Camera in preparation for a Hubble Space Telescope (HST) servicing mission. Extensive teamwork is required in a 6.2-million gallon pool in Houston, TX, to develop, refine, and practice the procedures to be used on spacewalks in orbit. Engineers from Goddard Space Flight Center in Greenbelt, MD, and Johnson Space Center in Houston work together to perfect the procedures and hardware, including specialized astronaut tools. The team uses models representing the flight items for conducting end-to-end tasks in the neutral buoyancy facility. This unique example of engineering teamwork has resulted in five very successful HST servicing missions involving complex astronaut spacewalks. The challenge to the team is to develop the nominal and contingency procedures and tools on the ground (and in the water!) to be used for mission success with HST in orbit 300 miles up.

R. Werneth

Teammate Evaluation: Practicing Accountability

As previously discussed, engineering is a self-governing profession. ABET is charged with accrediting engineering programs in the United States through membership from the profession. Among a set of required outcomes of engineering graduates, ABET requires that engineering students graduate with an ability to function on multidisciplinary teams. To ensure that each student achieves this outcome, individual accountability is needed. Realizing that much of the activity of a team happens when the team is meeting privately (without a professor), an effective and increasingly common way of addressing this tenet is to have team members rate one another's performance.

It is important to learn how to be an effective team member now, because most engineering work is done in teams, and studies show that most engineering graduates will have supervisory responsibility (at least project management) within 5 years of graduation. You have worked in teams before, so you have probably noticed that some team members are more effective than others. Consider these three snapshots of interactions with engineering students. All three are true stories.

- Three team members approach the professor, concerned that they have not seen the fourth team member yet. The professor speaks with the student, who quickly becomes despondent, alerting the professor to a number of serious burdens the student is bearing. The professor alerts an advisor and the student gets needed help.
- A student, acting as the team spokesperson, tells the professor that one team member never comes to meetings. The professor speaks to the nonparticipating student, who expects to be contacted about meetings by cell phone, not email. The professor explains that the student's expectations are unrealistic.
- A student is insecure about being able to contribute during team activities. After the team's ratings of that student are in, the professor talks to the class about the importance of participating and the different ways students can contribute to a team. In the next evaluation, the student receives the highest rating on the team.

Peer evaluations are a useful way for team members to communicate to one another and to their professor about how the members of a team are performing. Reviewing and evaluating job performance is a marketable skill and is as useful to the employee seeking a job or a job advancement as it is to the supervisor.

Focus on What Your Teammates Do Rather Than What You Think of Them

It is challenging to give a team member a single rating on their effectiveness as a teammate because some team members will be helpful to the team in some ways, but engage in some behaviors that hinder the team. Another difficulty is that each team member is likely to consider some ways of contributing more valuable than others, so the evaluation of a particular teammate will be overly influenced by that teammate's performance in certain areas. The only way to be fair is to focus on behaviors—what your teammates do—rather than opinions such as how you feel about them. One way to focus on behaviors would be to ask you to take an inventory of what behaviors your teammates demonstrate and how often. The result would be that you might need to answer 50 or more questions about each member of the team. It is difficult to stay focused on answering accurately when completing such a long survey. A better way to focus on behaviors is by using sample behaviors to anchor each point of a rating scale. A peer evaluation instrument that is widely used in engineering education is the

Comprehensive Assessment of Team-Member Effectiveness (CATME, see www. catme.org). CATME measures five different types of contributions to a team using such a behaviorally anchored rating scale. Each scale includes representative behaviors describing exceptional, acceptable, and deficient performance in each area. Recognizing that an individual team member may exhibit a combination of behaviors, the CATME instrument also includes "in-between" ratings. The five types of contributions are described below the associate behaviors.

Contributing to the Team's Work describes a team member's commitment to the effort, quality, and timeliness of completing the team's assigned tasks.

- A student who is exceptional at contributing to the team's work
  - Does more or higher-quality work than expected
  - Makes important contributions that improve the team's work
  - Helps to complete the work of teammates who are having difficulty
- A student who does an acceptable job at contributing to the team's work
  - Completes a fair share of the team's work with acceptable quality
  - Keeps commitments and completes assignments on time
  - Fills in for teammates when it is easy or important
- A student who is deficient at contributing to the team's work
  - Does not do a fair share of the team's work. Delivers sloppy or incomplete work
  - Misses deadlines. Is late, unprepared, or absent for team meetings
  - Does not assist teammates. Quits if the work becomes difficult

Interacting with Teammates measures how a team member values and seeks contributions from other team members.

- A student who is exceptional at interacting with teammates
  - Asks for and shows an interest in teammates' ideas and contributions
  - Improves communication among teammates. Provides encouragement or enthusiasm to the team
  - Asks teammates for feedback and uses their suggestions to improve
- A student who does an acceptable job at interacting with teammates
  - Listens to teammates and respects their contributions
  - Communicates clearly. Shares information with teammates. Participates fully in team activities
  - Respects and responds to feedback from teammates
- A student who is deficient at interacting with teammates
  - Interrupts, ignores, bosses, or makes fun of teammates
  - Takes actions that affect teammates without their input. Does not share information
  - Complains, makes excuses, or does not interact with teammates. Accepts no help or advice

Keeping the Team on Track describes how a team member monitors conditions that affect the team's progress and acts on that information as needed.

- A student who is exceptional at keeping the team on track
  - Watches conditions affecting the team and monitors the team's progress
  - Makes sure teammates are making appropriate progress
  - Gives teammates specific, timely, and constructive feedback
- A student who does an acceptable job at keeping the team on track
  - Notices changes that influence the team's success
  - Knows what everyone on the team should be doing and notices problems
  - Alerts teammates or suggests solutions when the team's success is threatened
- A student who is deficient at keeping the team on track
  - Is unaware of whether the team is meeting its goals
  - Does not pay attention to teammates' progress
  - Avoids discussing team problems, even when they are obvious

Expecting Quality is about voicing expectations that the team can and should do high-quality work.

- A student who is exceptional at expecting quality
  - Motivates the team to do excellent work
  - Cares that the team does outstanding work, even if there is no additional reward
  - Believes that the team can do excellent work
- A student who does an acceptable job at expecting quality
  - Encourages the team to do good work that meets all requirements
  - Wants the team to perform well enough to earn all available rewards
  - Believes that the team can fully meet its responsibilities
- A student who is deficient at expecting quality
  - Is satisfied even if the team does not meet assigned standards
  - Wants the team to avoid work, even if it hurts the team
  - Doubts that the team can meet its requirements

Having Relevant Knowledge, Skills, and Abilities accounts for both the talents a member brings to the team and those talents a member develops for the team's benefit.

- A student who has exceptional knowledge, skills, and abilities
  - Demonstrates the knowledge, skills, and abilities to do excellent work
  - Acquires new knowledge or skills to improve the team's performance
  - Is able to perform the role of any team member if necessary.
- A student who has an acceptable level of knowledge, skills, and abilities
  - Has sufficient knowledge, skills, and abilities to contribute to the team's work
  - Acquires knowledge or skills needed to meet requirements
  - Is able to perform some of the tasks normally done by other team members
- A student who has deficient knowledge, skills, and abilities is
  - Missing basic qualifications needed to be a member of the team
  - Unable or unwilling to develop knowledge or skills to contribute to the team
  - Unable to perform any of the duties of other team members

Research shows that team performance can be enhanced if team members reflect on their own and their teammates' performance and give each other high-quality feedback. "High-quality" ratings are consistent with observed behavior, which may or may not be "high" ratings. We also know that rating quality (again, consistency with observed behavior) improves with practice. Guided practice in giving and receiving feedback and in practicing self- and peer-evaluations using behavioral criteria will help you improve. Please take your time in evaluating the members of the fictitious team below.

Pat   Friendly and very well-liked, makes working fun, and keeps everyone excited about working together. Relies on teammates to make sure everything is going okay. Pays attention to keeping the team upbeat but does not seem to notice if the team's work is getting done. Struggles to keep up with the rest of the team and often asks teammates for explanations. The team has to assign Pat the least difficult jobs because Pat does not have the skills to do more complex work. Offers ideas when able, but does not make suggestions that add anything unique or important to the final product. Always shows up for meetings, prepares beforehand, and does everything promised. Is confident that the team can do everything that is essential. Agrees that the team should meet all explicit task requirements.

Chris   Okay as a person and does not interfere with the contributions of others but rubs teammates the wrong way by frequently griping about the work and making excuses for not following through on promises to the team. Chris has the brains and experience to make a unique and valuable contribution, but does not try. The fact that Chris is so smart frustrates some teammates who have to try hard to accomplish tasks that would be easy for Chris. Ignores assigned tasks or does a sloppy job because "Robin will redo the work anyway." Misses meetings or shows up without assigned work. Contributes very little during meetings. Was late to one meeting because "no one told me the meeting time." Missed another meeting because "the alarm clock did not go off." After missing meetings, he asks lots of questions to make sure that everyone is making progress and the team's work is being accomplished. Spends more time checking that everyone else is doing their work than getting the job done. Chris always seems sure that the team will do fine and says that the team should do good work that fully meets the standards for acceptable performance. In response to a teammate's question about Chris' failure to deliver a promised piece of work, Chris said, "Why should I bother? Robin won't let the team fail."

Robin   Very bright. Has far greater knowledge of the subject than any of the other team members. Extremely skilled in problem solving. Robin has very high standards and wants the team's work to be impressive, but Robin worries whether the team's work will be good enough to stand out. Robin completes a big chunk of the team's work and takes on a lot of the really difficult work. Does the work that Chris leaves unfinished. The quality of Robin's work is consistently outstanding. Tends to just work out the solutions and discourages teammates' attempts to contribute. Reluctant to spend time explaining things to others. Does not like to explain "obvious" things. Is particularly impatient with Pat's questions and once told Pat "You are not smart enough to be on this team." Complains that Chris is a "lazy freeloader." Sometimes gets obsessed with grand plans and ignores new information that would call for changes. Does not pay attention to warning signs that the current plan might not be effective until the problems are obvious. Then handles the situation as a crisis and takes over without getting team input. Robin is reluctant to acknowledge or discuss problems in the team until they affect his work.

Terry Not nearly as bright as Robin, but works to develop enough knowledge and skills to do the assigned tasks. Terry can usually fill in for other team members if given specific directions, but does not understand most of the tasks that other team members normally perform. Does more grunt work than any of the other team members, but does not do as good a job as Robin and does not take on difficult tasks. Sometimes makes mistakes on the more complex work. Super responsible, spends a lot of time giving one-on-one help to Pat. Always on time to meetings. Often calls to remind everyone (especially Chris) about meetings and usually makes some nice comment about one of the teammate's strengths or a valuable contribution that the teammate has recently made. Terry is outgoing and highly supportive of teammates when well-rested, but is sometimes too tired to get excited about teammates' ideas. Is not defensive when teammates' offer feedback, but does not ask for teammates' suggestions, even when teammates' input could help Terry to do better work. Terry thinks that the team can do great work and encourages teammates to do their best. When Robin expresses doubts if the team can do superior work, Terry reassures everyone that the team is capable of outstanding work. When the team is headed in the wrong direction, Terry is quick to notice and say something, but usually does not suggest a way to fix it. Terry reviews the team's objectives and alerts the team to anything that comes up that would affect the team. Terry was reluctant to press the issue when Robin's plan ignored one of the guidelines specified for the project.

To test your ability to focus on individual behaviors, go to https://www.catme.org/login/survey_instructions and rate each team member on each type of contribution to the team. On the Scenario Results page, a green arrow indicates that your rating matches the expected rating. If your rating does not match the expert rating, the blue arrow shows your rating and the red arrow indicates the rating experts would have assigned. If you count one point for every level separating your rating from the expert rating on the five different types of contribution, a low score is best, indicating the greatest agreement with the expert ratings. You can "mouse over" the red arrows to read the rationales underlying the expert ratings.

3.7 PROJECT TIMELINE

To complete a project successfully, on schedule and satisfying all constraints, careful planning is required. The following steps should help your team plan the completion of project work.

Step 1: **Create a project timeline.**

The first consideration is the project's due date. All team members need to note this on a calendar. Examine the due date within the context of other assignments and classes. For example, is there a calculus test in the fourth week? When is the first English paper due?

Next, look at the project itself and break into individual tasks and subtasks. Create a list, making it as specific, detailed and thorough as possible. Your list should include:

- All tasks needed to complete the project
- Decisions that need to be made at various times
- Any supplies/equipment that will need to be obtained

Carefully consider the order in which the tasks should be completed. Does one task depend on the results of another? *Then, working backwards from the project due date, assign each task, decision, or purchase its own due date on the calendar.*

Finally, your team should consider meeting at least once a week at a consistent time and location for the duration of the semester. More meetings will be necessary, but there should be at least once per week when the entire team can get together and review the project status. A standing meeting time will prevent issues of "I did not know we were going to meet" or "I did not get the message."

Step 2: **Create a responsibility matrix**.

List the project's tasks and subtasks one by one down the left side of the paper. Then, create columns beneath each team member's name, written side by side across the top. Put a check mark in the column beneath the name of the member who agrees to perform each task. It then becomes the responsibility of that team member to successfully perform the task by the due date that was agreed upon in Step 1. An alternate grid is shown in Table 3-4.

> **NOTE**
>
> Choose a weekly team meeting time and STICK TO IT!
>
> Divide the workload and require updates at your weekly meeting.
>
> If a team member is not completing assigned tasks as required, speak with your professor. Do not wait until the end of the project to raise concerns about a teammate who is AWOL.

Table 3-4 **Sample responsibility matrix**

Task	Completed by	Checked by
Purchase supplies	Pat and Chris by 9/15 team mtg	
Write initial proposal	Terry—Email to Robin by 9/22	Robin by 9/25 team mtg
Conduct preliminary calculations on height	Robin—Email to Pat by 9/22	Pat by 9/25 team mtg
Build prototype in lab	All—Lab: 7–9 p.m., 9/28	

In assigning the tasks, consider the complexity and time required for the job. One team member may have five small tasks while another may have one major task, with the goal being an equal distribution of effort. A second team member should be assigned to each task to assist or check the work completed by the first team member. Be sure all team members are comfortable with the assignments.

Step 3: **Consider team dynamics.**

Communication: The success of any project depends to a great extent on how well the team members communicate. Do not hesitate to share ideas and suggestions with the group and consider each member's input carefully. Do not be afraid to admit that you are having difficulties with a task or that the task is taking longer than expected. Be ready and willing to help one another.

Trust and respect: Remember the team is working toward a shared objective. Therefore, you must choose to trust and respect one another. Treat fellow team members with simple courtesy and consideration. Follow through with promises of completed tasks, remembering the team is counting on your individual contributions. Try to deal honestly and openly with disagreements. However, do not hesitate to ask for help from faculty if problems begin to escalate.

Nothing is carved in stone: It is important to plan the project as carefully as possible; however, unforeseen problems can still occur. Treat both the Project Timeline and Responsibility Matrix as working documents. Realize they were created to serve as guides, not as inflexible standards. Watch the project progress relative to the timeline, and do not hesitate to redesign, reallocate, or reschedule should the need arise. Review your matrix each week and adjust as needed.

Finally, do not forget to have fun!

In-Class Activities

ICA 3-1

With your team, compose a plan to build the longest bridge possible using the K'Nex™ pieces provided by your instructor. The longest part of your bridge will be defined as the longest stretch of K'Nex pieces that are not touching another surface (table, floor, chair, etc.).

During the planning phase (15 minutes), your team will only be allowed to connect as many pieces as your team has hands. For example, a team of four will only be allowed to have eight K'Nex pieces connected together at any one moment. In addition, every team member must have their hand on a K'Nex piece if it is connected together during planning. As soon as your team has finished the planning phase, disconnect all K'Nex pieces and place them in the provided container. The container will be shaken before you begin, so do not bother attempting to order the pieces in any way.

During the building phase (60 seconds), the restriction on the number of connected pieces goes away, but your team will not be allowed to talk. Your instructor will say go, and then stop after 60 seconds has elapsed. At the end of the building phase, your team must step away from the bridge and remove all hands and other body parts from the K'Nex bridge. If any pieces falls after time is called, you are not allowed to stabilize the structure in any way.

ICA 3-2

With your team, come up with a plan to build the tallest tower possible using the K'Nex™ pieces provided by your instructor. The tallest portion of your tower will be defined as the longest stretch of K'Nex pieces that are not touching another surface (table, floor, chair, etc.).

During the planning phase (15 minutes), your team will only be allowed to connect as many pieces as your team has hands. For example, a team of four will only be allowed to have eight K'Nex pieces connected together at any one moment. In addition, every team member must have their hand on a K'Nex piece if it is connected together during planning. As soon as your team has finished the planning phase, disconnect all K'Nex pieces and place them in the provided container. The container will be shaken before you begin, so do not bother attempting to order the pieces in any way.

During the building phase (60 seconds), the restriction on the number of connected pieces goes away, but your team will not be allowed to talk. Your instructor will say go, and then stop after 60 seconds has elapsed. At the end of the building phase, your team must step away from the tower and remove all hands and other body parts from the K'Nex tower. If any pieces fall after time is called, you are not allowed to stabilize the structure in any way.

ICA 3-3

Following the rules for brainstorming (encourage a lot of ideas, encourage a wide variety of ideas, and do not criticize), develop ideas for the following with your team.

(a) A better kitty litter box

(b) A new computer interface device

(c) A new kind of personal transportation device

(d) Reducing noise pollution

(e) Reducing light pollution

(f) A new board game

(g) A squirrel-proof bird feeder

(h) A no-kill mole trap

(i) A tub toy for children of 4 years or younger

(j) A jelly bean dispenser

(k) A new musical instrument

(l) A self-cleaning bird bath

(m) A new smart phone application

Chapter 3 MINI DESIGN PROJECTS

This section provides a wide range of design projects, varying in difficulty and time commitment. Your instructor may assign projects required for your specific course and provide more details.

Category I: Demonstrate a Physical Law or Measure a Material Property

1. Prove the law of the lever.
2. Demonstrate conservation of energy (PE + KE = constant).
3. Determine the coefficient of static and sliding friction for a piece of wood.
4. Prove that the angle of incidence is equal to the angle of reflection.
5. Demonstrate momentum conservation ($F = ma$).
6. Demonstrate the ideal gas law.
7. Obtain a series of data points from an experiment you conduct that, when plotted, exhibit a normal distribution.
8. Show that forces can be resolved into horizontal and vertical components.
9. Find the center of gravity of an irregular piece of plywood.
10. Show that for circular motion, $F = mv^2/r$.
11. Show that for circular motion, $v = \omega r$.
12. Measure the effective porosity of a sand sample.
13. Prove the law of the pendulum.
14. Prove Hooke's law for a spring.
15. Prove Hooke's law for a metal rod (in deflection).
16. Measure the coefficient of thermal expansion for a solid rod or bar.
17. Estimate the heat capacity for several objects; compare with published results.
18. Prove Archimedes' law of buoyancy.
19. Determine the value of pi experimentally.
20. Prove the hydrostatic pressure distribution.
21. Relate the magnetic strength to the radius.
22. Determine the density and specific gravity of a rock.

Category II: Solve a Problem

23. What is the volume of a straight pin?
24. Determine the thickness of a specified coin or a piece of paper.
25. How many pennies are needed to sink a paper cup in water?
26. Determine the specific gravity of your body.
27. What is the volumetric flow rate from your shower?
28. Use a coat hanger to make a direct reading scale for weight.

Category III: Design a Solution

29. THE GREAT EGG DROP

You have no doubt seen the "Odyssey of the Mind" type of assignment in which you are to design protection for an egg that is to be dropped from some height without being broken. This assignment is to have the same end product (i.e., an unbroken egg) but in a different way.

You cannot protect the egg in any way but are allowed to design "something" for it to land on. You will be allowed three drops per team, and will be assigned at random the heights from which you will drop the egg. The egg must free-fall after release. If the egg breaks open, the height will be taken as zero. If the egg shell cracks, the height from which you dropped it will be divided by 2. If you drop the egg and miss the catching apparatus, that is your tough luck (and a zero height will be used)—suggesting that you need to devise a way to always hit the "target."

Your grade will be determined by

Ranking = (height from which egg is dropped)/(weight of catching apparatus)

After demonstrations, the average ranking number for each team will be calculated, and the value truncated to an integer. The teams will then be ranked from highest to lowest value. The heights and weights will be measured in class. The actual grade corresponding to your class ranking will be determined by your instructor.

30. TREE HEIGHT

We have been contacted by a power company to conduct a study of tree height and interference with high-voltage wires. Among other requirements, the company is looking for a quick, easy, and inexpensive method to measure the height of a tree.

Your project is to develop different methods of measuring the height of a tree. As a test case, use a tree designated by your instructor. You may *not* climb the tree as one of the methods! In addition, you may not harm the trees or leave any trace of your project behind.

To sell your methods to the customer, you must create a poster. The poster should showcase your measurement methods, including instructions on how to conduct the experiment, any important calculations, graphs or photos, and your resulting measurements. The poster will be graded on neatness, organization, spelling and grammar and mechanics, formatting, and strength of conclusions. You may use any piece of poster board commercially available, or a "science fair" board. The poster can be handwritten, or typed and attached, or ... here is a chance to use your creativity! If you present more than one method, you must indicate and justify your "best" choice.

Your grade will be determined as follows:

- Method 1:   30 points
- Method 2:   20 points
- Method 3:   10 points
- Presentation Board: 40 points

31. FIRE EXTINGUISHER

Make a fire extinguisher for a candle. The candle will be lit, and the extinguisher will put out the flame at a predetermined time after the candle is lit (say, 20 seconds). The only thing that the participant can do to start the time is to light the candle. The candle can be mounted anywhere you like. The results will be scored as follows:

You will be allowed three trials. You will be allowed to use your best trial for grading.

You must extinguish the candle between 19 and 21 seconds; for every second or fraction thereof outside this range you will lose five points.

32. CLEPSYDRA

Construct a clepsydra (water clock). When you bring it to class to demonstrate its performance, the following test will be used:

You will have three times to measure: a short time, a medium time, and an extended period. The actual times to be measured will be given to you at the time of demonstration, and you will have 2 minutes to set up your apparatus.

- Short: Between 10 and 30 seconds (in 2-second increments)
- Medium: Between 1 and 4 minutes (in 30-second increments)
- Extended: Between 5 and 10 minutes (in 1-minute increments)

You will start the clock and tell the timekeeper to begin. You will then call out the times for each of the three intervals and the timekeeper will record the actual times. Your clock must "run" for the total time.

Your grade will be determined by the average percent error of your timings.

For example, if the specified "medium" time was 2 minutes and 30 seconds and you said "mark" at an actual time of 2 minutes and 50 seconds, the absolute value of the percent error would be $(20 \, s)/(150 \, s) = 13\%$. The absolute values of the three errors will be summed, divided by 3, and subtracted from 100% to get a numerical grade.

33. ON TARGET

Each team will design, build, and test a device that will allow you to successfully hit a target with a table tennis ball. The target will be a flat sheet of poster paper placed on the floor with a bull's-eye and two other rings around it for scores of 100, 90, and 80 with a score of 60 for hitting the paper. The target will be placed at a location of 15 feet from the point at which you release the ball. Once the ball is released, you cannot touch it again, and it must be airborne before it hits the target. When demonstrating your device, you will not be allowed any trial run.

Your grade will be determined as follows:

Average numerical score + bonus (10, 8, or 6 points for creativity and simplicity)

The class (each person) will be given a slip of paper on which they will rank their top three teams with respect to creativity and also with respect to simplicity. These will be tallied and the top three teams in each category will receive 10, 8, or 6 bonus points.

34. KEEPING TIME

Each team is to build a "clock." When you say "go," a stopwatch will be started, and you are to tell the timekeeper when 10, 30, and 60 seconds have elapsed. Differences between the actual times and the predicted times at the three checkpoints will be noted and the percent error calculated. Average the absolute values of these three errors and subtract from 100 to obtain your final score. You may not use any store-bought device that is designed to measure time. No electronic devices may be used.

Your final grade will be determined as follows:

Average numerical score + bonus points (10, 8, or 6 for creativity and simplicity)

The class (each person) will be given a slip of paper on which they will rank their top three teams with respect to creativity and simplicity. These will be tallied and the top three teams in each category will receive 10, 8, or 6 bonus points.

Category IV: Additional Projects

35. Develop a device that can be placed into a container of water and used to measure the pressure as a function of depth. Take measurements and plot them against theory for a hydrostatic pressure distribution.

36. A 2-liter soft-drink container, nearly full of water and open to the atmosphere, is placed on the floor. Where could you locate an orifice in the side of the bottle so that the jet of water that squirts out will have the maximum range? Keep the bottle filled by continuously pouring water in the container as the tests are conducted. Justify your answer with theory by discussion rather than equations.

37. Design and build a device that will allow a ping-pong ball to hit a target (small circle) between 5 and 15 feet away from the point at which you release the ball with the device on the floor. Points will be given for accuracy (distance from the target center). From a hat, you will draw two slips of paper: a short distance (3–7 feet) and a long distance (8–15 feet). The slips of paper will have values in 1-foot increments on them (3, 4, 5, 6, or 7 feet for the short distances, and similar for the long distances). When you set up your device, you will be given 2 minutes to set the device for the first test and 2 minutes to set the device for the second (long distance) test.

38. Build a vehicle that will travel over a flat surface (hallway in the building). Points will be awarded for the distance traveled divided by the total (initial) weight of the vehicle. The vehicle must move under its own internal "engine"—the team can only release the stationary vehicle when the test begins. You will have two attempts, and the best value will be recorded. Your instructor may impose an allowable maximum weight. No batteries or electricity can be used.

39. Build a thermometer. You are to be able to measure the temperature of cold water in a bucket, room temperature, and the temperature of hot water in a container (degrees Celsius). The total percent errors will be summed (absolute values), averaged, and subtracted from 100.

40. Without moving more than 10 feet from your initial location, position a person a distance of 50 feet (or 100 feet) away from your initial location; bonus points for doing it several ways; the person must initially start beside you. You cannot be connected to the other person in any way (e.g., string, rope). Points are given for accuracy.

41. Roll an object of your design down an inclined plane (provided and the same for all participants). The object is to knock over a small piece of wood placed at a distance of 5 feet from the base of the incline and 5 feet to one side.

42. We are interested in rolling plastic drink bottles across the floor. Rather than hold a race to see which bottle will roll the fastest, we want to determine which will roll the farthest. It is important that each bottle be given a fair chance, so the starting conditions must be the same for each. Each team will use the same ramp (18 inches wide by 24 inches long) and supported by the 4-inch dimension of a 2×4 inches board. The bottles to be used will be clear-plastic soft-drink bottles. The 2-liter size is probably the best, but smaller bottles could also be used. The objective is to determine the answer to questions. You must develop a defendable test program, carry out the tests, present your results in an easy-to-understand manner, and defend your conclusions.

(a) How much water should the bottle contain in order to roll the farthest distance (until it stops)?

(b) How much water should the bottle contain in order to roll the shortest distance (until it stops)?

(c) As a part of your test program, you will release two bottles simultaneously on the ramp (with differing amounts of water in them, including one empty). Do not let them roll all the way until they stop, but catch them about 1 foot after they leave the bottom of the ramp. Which moves the fastest, which the slowest, and why?

CHAPTER 4
ENGINEERING
COMMUNICATION

It is a common joke that most engineers cannot construct a grammatically correct sentence, and there is all too much truth in this anecdote. In reality, the most successful engineers have developed good communication skills, not only oral and written, but also those involving multimedia formats. You might have the best idea in the known universe, but at some point you are going to have to convince someone to supply the $200 million needed to develop it. You *must* be able to communicate effectively not only that you have this great idea for a practical antigravity device, but also that it will actually work and that you are the person to lead the team developing it.

Our intent here is not to make you expert communicators, but to at least make you aware of the importance of good communication skills in engineering, as well as to give you a bit of guidance and practice developing these skills.

**WISE WORDS: HOW IMPORTANT ARE
COMMUNICATION SKILLS AT YOUR JOB?**

When working with clients, we deliver our approach, analysis structure, status, findings, and final deliverable by presentation.

M. Ciuca, ME

Absolutely essential. While I thankfully have a job that allows me to dig into the math and analysis, I still deal with a lot of people. Being able to communicate effectively, where two people (or more) really understand what each is saying is very important on a complex project, and is often more difficult than one would think; or at least it involves more active participation than many are inclined to put into it.

J. Dabling, ME

I have to write design documentation, edit customer specs, produce design review presentations, and sometimes present to our customers.

E. D'Avignon, CpE

Being able to connect with customers, and internal team members, is the means to develop relationships and win new business.

B. Dieringer, ME

Absolutely critical. I can think of people that I have worked with who do not have these skills, and they are not easy or fun to work with.

S. Forkner, ChE

Social skills are crucial to success when working at a company. Many times the person who is most successful is not necessarily the one who has the best or brightest ideas, but rather the individual who has solid ideas and is able to communicate in a manner that allows others to easily understand the vision and path to goal achievement.

L. Gascoigne, CE

Good social skills are very important because they improve productivity, teamwork, and goodwill. I have also found socials skills can be a deciding factor in job advancement.

R. Holcomb, IE

4.1 BASIC PRESENTATION SKILLS

Since most students consider giving an oral presentation a more daunting task than submitting written documents, we focus on live presentations first, although many of the suggestions apply to all forms of engineering communication.

Many years ago, one of us was responsible for a program to recruit high school students into engineering. Each engineering department made a short presentation to the visiting students, extolling the glories of its particular discipline. One department sent its most personable and able communicator about half the time, and Professor X came the other half. Both used the same set of PowerPoint™ slides, but when Professor X showed up, every single student seemed to be completely brain-dead within 3 minutes. It was *awful*! The other professor maintained their rapt attention for the entire 15 minutes, with supposedly the same presentation.

With this in mind, you need to focus on several factors when planning a presentation. Note that the first item in our list is *who* the audience is, although the other factors mentioned are equally important.

Preplanning

NOTE

5 Ws and 1 H

- Who
- What
- Where
- When
- Why
- How

- **Who is my audience?** Know the age group, demographics, prior knowledge about the topic, and what positions or opinions they may hold.
- **What is my purpose?** What do I hope to accomplish? What response do I expect? What will the audience get out of my speech?
- **Where is all the equipment I need?** Where will the talk be held?
- **When am I on the program agenda?** Will I be the first presenter (when audience is most alert) or the last one before lunch (when they are becoming restless) or after lunch (when they are sleepy)? What will I need to do to keep my listeners attentive?
- **Why am I giving this talk?** Why is the audience here?
- **How long should I talk?** Remember that only few people can focus for more than 20 minutes. Trim your talk so that people will ask for more information rather than thinking "When will he sit down?"

Preparing the Verbal Elements

The preceding list focused primarily on logistics. In addition to these considerations, the structure of your presentation is vital. As a simple example, which of the following two sentences is easier to understand?

> Sentence A: While perambulating in the antithesis of the metropolis to evade the intemperate brouhaha thereof, my visual cortex perceived an ophidian.
>
> Sentence B: I saw a snake while taking a relaxing walk in the woods.

Although sentence A may be phrased in a more intriguing manner, it tends to obscure the underlying meaning. This is perhaps desirable in poetry or fancy fiction but generally detrimental to a professional engineering presentation.

To help you avoid such pitfalls, we offer the 4-S formula for structuring presentations.

NOTE

The 4-S Formula

- Short
- Simple
- Strong
- Sincere

- **Shortness:** Use short sentences, avoid too many details, and do not talk too long.
- **Simplicity:** Avoid wordy, lengthy phrases. Remember the old saying: "Eschew obfuscation!"
- **Strength:** Use active voice and action verbs, not passive voice and "to be" verbs.
- **Sincerity:** Convey empathy, understanding, and respect for the audience.

Three Structural Parts

Keep in mind the purpose of discrete elements of a speech.

- **Introduction:** Purpose: to capture the interest of the audience. Your first task is to *hook your audience.* What is it about your subject that *they* (and not necessarily you) would find most interesting and relevant?
- **Body:** Purpose: to keep your audience interested. They will continue to pay attention if you keep the material interesting and relevant to them.
  - Divide the presentation into two or three main points, and organize your thoughts and ideas around them.
  - Use one or more simple examples to illustrate each major point.
  - Include slides, transparencies, or other visual aids.
- **Conclusion:** Purpose: to pull it all together.
  - Summarize major points.
  - Show appreciation for your audience's attention.
  - Allow for a few questions, but be sensitive to your audience and the other speakers.

Preparing Visual Aids

Most of you have seen presentations that used slides with unreadable text, incomprehensible graphics, or annoying special effects. Well-designed graphics can greatly enhance your presentation, not only making it easier for the audience to understand, but also keeping their attention focused. A picture really is worth about 2^{10} words! The guidelines below will help you design visual aids that are easily understood without being boring. Although our focus is on PowerPoint presentations, these suggestions apply to other media as well.

Helpful Hints

- Keep each slide simple, with one concept per slide. As a rule, use no more than *six lines per slide*. Each slide should correspond to an average of *60 seconds* of speech.
- If possible, make slides in *landscape* format.
- Present data in simple graphs rather than in lists or tables. Avoid excessively complex graphs with extensive data. If you must present tables, divide them among several slides.
- Pictures, diagrams, and video simulations all may enhance your presentation. Be sure that all are large enough to be seen by the audience, and have color schemes that do not appear washed out when projected. Often, such items are designed for viewing on a small screen and do not project well. Be sure to test them prior to your presentation.
- Use bullet points with important phrases to convey ideas. Avoid complete sentences.
- Large size text is best. A font size of at least 18 points and preferably no less than 24 points should be used. This includes *all* objects, such as axis and legend captions, table headings, figure symbols, and subscripts.
- Use high-contrast colors. Avoid fancy fonts, such as cursive, or light colors, such as yellow or other pastels. Avoid using all capitals.
- Use a light background and dark print to keep the room brighter. Avoid black slides with white text.
- Keep background styles simple and minimize animation to avoid distracting from the presentation. Keep all the slide backgrounds the same throughout a single presentation.

4.2 SAMPLE PRESENTATIONS

To illustrate the visual aids caveats, we critiqued three student presentations.

Sample Student Presentation 1

Original Presentation: Critique

- Slide 1 font is difficult to read, poor choice of abbreviation for *approximately*.
- Slide 2 dates and text appear disjointed due to text size and graphic; graphic is too large.
- Slide 3 graph is difficult to read; too many gridlines.
- Slide 4 too many words; graphic is too large.

(1)

(2)

(3)

(4)

Improved Presentation:

(1)

(2)

(3)

(4)

Sample Student Presentation 2

Original Presentation: Critique

- Different graphics on every page is distracting.
- White color is hard to project unless on black background.
- Slide 4 graphic is difficult to read; yellow highlights make it worse.

(1)

(2)

(3)

(4)

Improved Presentation:

(1)

(2)

(3)

(4)

Sample Student Presentation 3

Original Presentation: Critique

- Green backgrounds with white text do not project well; blue text is especially hard to read.
- Slides 2 and 4 have too many words; should use bullets, not sentences.
- No graphics; some pictures of acid rain damage would be nice.

(1)

(2)

(3)

(4)

Improved Presentation:

Acids and Bases
Arrhenius Definition

o **Acid:** A substance that dissociates in water to yield hydrogen ions (H+)

o **Base:** A substance that dissociates in water to yield hydroxide ions (OH-)

(1)

pH

o Molar H_3O^+ concentration in solution

o Higher H_3O^+ concentration = lower pH

o Acids = high H_3O^+ concentrations = low pH

o pH ranges:
   - pH < 7   acid
   - pH = 7   neutral
   - pH > 7   basic

(2)

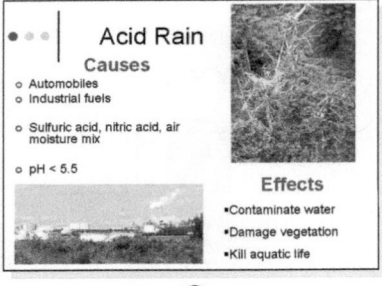

Acid Rain
Causes

o Automobiles
o Industrial fuels

o Sulfuric acid, nitric acid, air moisture mix

o pH < 5.5

Effects
- Contaminate water
- Damage vegetation
- Kill aquatic life

(3)

Radicals in Atmospheric Change

o Main components of atmospheric change = existence of free radicals

o Nitric Oxide (NO)
   - Main sources
   - Most common free radical

(4)

Making the Presentation

Oral presentations present several challenges for effective communication. How many of you have had an instructor who simply reads the contents of the slides with no embellishment? How many have had an instructor who seems to be terrified of the audience, cowering in fear and trying to disappear into the wall? How many have tried desperately to read the contents of a slide containing hundreds of words in a minuscule font? If you have not yet suffered through one or more such painful presentations—you will! Do not inflict such things on your own audiences.

Presentation Dos and Don'ts

NOTE

The key to improving presentation skills is practice, practice, practice!

When delivering a presentation, do:

- Relax!
- Speak slowly and clearly, making good eye contact.
- When your hands are not busy, drop them to your sides.
- Rehearse your presentation *out loud* multiple times. If possible, have a friend critique.
- Arrive early enough to make sure that all technology is present and working, and resolve any problems you may discover.

When delivering a presentation, do not:

- Lean on your surroundings, turn your back to the audience, or cover your mouth while speaking.
- Read your presentation from a prepared text.
- Tell inappropriate jokes.
- Stammer, overuse the pronoun "I," or repeatedly say "um" or "uh." Do not be afraid of a little silence if you need to glance at notes or collect your thoughts.
- Chew gum, remove coins from pockets, crack your knuckles, etc.
- Shuffle your feet or slouch; move repetitively, for example, pace back and forth or sway.
- Play with your notes.

4.3 BASIC TECHNICAL WRITING SKILLS

Although most of you probably consider written communications much easier than oral presentations (the fear factor is largely absent), technical documents you produce will often be far more important to your company and your career than a live presentation of the same information.

General Guidelines

In addition to many of the points made earlier, effective technical writing requires its own set of guidelines.

- **Be clear**; use precise language. Keep wording efficient without losing meaning. Do not exaggerate.
- Ensure that the finished copy logically and smoothly **flows** toward a conclusion. Beware of "choppiness" or discontinuity. Avoid extremely long sentences because they may confuse the reader.
- If possible, use **10-point font size and 1.5 line spacing**.
- **Generally, prefer past tense verbs.** Keep verb tenses in agreement within a paragraph.

- **Define any terms** that might be unfamiliar to the reader, including acronyms and symbols within equations.
- **Present facts or inferences** rather than personal feelings.
- **Maintain a professional tone.** Do not be emotional or facetious.
- **Number and caption all tables, figures, and appendices.** Refer to each from within the body of the text, numbering them in order of appearance within the text.
  - Tables are numbered and captioned *above* the table.
  - Figures are numbered and captioned *below* the figure.

Table 4-1 Example of a properly formatted table

Current (I) [A]	2	6	10	14	16
Energy of Inductor #1 (E1) [J]	0.002	0.016	0.050	0.095	0.125
Energy of Inductor #2 (E2) [J]	0.010	0.085	0.250	0.510	0.675
Energy of Inductor #3 (E3) [J]	0.005	0.045	0.125	0.250	0.310

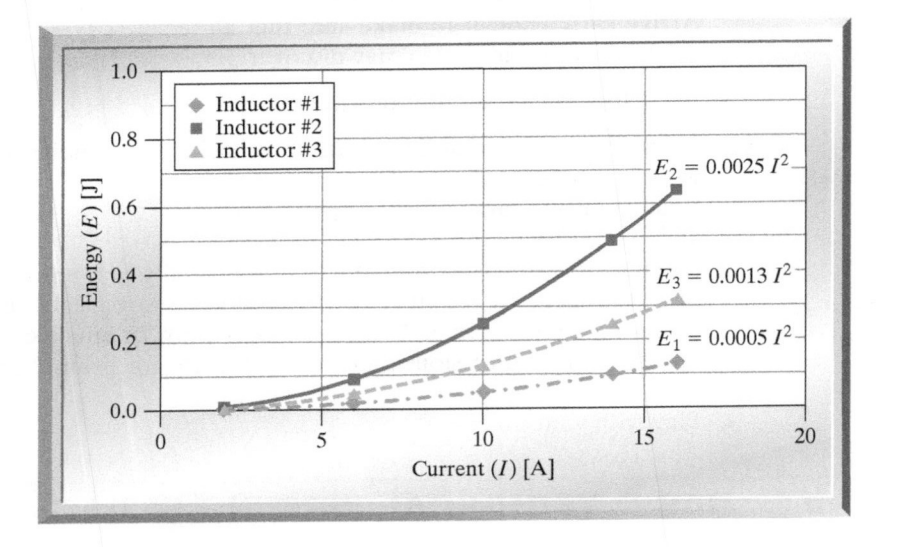

Figure 4-1 Example of a properly formatted figure.

- **Proofread and edit several times.**
  - **Remember to include** headings, figures, tables, captions, and references.
  - Do not assume that the spell check on the computer will catch everything! It will not distinguish between such words as *whether* and *weather*, or *was* and *as*.
- **Read it twice:** once for technical content and once for flow.
  - As you proofread, look for and *remove* the following: unnecessary words; sentences that do not add to the message; superfluous paragraphs.
  - Do one proofreading aloud. When you encounter commas, semicolons, colons, or periods, pause. Read a comma as a brief pause. Read a colon or semicolon as a longer pause. Read a period as a complete stop before the next sentence. Read what is actually written, not what you "think" it should say. If the text sounds stilted or blurred when read, you probably need to reconsider your use of these punctuation marks.
  - If possible, have someone not associated with the project (a roommate, a friend, or a mentor) read it, and ask that person for suggestions.

- **Spell out a number that starts a sentence.** If the number is large (e.g., a date), reword the sentence.

  - 23 points were outliers. (Unacceptable)
  - Twenty-three points were outliers. (OK)

- **Keep the leading zero with a decimal.**

  - The bridge cost .23 dollars per gram. (Unacceptable)
  - The bridge cost $0.23 per gram. (OK)

- **For long numbers, do not spell out.**

  - The average was one thousand, two hundred fifty-five grams. (Unacceptable)
  - The average was 1,255 grams. (OK)

- **Use the dollar symbol.**

  - The bridge cost four thousand dollars. (Unacceptable)
  - The bridge cost $4,000. (OK)

- **Watch for significant figures. Keep it reasonable!**

  - The bolt is 2.5029 inches long. (Unacceptable)
  - The bolt is 2.5 inches long. (OK)

WISE WORDS: HOW IMPORTANT ARE COMMUNICATION SKILLS AT YOUR JOB?

Projects are successful when the people who work together on them are able to communicate clearly with each other and work together to achieve a common goal. Misunderstanding and miscommunication leads to delays, poor quality, and frustration.

A. Hu, EE

As an engineer you communicate at all levels from the least senior production employee on the factory floor to the president of the company. Tailoring the message to the audience is the difference in acceptance and rejection.

J. Huggins, ME

Writing clear and concise specifications for construction can make the difference between an under-budget, on-time project and an over-budget, late, and unsafe final product.

L. Johnson, CE

As a consultant, extremely. If clients can't get along with you, they won't hire you. Every job requires a proposal and an interview.

J. Meena, CE

Much of my work in my current job involves researching what is going on in the world, and then putting that information into a format that makes sense to people and helps other people draw conclusions from it. Good written communication skills are essential for what I do every day.

M. Peterson, EE

All the social skills are *extremely* important because of the different functions and technical levels that I interface with.

E. Styles, EE

Communication—along with teamwork—really separates bad engineers from good ones. Someone could have the best idea in the world, but if he isn't able to describe the invention or provide reasons as to why it should be developed, the idea is useless. Plus, engineers are trained to be rational and thus perfect for managerial positions. If you have good communication skills, one can easily expect you to climb quickly up the corporate ladder.

A. Thompson, EE

Proper Use of References

Contributed by Ms. Jan Comfort — Engineering Reference
Librarian, Clemson University Libraries

In today's wired age, most students immediately go to the Internet to find information. Although this can be an excellent source, particularly for preliminary research, there are definite risks associated with using online sources, since essentially anyone can put anything they want on the web. For example, type "flat earth society" into your favorite search engine and check out the "truth" concerning our home planet, or explore how you can save the endangered Pacific Northwest Tree Octopus.

When making presentations or writing reports, it is important to verify the veracity of any sources you consult. These guidelines will help you avoid egregious errors in your own technical communications.

The **ABCs of evaluating information** offer a useful start.

- **Authority:** Is it clear who is responsible for the site? What are the author's credentials? Is the author an expert in the field? Is it a .com or .gov or .edu site?
- **Bias:** What is the purpose of the article? Is it free of obvious bias? Is the author presenting an objective view of the subject matter?
- **Currency:** When was the information created or last updated?

But there is more to evaluating resources than that. Good students take it to the next level. Here is how you can, too.

- **Use sources that have been reviewed by experts.** Instead of searching for hours trying to find websites that meet stringent requirements, try using library sources to identify good quality sources that have already been through a review process.
- **Secure a peer review:** An expert in the appropriate field evaluates something proposed (as for research or publication).[1] Academic Search Premier and Expanded Academic ASAP are the names of two very good multisubject databases that contain scholarly (peer-reviewed) as well as popular articles. One or both of them should be available at your library.
- **Compare the information found in your article or website with content from other websites, or from reviewed sources.** Comparing sources can also alert you to controversial information or bias that will need further study. Are facts from one website the same as those of another? How about depth of coverage? Maybe one site has better-quality information. Does the site have photos or other unique features that make it a good choice? Or perhaps a journal article from a library database is a better source. Until you compare several sources, you will not know what you are missing!
- **Corroborate the information.** Verify the facts from your source — regardless of where you found it — against one or more different sources. Do not take the word of one person or organization. A simple rule might be: "Do not use information unless you have corroborated it. Corroboration with varied and reviewed sources increases the probability of success."[2]

---

[1]Peer review. (2009). In *Merriam-Webster Online Dictionary*. Retrieved May 13, 2009, from http://www. merriam-webster.com/dictionary/ peer review
[2]Meola, Marc. (2004). "Chucking the checklist: A contextual approach to teaching undergraduates web-site evaluation." Portal: *Libraries and the Academy*, 4(3), 331–344.

4.4 COMMON TECHNICAL COMMUNICATION FORMATS

Technical communications can take on a variety of formats. Here, we will specifically address e-mail, memos, and short technical reports. Other, usually longer formats will probably be addressed later in your engineering career, but the same general guidelines apply regardless of form or length of content.

E-mail

Many students believe that the rules they use for instant messaging (IM), Twitter, etc. apply to e-mail also. When sending informal messages to friends, this is acceptable. However, when using e-mail in a professional context (including e-mail to professors!), more formal rules should be followed. The suggestions below will help you write e-mail that is clear, concise, and appropriate for the recipient.

After you have composed your e-mail, ask yourself if you would mind the president of the university, the CEO of your company, or your parents reading it. If the answer to any of these is no, then you probably should reword it.

E-mail Etiquette

NOTE

Keep two e-mail accounts: one for professional use, and the other for personal use.

Choose e-mail names carefully. Some of our favorites are as follows:

- sugarbritches
- guitarfreak
- cdbpimpman
- jessiethestudent
- Bombom bombombo
- YoltsPreston
- fatmarauder

- Be sure to correctly address the recipient. If you are unsure of a person's proper title (Dr., Mrs., Prof.), look it up!
- Use an appropriate subject line. Avoid silly subjects (Hey—Read this!) or omitting the subject line—this may cause the e-mail to end up in the Junk Mail folder.
- Sign your *full* name and include contact information for e-mail, phone, fax, or mailing address if appropriate. When sending e-mail about a class, including your course number and course day and time is often helpful.
- Change your sending name to your full name (such as Elizabeth Stephan) or an appropriate nickname (Beth Stephan). Do not leave your account as Student or the computer default setting (such as Noname Stephan). The easier it is for your reader to identify who you are, the better your chance for a response.
- Keep it brief. Do not use one continuous paragraph—make it easy to read.
- If you expect a response from your reader, be sure that action items are clearly defined.
- Use correct capitalization and punctuation. Spelling does count—even in e-mail! Avoid IM speak (e.g., LOL, IMHO, IIRC).
- Avoid putting anything in e-mail you would not say in person. Do not use e-mail to "vent" or write anything that can be easily misinterpreted by the reader.
- To avoid sending an e-mail before you have a chance to check over your work, fill in the To: and CC: lines last.
- When waiting for a reply, allow a grace period of 48 to 72 hours. If you have not received a reply after 48 hours and a deadline is approaching, you can resend your message, inquiring politely if it was received. Items do sometimes get lost in cyberspace! If the matter is critical, try the phone or request a face-to-face meeting if the first contact does not elicit a response.

Sample E-mail

To...	R. Swarthmore, Ph.D. [swart@reactorsealsrus.com]
cc...	C. Ohland [carson@reactorsealsrus.com];
	K. Stephan [katie@reactorsealsrus.com]
Subject:	Leaky gel reactor seal

Dr. Swarthmore:

The gel reactor seals in B4L3 are leaking and causing production losses (over 200K for FY 2001). The Materials Engineering Lab was asked to test other seal materials. Laboratory tests identified six material couples that produced better wear resistance than the current seal. A prototype seal was made with a new material, self-mated cemented carbide, but the carbide on the seal cracked during fabrication.

The purpose of this e-mail is to request an additional $40,000 and four months' project time to fabricate and test another new seal configuration.

Your approval of this program before Friday noon will allow us to proceed with the project as quickly as possible without any delay. If you have further questions or would like more information, please contact me.

Sincerely,
J. Brock
Design Team Manager, Reactor Seals R Us
(123) 456-7890 x 1234
jbrock@reactorsealsrus.com

● **EXAMPLE 4-1**

Samples of poorly written (actual student) e-mail

Subject: Carrier Fair
I hoping to be balle to show up to the Friday class, or take the quiz early on Wed. to allow more time for myself at the Carrier Fair on Wed.

Subject: FW: John Doe fri 8
Im sorry for missing class this morning, I stayed up really lait working on an english paper. Im not really doing that well in any of my classes, but im confident that im going to pass the other ones. Thank god for that. Anyway last night i ate a bunch of fish too, and i think fish doesn't go to well on my stomach because i feel really sick. Could i meet with you sometime this weekend?

Subject: excel
I don't know why it sent 10 other e-mails but sorry. I'm writing to you about the excell test today. I've been sick for the last three days and i wasn't feeling great today either. Also i had a hard time getting started on the test because of downlad problems. Anyway by the time I had figured out the format of the test there were only 15 minutes left so if i could come and talk to you about that then that and one other thing then that would be great.

Subject: Hey, I need help
Hey,
I can't figue out how to do a complex interpolation problem. I understand how to do the simple one, and i used to no how to do the complex one but now everytime I do it i get it wrong. Do you have any office hours I can come in a lean how to do it? If you can't could you send my a worked example of how to do one?
Thank You

Subject: classes for next semester
from what I have heard the math classes we pick at our time pick classes are only for a time. and that we dont pick the teacher we want. is there any way where we can pick the teacher we want for next semester?

Memo (One Page Limit)

The following is a template for a brief memo. Your professor may ask you to adhere to this format, or may suggest a different one.

NOTE
You should use a 10-point font such as Times New Roman or Verdana, with 1 to 1.5 line spacing.

Margins should be set to 1 inch all around.

Be sure to use correct spelling and grammar.

Include the headings given here, in bold.

To:	Dr. Engineering
From:	Ima Tiger, Section 000 (IMT@school.edu)
Subject:	Memo Guidelines
Date:	May 21, 2011

Introduction: The first three or four sentences should explain the purpose behind the memo. You should attempt to explain what you were asked to do, what questions you are trying to solve, what process you are attempting to determine, etc.

Results: Place any experimental results, in tabular and/or graphical format, here. As space is limited, this normally only includes two items: two tables, two figures, or one table and one figure. Be sure that each is clear enough to stand alone, with one to two sentences of explanation. Include a table caption at the top of each table, and a figure caption at the bottom of each figure. The caption should include a number and a word description. When a figure is used within a document, a title is not necessary on the graph and is replaced by the caption. The two items should be pasted side by side from EXCEL into WORD using the **Paste Special > JPEG** command or similar picture format command (PNG, Bitmap) and then sized appropriately.

Discussion: In this section, discuss how you obtained your data, the meaning of any trends observed, and significance of your results. Refer to the tables or figures shown in results by name (Table 1 or Figure 1). Explain any errors in your data (if possible) and how your data differs from theory. If you are deciding among several alternatives, be sure to explain why you did NOT choose the other options.

References: List any sources you use here. You do not need to reference your textbook (Thinking like an Engineer). You may use a new page for references if necessary. Any reference format is acceptable; Modern Language Association (MLA) citation style is preferred.

● **EXAMPLE 4-2**   **Sample of a poorly written student memo**

To: Dr. Engineering
From: Ima Student
Subject: Memo
Date: April 1, 2009

Introduction: We are given the job to analyze the cost of upgrade a machine line, which produces widgets. We were given three companies to choose from, to figure out witch would be the best for the cost and its production. Just by graphing the variables would allow us to find our answer.

Results:

	Klein Teil	
Varible Cost	0.95	
Fixed Cost	*5.00E+06*	
Material Cost	*0.75*	
Energy Cost	*0.15*	
Labor Cost	*0.05*	
Selling Price	*3*	
apacity per da	*6500*	
antity Produc	*ein Teil Total Co*	*Revenue*
0.00E+00	*5.00E+06*	*0.00E+00*

Discussion: We got the data by taking all variables from the information provided, then graphing the results together. This allowed us to see which machine line would provide the better outcome for the situation at hand. Considering the cost of the machine, material, labor, and energy into consideration with what would produce the quantity and quality product we're striving for. Figure 1 display all three solutions': total cost, revenue for us, and our breakeven point to ensure us of our choice. From observation of the graph we see that the Klein Teil machine is better. Its breakeven is at $2,400,000 and the profit is twice as much.

Summary: So to answer the question, Klein Teil would be our best option. The results yielded that the Klein Teil machine would give us the most quality for its price, a better production rate, and more money in return. From this research I hope you choose to take the Klein Teil machine.

Comments on this memo:
There are so many problems with this submission that we address only the major problems.

■ *The subject line simply informs us that this is a memo.*
■ *The introduction tells us very little about what the memo will address.*
■ *The same data is presented in both the graph and the table. The formatting of the table is very poor; the formatting of the graph is worse.*
■ *The Discussion does not explain how the data was analyzed, and the justification of the final recommendation is essentially nonexistent.*
■ *Similarly, the Summary says almost nothing. Although not an appropriate summary, the three words "Buy Klein Teil" would probably have been more effective.*

How many more problems can you find in this sample memo?

Short Report (Two to Four Pages)

The following template is for a short report. Again, your professor may ask you to follow these guidelines or provide a somewhat modified version.

Introduction Type the introduction here. This should be four or five sentences. What is the problem that will be addressed in this memo? What can the reader expect to learn by reading your report?

Procedure Type the procedure here. This should be at most ¾ page. It must be in bulleted format. You should generalize the procedure used to include the basic steps, but you do not need to include every detail. The reader should gain an understanding of how you collected your data and performed your analysis.

Results Insert the results here, but do not discuss them or draw any conclusions. This may include a maximum of three illustrations, in a combination of figures and tables. Be sure that each is clear enough to stand alone, with one or two sentences of explanation. Include a table caption at the top of the table, and a figure caption at the bottom of the figure. The caption should include a number and a word description.

Be aware that your tables and figures should illustrate *different* ideas; they should not contain the same data. Do *not* include large tables of raw data or *every* graph generated. This section should be a *sample* of those items, used to illustrate the points of your discussion below.

Table 4-2 Example of a properly formatted table

Section	Instructor	E-mail	Time
−030	Dr. Stephan	beths	M 8:00–9:55
−031	Dr. Park	wpark	M 12:20–2:15
−032	Dr. Sill	sillb	W 8:00–9:55

Figure 4-2 Example of a properly formatted figure.

Discussion Talk about your results here. This can be up to a maximum of one page. Refer to the table and figure shown in results by name. Be sure to include the items specifically requested in the original project description.

Summary What is the final conclusion? As your boss, I may only have time to read the introduction (what the problem is) and the summary (what the answer is) and glance at the results (how you got the answer) before I head to a big meeting. This should be four to five sentences long, and answer the initial questions asked in the introduction and summarize any important findings.

Poster Presentation

The following template is for posters. Again, your professor may ask you to follow these guidelines or provide a somewhat modified version. The template provided online is a PowerPoint format, but is meant to be printed. The default is set to 8½ × 11 printing, which will allow you to submit this to your instructor without the need for a plotter. This could easily be changed, however, and this template be used to create a large poster.

LOGO

Project Title
Course- Section
Team Names

LOGO

BACKGROUND

What important information does the reader need to know before understanding your discussion? Have you built upon someone else's previous work? Why is this work important?

CHART or PICTURE
Illustrating the Purpose
or Background

PURPOSE

Type the introduction here. What is the problem that will be addressed? What can the reader expect to learn?

You may present this as a bulleted list or short sentences. Should be concise and easy to read.

RESULTS

Insert the results here, but do not discuss them or draw any conclusions. Include a table caption at the top of the table, and a figure caption at the bottom of the figure. The caption should include a number and a word description.

Be aware that your tables and figures should illustrate DIFFERENT ideas; they should not contain the same data. Do NOT include large tables of raw data. This section should be a SAMPLE of your work, used to illustrate the points of your discussion. Be sure to follow proper plot rules. Be sure your graphs can be easily read from a distance.

Replace these words with
FIGURE or TABLE

FIGURE or TABLE
of Results

DISCUSSION

Talk about your results here. Refer to the table and figure shown in results by name. Be sure to include the items specifically requested in the original project description.

You may present this as a bulleted list or short sentences. Should be concise and easy to read.

CONCLUSIONS

What is the final conclusion? I may only have time to read the purpose (what is the problem) and the conclusion (what is the answer) and glance at the results (how did you get the answer. This should be short, answer the initial questions asked in the introduction and summarize any important findings. Do NOT introduce any new information here.

REFERENCES (if needed)

(1) Put references here, if you used any

(2) If not, put something else creative here!

In-Class Activities

POWER POINT

ICA 4-1

Critique the following student presentation, discussing improvement strategies.

Purpose

In this Business and Engineering Collaborative Project we were given to task to design a product that would make dorm life safer, more enjoyable, or more productive. Our design was driven by our desire to meet customers needs, which would correspond to the ability to make a profit. We will show you all the steps it took to make our product marketable. Finally, we would like to thank everyone for coming, and we hope that you agree with us that our product is marketable and of course a masterpiece.

Idea Generation

Here are some of our best ideas...

Screening

In our next step we took all the ideas that we had come up with and narrowed them down to a select three. The reason all the others were thrown out is because some of them already existed on the market, some of them would be too complex to the manufacture, and some of them we didn't think that we had technical expertise needed to produce them. The three products we chose are...

Marketing Programs

- Each person worked 40 hours per week
- Insurance is $200 per quarter
- 30 people were employed for the quarter at $9.00 per hour
- Assembly average completing 90 lofts a day
- Raw materials for the loft cost $35.00 wholesale each
- Circular saw (8"50") 168 per month = $2016.00 per year
- Drill 3" 144 per month = $1728 per year
- Palm Sander $39 per month $390 per year
- Miscellaneous tools and manual expenses $5000 per year
- Supertech to pad $1000 per quarter
- The rent on our building is $2000 per quarter
- Miscellaneous overhead expenses are $200 per quarter
- 12 weeks a quarter (1 week off/quarter)

Production Processes

1st: The wood comes off of the trucks and goes strait to cutting

2nd: After the wood is cut, it is sent to be drilled.

3rd: Then all of the wood is sanded down, to make a nice surface.

4th: The loft is then put together by 5 employees.

5th: While the loft is still together it is tested for any flaws.

6th: The loft is then taken back apart by another 5 employees.

7th: The loft is then packaged and sent to be shipped.

8th: The last and final step, the loft is loaded into trucks.

Conclusion

Developing and introducing new products is frequently time-consuming, expensive, and risky. Thousands of new products are introduced annually but the failure rate is between 60 and 75 percent. If our product was put into production, we are confident that we would not be a part of that percentage. We think we have a feasible and well thought out marketing plan. We would like to thank you for coming and listening to our marketing pitch!

ICA 4-2

Critique the following student presentation, discussing improvement strategies.

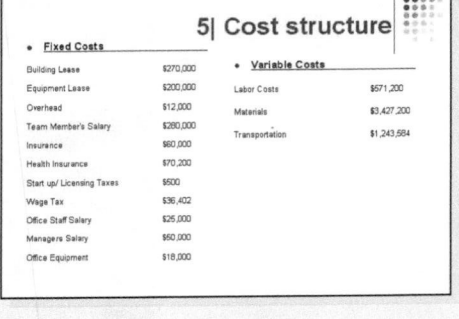

The following three ICAs are possible presentations you may be asked to make in this course. For your presentation, you may be required to choose one of the topics from the list provided, your instructor may specify different topics, or you may even be allowed to choose one of your own. Your instructor will make clear which options you have. Remember, you are giving a *technical* presentation. *Any discussion of the topic that is considered inappropriate by the instructor will be subject to a grade reduction.*

ICA 4-3

This ICA is meant to give you practice getting up in front of a group. The topics are informal, as the purpose is simply to help you gain confidence in public speaking. The presentation topic will be assigned to you at random shortly before your scheduled presentation; your instructor will determine how "shortly" before. The presentation should last *one minute*. If your speech is shorter or longer by more than 15 seconds, 10 points will be deducted from your presentation grade. For your presentation, here are some possible approaches you may want to take.

Make it informative.
Suppose your word is "WHALE." To give an informative talk, make a mental note of important things you know about whales. They are big. Some species are almost extinct. They are mammals. The blue whale is the largest animal that has ever lived on Earth. They were hunted for their blubber and oil that was used in lamps before electric lights. They hold their breath while under the water.

Tell a story.
If you know *Moby Dick*, you could give a brief outline of the most important points or of a particular scene in the book. You could tell of a visit to Sea World where you saw the trained killer whales perform. You could make up a short bedtime story that you relate as one you would tell your child or that was told to you as a child.

Be innovative.
You could do something like this: Whale is spelled W-H-A-L-E. The W stands for "water" where the whales live (talk about the ocean for a while); H stands for "huge," which is what we think of when we say whale; A stands for "animal" and the whale is the largest; L stands for "large," which is a lot like huge; and E stands for "eating" since the whale has to eat a lot, or E could stand for "enormous" like huge and large.

Or

You could do something like this: I dreamed about a whale that was in the parking lot at K-Mart. It kept smiling, and let out an enormous burp every few minutes. Being an animal lover, I went up next to the whale and stroked its sides. I was amazed at how smooth it was.

Or

You could do something like this: I have always wanted to scuba dive and in particular to ride on the back of a killer whale. I know that it would be dangerous, but it would be something I could remember the rest of my life.

ICA 4-3: Presentation Topic Suggestions

- Person who impressed you
- A hobby
- Favorite sport
- Favorite team mascot
- Favorite course
- Importance of cars
- Importance of space exploration
- Why engineers are neat
- Why calculus is important
- My favorite food
- My favorite dessert
- The worst insect
- How I would improve my school
- Coolest animal
- Favorite day of the week

- A childhood memory
- My favorite relative
- Someone I admire and why
- The best car
- Favorite month of the year
- Why I came to this college
- My dream job (after college)
- Why I want to be an engineer
- Place I would like to visit
- If I had a million dollars
- The ultimate dorm room
- Favorite phone app
- Favorite vacation
- Why I would like to be a professor
- The best thing about being in college

- The best thing about computers
- What kind of boss I would make
- Why I would like to be the president
- My opinion on Napster
- Something I learned this week
- The best thing about my school
- Advice for incoming freshman
- How to improve this classroom
- A feature to add to the car
- A good book I have read
- My favorite year in grade school
- The farthest I have ever been from my hometown

ICA 4-4

In this ICA, the speeches will discuss the graphical representation of various phenomena, such as "A total eclipse" or "Using a toaster." The presentations should last 1 *minute*, 30 *seconds*. If your speech is more than 15 seconds longer or shorter than this, 10 points will be deducted from your presentation grade.

Later in this text, much time is spent on graphing mechanics and interpretation. You are to choose a topic from the following list and represent it graphically. A variety of presentations of the available data that tell different things are possible. Do not forget to use all your senses and imagination.

You must prepare a proper graph, incorporated in PowerPoint, and use it during your presentation. You are not allowed to copy a premade graph from the Internet! In your speech, you should discuss the process, explain how information is shown on the graph, and be prepared to answer questions about your process. *You are limited to three slides*: (1) a title slide, (2) an introductory slide, and (3) a graph. If needed, you will be allowed a single 3 × 5 inch index card with notes on one side only.

ICA 4-4: Presentation Topic Suggestions

- Moving a desk down a set of stairs
- Letting go of a helium balloon
- Feedback from an audio system
- A cow being picked up by a tornado
- A kangaroo hopping along
- A glass of water in a moving vehicle
- People in Florida
- People in Michigan
- The flight of a hot air balloon
- Using a toaster
- A train passing
- Dropping ice in a tub of warm water
- Slipping on a banana peel
- Sound echoing in a canyon
- Detecting a submarine using sonar
- Pouring water out of a bottle
- Boiling water in a whistling teapot
- Hammering nails
- Spinning a Hula-Hoop™
- Playing with a yo-yo
- Snow blowing over a roof
- Climbing a mountain
- Pumping air into a bicycle tire
- The plume from a smokestack
- Formation of an icicle
- A rabbit family
- Firing a bullet from a rifle
- Hiking the Appalachian Trail
- Eating a stack of pancakes
- A solar eclipse

- Taking a bath
- Throwing a ball
- Driving from Clemson to Greenville
- Diving into a swimming pool
- A person growing up
- Burning a pile of leaves
- Driving home from work
- An oak tree over the years
- Airplane from airport to airport
- Football game crowd
- Train passing through town
- A coastal river
- The moon
- Daily electric power consumption
- A typical day
- A thunderstorm
- A day in the life of a chicken
- Popping corn
- Feeding birds at a bird feeder
- Skipping a stone on water
- A burning candle
- Pony Express
- Talking on a cell phone
- Using Instant Messenger
- An engineer's salary
- Baseball in play
- Exercising
- Running of the bulls
- Drag racing
- D.O.R. possum ("dead on the road")

- Political affiliations
- Traffic at intersections
- River in a rainstorm
- A tiger hunting
- Hair
- Grades in calculus class
- Forest fire
- Cooking a Thanksgiving turkey
- Brushing your teeth
- Baking bread
- Eating at a fast-food restaurant
- Studying for an exam
- Power consumption of your laptop
- Power usage on campus
- Oil supply
- Air temperature
- Student attention span during class
- Baseball
- A diet
- Sleeping
- Bird migration
- Strength of concrete
- Human population
- A mosquito
- A video game
- Taking a test
- A trip to Mars
- The North Pole
- Space elevators

ICA 4-5

This presentation covers topics related to your future major. The presentations should last *three minutes*. If your speech is more than 15 seconds longer or shorter than this, 10 points will be deducted from your presentation grade.

In 2000, the National Academy of Engineering compiled a list of "Greatest Engineering Achievements of the 20th Century." The following list contains some of the achievements listed, as well as some of the greatest failures of the past century. The full list can be found at www.greatachievements.org.

It is your responsibility to research the topic you choose so that you can intelligently discuss it in reference to the engineering involved and how it affects everyday life, both then and now.

You must prepare a PowerPoint presentation and use it in this speech. You should have between five and eight slides, of which the first must be a title slide, and the last must be a slide listing references. Other visual aids may be helpful and are encouraged. If needed, you will be allowed a single 3×5 inch index card with notes on one side only.

ICA 4-5: Presentation Topic Suggestions

Electricity
- Grand Coulee Dam (1942)
- Electric light bulbs

Automobiles
- Mass production (1901: Olds; 1908: Ford)
- Octane ratings (1929)
- Goodrich "tubeless" tires (1947)

Airplanes
- Hindenburg (1937)
- Concord

Water Supply and Distribution
- Purification of water supply (1915: Wolman)
- Cuyahoga River pollution (1970s)
- Hinkley, California

Electronics
- Integrated circuits (1958: Kilby)
- Handheld calculator (1967: TI)

Radio and TV
- Color television (1928; 1954)
- Phonograph (Edison)

Agricultural Mechanization
- Mechanical cotton picker (1949: Rust)
- Irrigation equipment (1948: Zybach)

Computers
- Language compiler (1952: Hopper)
- Transistor (1947)

Telephones
- Touch-tone dialing (1961)

Air Conditioning and Refrigeration
- Air conditioning (1902: Carrier)
- Freezing cycle for food (1914: Birdseye)

Highways
- PA turnpike
- Tacoma Narrows Bridge
- Golden Gate Bridge
- Chunnel

Spacecraft
- Space shuttle *Challenger* explosion
- Hubble telescope
- *Apollo 1* and *Apollo 13* failures
- *Gemini* spacecraft

Internet
- E-mail (1972: Tomlinson)
- WWW (1992)

Imaging
- Sonar (1915: Langevin)
- Radar (1940)
- Ultrasound (1958)
- MRI (1980)

Household Appliances
- Dishwasher (1932)
- Clothes dryer (1935: Moore)
- Microwave (1946)

Health
- Defibrillator (1932: Kauwenhoven)
- Artificial heart (1980: Jarvik)

Petroleum
- Distillation (1920s: Fischer and Tropsch)
- Ethyl gas (1921)
- Alaskan pipeline

Laser and Fiber-optics
- Chemical vapor deposition (1974)
- Optical fibers (1970: Maurer, Corning)

Nuclear Technologies
- Van de Graff generator (1937)
- Manhattan Project (1939–1945)
- Three Mile Island power plant (1979)

High-Performance Materials
- Vulcanization of rubber (1926)
- Polyvinyl chloride—"PVC" (1927)
- Teflon (1938: Plunkett)
- Kevlar (1971: Kwolek)

ICA 4-6 and 4-7 were written to address the question of what obligations humans may have to protect extraterrestrial life if it is discovered.

ICA 4-6

Critique the following writing assignment, discussing improvement strategies.

If life were to be discovered elsewhere in the universe, it would be our duty to protect that life only to the extent in which we do not compromise our own stability. The nation as a whole currently already has debt issues and is going through a depression. America could not afford to spend money on a life when they are struggling to take care of themselves. According to Hodges, "America has become more a debt 'junkie'—than ever before with total debt of $53 Trillion—and the highest debt ratio in history." (2) Globally there are people who are dying from starvation each day. "On Tuesday September 11, 2001, at least 35,615 of our brother and sisters died from the worst possible death, starvation. Somewhere around 85% of these starvation deaths occur in children 5 years of age or younger." (1) What would make this new life form a higher priority than the neighbors right around the corner? If they have managed to survive this long we shouldn't worry about helping them until we have taken care of ourselves. Even if they are extremely advanced with many discoveries we have not made, what good would it do to spend billions on reverse engineering but leave our own world in desperation. Now if we were to reach a point in the future in which we could help them; we would naturally have to approach with caution. Politically one of the worst first impressions is when new people meet and one group starts a biological plague. In 1493 right after Columbus came to America he went back to Hispaniola, bringing livestock in order to start a colony there. "Influenza, probably from germs carried by the livestock, swept through the native people, killing many of them. Modern researchers believe that American Indian traders carried the disease to Florida and throughout the Caribbean." (3) We would not know what would hurt them as well as what could hurt us. In order to avoid this terrible introduction, we would need to do research with probes and satellites. These observations from afar would make a seamless introduction possible. After the introduction it would be top priority to keep diplomatic relations intact. Finding another life out in space would be great, but not if we made them our enemies.

ICA 4-7

Critique the following writing assignment, discussing improvement strategies.

For centuries, people have wondered if we were all alone in our universe. Still today, even with our advancements in science we still have not been able to find life anywhere else. Recently the Phoenix Lander discovered what seems to be incontrovertible evidence that water exists on Mars. Since life is dependent on water eye brows have again been raised about the probability that life may exist, or has existed on Mars. So what if life is discovered somewhere other than on earth? Are we obligated to protect that life? Does that obligation depend on how advanced the life is? How do we stop ourselves from not destroying the non-terrestrial life? If life is discovered somewhere other than earth, some people will feel threaten, others will feel that maybe somehow human life could be supported by the non-terrestrial's planet and that life is elsewhere out there, maybe life like ours. As far as our obligation to protect that life, it is recommended that we do not interfere. We are having problems with our own planet, people pollute, litter, kill wildlife, start wildfires, cut down forests, and destroy whole ecosystems. Imagine what we will do to life if it doesn't matter to us if it lives or not. No matter how advance the life is we should leave the life to itself, unless the life was able to communicate with us somehow. The only way to keep ourselves from destroying the non-terrestrial life is to just to leave it alone. If we leave it, it wouldn't be our fault if it survives or eventually dies off. Yet still we haven't been able to find life anywhere besides earth so until we do we should try finding ways to turn our planet in the right direction before we lose what supports us.

ICA 4-8 and 4-9 were written to address the question of whether we should pursue manned exploration of space or restrict such activities to unmanned robotic devices.

ICA 4-8

Critique the following writing assignment, discussing improvement strategies.

Manned, unmanned space travel has been a big controversy for many years; it's too risky or space bots gets just as much done as humans. I agree 100% that robots are far better off into space than humans; manned space travel is too dangerous. Almost all the money for such a mission would be spent simply to keep the people alive. (John Tierney) Space bots are more reliable, don't get tired, and do what it's programed to do, but more proficient. Things humans need for survival includes: air, food, water, things we must take with us for space travel, which adds to the cost for each individual we fly out into space. While space bots don't need any of these sources for survive, which makes space travel less expensive and more productive. Also the bots can retrieve more data because there aren't any stopping periods for breaks or any other reasons for that matter. It cost about 1.3 billion dollars per shuttle launched out into orbit, while it cost far more per individual we send out into space. Manned space travel is not all bad; things humans can do like, making quick and on the spot decision or human senses to evaluate our surroundings are things robots can't imitate. It's nothing like being somewhere physically and knowing what's there instead of watching it through another pair of eyes. By using unmanned space travel, in reality we can only see what the robot sees, but is a human life worth the risk just for data. A human life is priceless, it like time when it's gone; it's gone, so why not send robotic material into space to collect data. It's only scrap metal, but the life of any human is far more valuable just for the expense of useless data.

ICA 4-9

Critique the following writing assignment, discussing improvement strategies.

Since the early 1960s, humans have been venturing beyond the Earth's atmosphere, a few times as far as the moon, a quarter of a million miles away. NASA currently plans to return humans to the moon by 2020, and plans Mars missions after that. Much criticism has been leveled at the entire idea of manned spaceflight, claiming that unmanned craft can do essentially all of the jobs people can with less cost and less risk. There are of course two sides to the situation. The idea for space exploration and those against it.

Space flight is a very integral part of exploration and adventure. Discovering the worlds around us I a very key part to discovering space. NASA's mission is to pioneer the future in space exploration, scientific discovery and aeronautics research. To do that, thousands of people have been working around the world—and off of it—for almost 50 years, trying to answer some basic questions. What's out there in space? How do we get there? What will we find? What can we learn there, or learn just by trying to get there, that will make life better here on Earth? (NASA). The ideal of many working together to the common goal of space exploration makes it a very important part. Manned spaceflight can be very dangerous. Many deaths and tragedies have occurred because of the exploration of space.

I think that space should still be explored by mankind. With technology advances mentioned in In the first 25 years of its existence, NASA conducted five manned spaceflight programs: Mercury, Gemini, Apollo, Skylab, and Shuttle.

The latter four programs produced spacecraft that had on-board digital computers. The Gemini computer was a single unit dedicated to guidance and navigation functions. Apollo used computers in the command module and lunar excursion module, again primarily for guidance and navigation. Skylab had a dual computer system for attitude control of the laboratory and pointing of the solar telescope. NASA's Space Shuttle is the most computerized spacecraft built to date, with five general-purpose computers as the heart of the avionics system and twin computers on each of the main engines. The Shuttle computers dominate all checkout, guidance, navigation, systems management, payload, and powered flight functions. The computers helped and as they advance manned spaceflight gets better. In the long run the risk is worth the gain for knowledge.

Writing Assignments

For each question, write a response according to the directions given by your instructor. Each response should contain correct grammar, spelling, and punctuation. Be sure to answer the question completely, but choose your words carefully so as to not exceed the word limit if one is given. There is no right or wrong answer; your score will be based upon the strength of the argument you make to defend your position.

1. In August 2007, the space shuttle *Endeavor* suffered minor damage to the heat shield tiles during liftoff. After the *Columbia* burned up on reentry in 2003 due to damaged tiles, NASA developed a protocol for repairing damaged tiles while in orbit. After much consideration, NASA decided *not* to attempt to repair the tiles on *Endeavor* while in orbit on this mission.

   Find a minimum of three different references discussing this incident and NASA's decision. Summarize the reasons both for and against repairing the tile while in orbit. If you had been on the team making this decision, would you have argued for or against the repair and why?

2. Research the failure of the Teton Dam. Describe what you think are the fundamental ethical issues involved in the failure. In terms of ethics, compare the Teton Dam failure in 1976 to the failure of levees in New Orleans in 2005.

3. In recent years, many studies have been conducted on the use of cell phones while driving. University of Utah psychologists have published a study showing that motorists who talk on handheld or hands-free cellular phones are as impaired as drunken drivers.

   > *"We found that people are as impaired when they drive and talk on a cell phone as they are when they drive intoxicated at the legal blood-alcohol limit of 0.08 percent, which is the minimum level that defines illegal drunken driving in most U.S. states," says study co-author Frank Drews, an assistant professor of psychology. "If legislators really want to address driver distraction, then they should consider outlawing cell phone use while driving."*

   > (*Strayer and Drews, "Human Factors."* The Journal of the Human Factors and Ergonomics Society, *Summer 2006.*)

   Another way to approach this problem is to force manufacturers of cell phones to create devices on the phones that would restrict usage if the user is driving, much like a safety on a gun trigger. Research and report current statistics on cell phone or other texting device usage during driving. Discuss the hazards (or lack of hazards) of driving while using a cell phone or other texting device. Discuss and justify whether cell phone manufacturers should be required to provide "safety" features on their devices to prevent usage while driving.

4. According to an article in the *Christian Science Monitor* (January 16, 2008, issue), environmentalists claim that a development around a remote lake 140 miles north of Augusta, Maine, would emit 500,000 tons of carbon dioxide over 50 years, including estimated emissions from cars traveling to and from the development. An environmental group has presented this "carbon footprint" to the state, and is requesting that the impact on the environment become part of the process for granting development permits.

   As many as 35 states have adopted climate-action plans, but there are few cases like this in which environmental impact factors into government approval of land development. This could have a significant effect on engineers involved with land development, structures, land-use planning, or environmental impact assessments in the future. The original article can be found at: http://www.csmonitor.com/2008/0116/p01s04-wogi.html.

   Discuss both sides of this issue, and take a stance for or against mandating carbon footprint assessment for new developments. Justify your position, including information from at least three sources. Ideas to include in your essay are cases in other states, climate-action plans, calculation of a "carbon footprint," or the land-development approval process. Most importantly, consider how an engineer would view this issue.

   Thank you to Dr. Lisa Benson for contributing this assignment.

5. From 2005 to 2009, much of the southeast experienced a serious rainfall deficit. Lake levels were at record lows, water restrictions were debated and enacted, and the ecology of the area was changed. Amid all of this are nonessential services that are extremely heavy users of water. Perhaps the most egregious examples are sports fields, and in particular, golf courses. On average, an 18-hole golf course in the United States uses about 100 million gallons per year.

Summarize the arguments both in favor and against the heavy use of water for nonessential services, particularly in areas where water supply is limited. Consider the following:

- If you were in a position to recommend legislation for such water use, what policies would you recommend and why? Consider this from an engineer's point of view.
- Consider the impact on local environments for building dams for water supplies and hydropower. As an engineer, what would you consider to be the benefits and drawbacks of this type of project, and why?

6. Since the early 1960s, humans have been venturing beyond Earth's atmosphere, a few times as far as the moon, a quarter of a million miles away. NASA currently plans to return humans to the moon by 2020, and plans Mars missions after that.

Much criticism has been leveled at the entire idea of manned spaceflight, claiming that unmanned craft can do essentially all the jobs people can with less cost and less risk.

Summarize the arguments on both sides of this issue.

7. In summer 2008, the *Phoenix Lander* discovered what seems to be incontrovertible evidence that water exists on Mars. Since life as we know depends on water (for a variety of reasons), this discovery raises the probability that life may exist, or did exist in the past, on Mars.

If life is discovered somewhere other than on Earth, what are our obligations to protect that life? Does that obligation depend on how "advanced" we perceive that life to be? What steps, if any, should be taken to ensure that we do not destroy the non-terrestrial life?

8. Advances in genetic engineering may make it possible to bring extinct species back to life.

(a) Should we attempt to restore populations of recently extinct animals, such as the Passenger pigeon, Carolina parakeet, ivory-billed woodpecker, Tasmanian tiger, or Formosan clouded leopard, for which there are many preserved specimens from which DNA could be acquired? There is currently an effort to obtain enough DNA to reestablish a population of Woolly mammoths. What are the ethical issues involved with bringing back a mammal extinct for 3,500 years?

(b) It was announced in February 2009 that a first draft of the genome of *Homo sapiens neanderthalensis* (Neanderthal), comprising about two-thirds of the base pairs, has been completed. If future advances make it possible, should we attempt to bring Neanderthals back to life?

9. If you could go back in time and be part of any engineering achievement in the past, what would you choose?

Your choice must involve something that was accomplished before 1970, although it might still be in use today. You may go as far back in time as you wish, but not more recently than 1970.

Your essay must include the following.

- Why did you choose this specific thing?
- Discuss the actual development of the item in question. Include issues such as why the item was desired, what problems the designers confronted, and specific design decisions that were made.
- What effects has the development of this device (or process) had on society and the planet, including positive, negative, and neutral effects.
- A bibliography with at least three distinct entries. All may be online references, but no more than one may be Wikipedia or similar sites.

10. Choose a bridge innovation to research from a list of potential topics given below, and write a memo or presentation that includes the following:

■ The name and location of the structure, when it was constructed, and other significant attributes.

■ If possible, a photo or sketch.

■ A summary table of the design features. Potential features to consider including, if appropriate:

  • Type of bridge design (arch, beam, suspension, etc.)
  • Dimensions (span, height)
  • Unique design features
  • Cost
  • Awards or superlatives (longest, highest, most cost-effective, costliest)

■ A discussion of the aspects of the bridge design that contributed to its success (materials, structural design, geographical, topographical, or climatic challenges, aesthetic qualities, etc.).

(a) Akashi Kaikyo Bridge, linking the islands of Honshu and Shikoku in Japan
(b) Cooper River Bridge in Charleston, South Carolina
(c) Forth Bridge, Scotland
(d) Gateshead Millennium Bridge, spanning the River Tyne in England
(e) Hanzhou Bay Bridge, China
(f) Humber Bridge, England
(g) Lake Pontchartrain Causeway, Louisiana
(h) Mackinac Bridge, Michigan
(i) Millau Viaduct, Millau, France
(j) Natchez Trace Bridge in Franklin, Tennessee
(k) Penobscot Narrows Bridge, Maine
(l) Rio-Antirio Bridge, Greece
(m) Sundial Bridge at Turtle Bay in Redding, California
(n) Sunshine Skyway Bridge in Tampa, Florida
(o) Sydney Harbor Bridge, Australia
(p) Tower Bridge, London
(q) Woodrow Wilson Bridge (proposed), Washington, DC
(r) Zakim Bunker Hill Bridge in Boston in Massachusetts.

11. Choose a major transportation structure failure to research from the list of potential topics that follows, and write a memo or presentation that includes the following:

■ The name and location of the structure, when it was constructed, and other significant attributes.

■ If possible, a photo or sketch.

■ A summary of the event(s) surrounding the structure's failure, including dates. Discuss aspects of the design that contributed to its failure (materials, structural flaws, misuse, improper maintenance, climatic conditions, etc.). If it was rebuilt, repaired, or replaced, how was the design modified or improved?

(a) Angers Bridge over the Maine River in Angers, France
(b) Autoroute 19 Overpass, Quebec
(c) Arroyo Pasajero Twin Bridges in Coalinga, California
(d) Banqiao Dam, China
(e) Charles de Gaulle Airport, France
(f) Hartford Civic Center, Connecticut
(g) Hyatt Regency hotel walkway in Kansas City, Missouri
(h) Kemper Arena, Missouri
(i) L'Ambiance Plaza in Bridgeport, Connecticut

    (j) Loncomilla Bridge, Chile

    (k) Mianus River Bridge in Greenwich, Connecticut

    (l) Millennium Footbridge, London

    (m) Sampoong Department Store, South Korea

    (n) Seongsu Bridge, spanning the Han River in Seoul, South Korea

    (o) Sgt. Aubrey Cosens VC Memorial Bridge in Latchford, Ontario

    (p) Silver Bridge, between Point Pleasant, WV, and Kanauga, Ohio

    (q) The Big Dig in Boston, Massachusetts

    (r) West Gate Bridge in Melbourne, Victoria, Australia

12. Choose an environmental issue to research from a list of potential topics given below, and write a memo or presentation that includes:

- A clear definition of the problem.
- If possible, a photo or sketch.
- Discussion of the issue; potential features to consider include, if appropriate:
  - Affected areas (local, region, continent, global)
  - Causes, sources
  - Effects (human, animal, vegetation, climate)
  - Prevention or reversal options (including feasibility and cost)
  - Important legislation (or lack thereof)

The topic should be discussed from an *engineering* viewpoint.

    (a) Acid rain

    (b) Air purification

    (c) Bioremediation

    (d) Clean Air Act

    (e) Cuyahoga River pollution/Clean Water Act

    (f) Deforestation

    (g) Erosion control

    (h) Groundwater pollution

    (i) Kyoto Protocol

    (j) Lake eutrophication/hypoxia

    (k) Loss of wetlands/ecosystems/pollinators

    (l) Ocean acidification/pollution

    (m) Purification/safe drinking water

    (n) RCRA (Resource Conservation and Recovery Act)

    (o) Smog/particle reduction

    (p) Soil contamination

    (q) Solar energy

    (r) Superfund/CERCLA

    (s) Water Pollution Control Act

    (t) Wind energy

13. Technology promises to revolutionize many aspects of life and society. In a memo or presentation, discuss the advantages and disadvantages of one or more of the following. You may need to research some of these topics first.

    (a) Nano-robots designed to destroy cancer cells

    (b) More powerful particle accelerators for probing the structure of matter

    (c) The James Webb Space Telescope

    (d) Cloaking technology at visible wavelengths

    (e) Practical antigravity devices

    (f) Drugs to inhibit soldiers' fears

    (g) Nano-devices to rewrite an organism's DNA

    (h) Practical (time and cost) interplanetary travel

    (i) Artificial chlorophyll to harness energy from the sun

(j) Genetically engineered microbes to attack invasive species
(k) Direct neural interface to computers
(l) Replacement human limbs with full functionality
(m) Terraforming Mars, Venus, or the moons of Jupiter or Saturn
(n) Quantum computers
(o) Room-temperature superconductors
(p) Materials harder than diamonds
(q) Artificial spider silk
(r) Full-color night-vision goggles
(s) Home-scale fusion reactors
(t) Fully automated cars
(u) Space elevators
(v) Bionic implants for enhancing sight, sound, and/or smell

CHAPTER 5
ESTIMATION

Enrico Fermi was a Nobel laureate and one of many brilliant scientists and engineers involved in the Manhattan Project, which developed the first nuclear weapons during World War II. He wrote the following after witnessing the first test of an atomic bomb, called the Trinity Test (see Figure 5-1). Of particular note is the final paragraph.

> *On the morning of the 16th of July, I was stationed at the Base Camp at Trinity in a position about ten miles from the site of the explosion.*
>
> *The explosion took place at about 5:30 A.M. I had my face protected by a large board in which a piece of dark welding glass had been inserted. My first impression of the explosion was the very intense flash of light, and a sensation of heat on the parts of my body that were exposed. Although I did not look directly towards the object, I had the impression that suddenly the countryside became brighter than in full daylight.*
>
> *I subsequently looked in the direction of the explosion through the dark glass and could see something that looked like a conglomeration of flames that promptly started rising. After a few seconds the rising flames lost their brightness and appeared as a huge pillar of smoke with an expanded head like a gigantic mushroom that rose rapidly beyond the clouds probably to a height of the order of 30,000 feet. After reaching its full height, the smoke stayed stationary for a while before the wind started dispersing it.*
>
> *About 40 seconds after the explosion the air blast reached me. I tried to estimate its strength by dropping from about six feet small pieces of paper before, during and after the passage of the blast wave. Since at the time there was no wind I could observe very distinctly and actually measure the displacement of the pieces of paper that were in the process of falling while the blast was passing. The shift was about 2½ meters, which, at the time, I estimated to correspond to the blast that would be produced by ten thousand tons of T.N.T.*
>
> **Citation: U.S. National Archives, Record Group 227, OSRD-S1 Committee, Box 82 folder 6, "Trinity."*

Before the test, no one knew what would happen. Speculation among the many people involved concerning the results of the test ranged from nothing (no explosion at all) to setting the planetary atmosphere on fire and destroying all life on Earth. When all the data from the blast were analyzed, the true strength of the blast was calculated to be 19 kilotons. By simply observing the behavior of falling bits of paper 10 miles from ground zero, Fermi's estimation of 10 kilotons was in error by less than a factor of 2.

After the war, Fermi taught at the University of Chicago, where he was noted for giving his students problems in which so much information was missing that a solution seemed impossible. Such problems have

Figure 5-1 The first atomic bomb test, Alamogordo, New Mexico.

Courtesy of: Truman Presidential Museum & Library.

been named **Fermi problems**, and in general they require the person considering them to determine an answer with far less information than would really be necessary to calculate an accurate value. Engineers are often faced with solving problems for which they do not have all the information. They must be adept at making initial estimates. This skill helps them identify critical information that is missing, develop their reasoning skills to solve problems, and recognize what a "reasonable" solution will look like.

Most practical engineering problems are better defined than Fermi problems and can be estimated more easily and accurately in general. The following are just a few examples of real engineering problems. See if you can estimate answers for these problems. These should be done without reference to the web or any other source of information.

- How many cubic yards of concrete are needed to pave 1 mile of interstate highway (two lanes each direction)?
- How many feet of wire are needed to connect the lighting systems in an automobile?
- What is the average flow rate in gallons per minute of gasoline moving from the fuel tank to the fuel injectors in an automobile cruising at highway speed?

An accomplished engineer knows the answer to most problems before doing any calculations. This does not mean an answer to three significant figures, but a general idea of the range of values that would be reasonable. For example, if you throw a baseball as high as possible, how long will it take for the ball to hit the ground? Obviously, an answer of a few milliseconds is unreasonable, as is several months. Several seconds seems more realistic. When you actually do a calculation to determine this time, you should ask yourself, "Is my answer reasonable?"

Sample Fermi Problems

- Estimate the total number of hairs on your head.
- Estimate the number of drops of water in all of the Great Lakes.
- Estimate the number of piano tuners in New York City.

● EXAMPLE 5-1

Every year, numerous people run out of fuel while driving their vehicle on the road. Determine how many gallons of gasoline are carried to vehicles with empty fuel tanks each year in the United States so that the vehicle can be driven to the nearest gas station. Do this without reference to any other material, such as the Internet or reference books.

Estimations

In almost all cases, the first step is to estimate unknown pieces of information that are not available. In general, there are numerous paths to a solution, and different people may arrive at different answers. Often, the answer arrived at is only accurate to within an order of magnitude (a factor of 10) or less. Nonetheless, such problems can provide valuable insight not only into the problem itself but also into the nature of problem solving in general.

Remember, these are estimates, not accurate values. Someone else making these estimates might make different assumptions.

- *Number of people in the United States: 500,000,000 persons.*
- *Fraction of people in the United States that drive: drivers per 10 persons.*
- *Average times a person runs out of gas per year: one "out of gas" per 4 years per driver.*
- *Fraction of "out of gas" incidents in which gas is brought to the car (rather than pushing or towing the car to a station): 24 "bring gas to car" per 25 "out of gas".*

■ *Average amount of gas carried to car: 1.5 gallons per "bring gas to car".*

Calculation

This is where you combine your estimates to arrive at a solution. In the process, you may realize that you need further information to complete the computation.

$$\text{Drivers in United States} = (5 \times 10^8 \text{ people})\left(\frac{7 \text{ drivers}}{10 \text{ people}}\right) = 3.5 \times 10^8 \text{ drivers}$$

$$\text{Number out of gas per year} = (3.5 \times 10^8 \text{ drivers})\left(\frac{1 \text{ out of gas}}{(4 \text{ years})(1 \text{ driver})}\right)$$

$$= 8.75 \times 10^7 \frac{\text{out of gas}}{\text{year}}$$

$$\text{Number bring gas to car per year} = \left(\frac{8.75 \times 10^7 \text{ out of gas}}{\text{year}}\right)\left(\frac{24 \text{ bring to car}}{25 \text{ out of gas}}\right)$$

$$= 8.4 \times 10^7 \frac{\text{bring gas to car}}{\text{year}}$$

$$\text{Amount of gas to cars} = \left(\frac{8.4 \times 10^7 \text{ bring gas to car}}{\text{year}}\right)\left(\frac{1.5 \text{ gallons of gas}}{\text{bring gas to car}}\right)$$

$$= 1.26 \times 10^8 \frac{\text{gallons}}{\text{year}}$$

Thus, we have estimated that about 125 million gallons of gas are taken to "out of fuel" vehicles each year in the United States. It would be perfectly valid to give the answer as "about 100 million" gallons, since we probably have only about one significant digit worth of confidence in our results, if that.

A few things to note about this solution:

■ *"Units" were used on all numerical values, although some of these units were somewhat contrived (e.g., "out of gas") to meet the needs of the problem. Keeping track of the units is critical to obtaining correct answers and will be highly emphasized, not only in this text but also throughout your engineering education and career.*

■ *The units combine and cancel according to the regular algebraic rules. For example, in the first computation, the unit "persons" appeared in both the numerator and the denominator, and thus canceled, leaving "drivers."*

■ *Rather than the computation being combined into one huge string of computations, it was broken into smaller pieces, with the results from one step used to compute the next step. This is certainly not an immutable rule, but for long computations it reduces careless errors and makes it easier to understand the overall flow of the problem.*

Many cars today use a plastic fuel tank. It is more durable and lighter than a conventional steel tank. The picture below shows a blow-molded fuel tank with six layers of plastics. Six layers are required to eliminate any permeation of the fuel through the tank.

The picture on the right shows a model of how the melted plastic flows through the extruder head of a blow-molding machine. The six layers are combined at the bottom to form a parison, which is then blow molded to form the fuel tank.

Photos courtesy of Kautex Machines.

5.1   GENERAL HINTS FOR ESTIMATION

As you gain more knowledge and experience, the types of problems you can estimate will become more complicated. Here we give you a few hints about making estimates.

- Try to determine the accuracy required. Is order of magnitude enough? How about ±25%?
  - What level of accuracy is needed to calculate a satellite trajectory?
  - What level of accuracy is needed to determine the amount of paint needed to paint a specified classroom?

The term "**orders of magnitude**" is often used when comparing things of very different scales, such as a small rock and a planet. By far the most common usage refers to factors of 10; for example, three orders of magnitude refer to a difference in scale of $10^3 = 1,000$. If we wanted to consider the order of magnitude between 10,000,000 and 1,000, we would calculate the logarithm of each value ($\log(10,000,000) = 7$ and $\log(1,000) = 3$), thus there are $7 - 3 = 4$ orders of magnitude difference between 10,000,000 and 1,000.

- Remember that a "ballpark" value for an input parameter is often good enough.
  - What is the square footage of a typical house?
  - What is the maximum high temperature to expect in Dallas, Texas, in July?
  - What is the typical velocity of a car on the highway?

- Always ask yourself if it is better to err on the high side or the low side. There are two primary reasons for asking this question.
  - Safety and practical considerations. Will a higher or lower estimate result in a safer or more reliable result?
    - If estimating the weight a bridge can support, it is better to err on the low side, so that the actual load it can safely carry is greater than the estimate.
    - For the bridge mentioned above, if estimating the load a single beam needs to support, it is better to err on the high side, thus giving a stronger beam than necessary. Be sure you understand the difference between these two points.
- Estimate improvement. Can the errors cancel each other?
  - If estimating the product of two numbers, if one of the terms is rounded low, the other should be rounded high to counteract for the lower term.
  - If estimating a quotient, if you round the numerator term on the low side, should the denominator term be rounded low or high?
- Do not get bogged down with second-order or minor effects.
  - If estimating the mass of air in the classroom, do you need to correct for the presence of furniture?
  - In most instances, can the effect of temperature on the density of water be neglected?

The best way to develop your ability to estimate is through experience. An experienced painter can more easily estimate how much paint is needed to repaint a room because experience will have taught the painter such things as how many coats of one paint color it will take to paint over another, how different paint brands differ in their coverage, and how to estimate surface area quickly. In *Outliers: The Story of Success*, Malcolm Gladwell provides examples from diverse career pathways that demonstrate 10,000 hours of practice are required to develop world-class expertise in any area. Fortunately for aspiring engineers, much of this expertise can be developed starting at a young age and outside of formal schooling. For example, how many hours have you spent observing the effects of gravity? Of course, some important engineering concepts stem from phenomena that are not so easily observed, and some lend themselves to misinterpretation. As a result, it helps to have a systematic approach to developing estimates—particularly where we have less experience to guide us. Estimating an approximate answer of a calculation including known quantities is a valuable skill—such as approximating the square root of 50 as about 7, approximating the value of pi as 3 for quick estimates, etc. These mathematical approximations, however, assume that you have all the numbers to begin with, and that you can use shortcuts to estimate the precisely calculated answer to save time or as a check against your more carefully calculated answer. Estimation is discussed here in a broader sense—estimating quantities that cannot be known, are complicated to measure, or are otherwise inconvenient to obtain. It is in these cases that the following strategies are recommended.

The Windows interface estimates the time needed to copy files. The estimate is dynamic and appears to be based on the total number of files and the assumption that each file will take the same amount of time to copy. As a result, when large files are copied, the estimate will increase—sometimes significantly. Similarly, as a large number of small files are copied, the estimate will decrease rapidly. A better estimation algorithm might be based on the percentage of the total file size.

5.2 ESTIMATION BY ANALOGY

One useful strategy for estimating a quantity is by comparison to something else we have measured previously or otherwise know the dimension of. The best way to prepare for this approach to estimation is to learn a large number of comparison measures for each type of quantity you might wish to estimate. Each of these comparison measures becomes an anchor point on that scale of measurement. This book provides some scale anchors for various measurable quantities—particularly in the case of power and energy, concepts with which many people struggle.

● **EXAMPLE 5-2**

Estimate the size of a laptop computer using analogy.

Laptop computers come in different sizes, but it is not difficult to estimate the size of a particular laptop. Laptops were first called "notebook" computers—a good starting estimate would be to compare the particular laptop to notebook paper, which is 8.5 inches by 11 inches in the United States.

● **EXAMPLE 5-3**

Estimate the size of an acre and a hectare of land using analogy.

American football field—playing area is 300 feet by 160 feet = approximately 50,000 square feet. An acre is 43,560 square feet. Using this data, we have a better sense of how much land an acre is—about 90% of the size of the playing area of an American football field. Soccer fields are larger, but vary in size. The largest soccer field that satisfies international guidelines would be about 2 acres.

A hectare, or 10,000 square meter, is equivalent to 108,000 square feet and is much larger than an acre—about the maximum size of the pitch in international rugby competition.

5.3 ESTIMATION BY AGGREGATION

Another useful strategy is to estimate the quantity of something by adding up an estimate of its parts. This can involve multiplication in the case of a number of similarly sized parts, such as estimating the size of a tile by comparing it to your foot (estimation by analogy), counting the number of floor tiles across a room, and multiplying to estimate the total length of the room. In other cases, aggregation may involve adding together parts that are estimated by separate methods. For example, to estimate the volume of a two-scoop ice cream cone, you might estimate the volume of the cone and then separately estimate the volume of each scoop assuming they are each spheres.

● **EXAMPLE 5-4**

Estimate by aggregation the amount of money students at your school spend on pizza each year.

Ask students around you how often they purchase a pizza and how much it costs;
Convert this estimate into a cost per week;
Multiply your estimate by the number of weeks in an academic year;
Multiple that result by the number of students at your school.

5.4   ESTIMATION BY UPPER AND LOWER BOUNDS

An important part of estimating is keeping track of whether your estimate is high or low. In the earlier example of estimating the volume of a two-scoop ice cream cone, we would have over-estimated, because one of the scoops of ice cream is pressed inside the cone. The effect of pressing the scoops together is not that important, because the same amount of ice cream is still there, but if the scoop is pressed into an ellipsoid, it may be difficult to estimate the original radius of the scoop.

Engineers frequently make "conservative" estimates, which consider the "worst-case" scenario. Depending on the situation, the worst case may be a lower limit (such as estimating the strength of a structure) or an upper limit (such as estimating how much material is needed for a project).

● EXAMPLE 5-5

If you are to estimate how many gallons of paint are needed to paint the room you are in, what assumptions will you need to make? Where will you need to make assumptions to ensure that you have enough paint without running out?

In estimating the wall area, you should round up the length and height.

Noting that paint (for large jobs) is sold in 5-gallon pails, you will want to round your final estimate to the next whole 5-gallon pail.

Close estimates allow for subtracting 21 square feet per doorway (if the doors are not being painted the same color). In making a rough estimate, if there are not a lot of doorways, it would be conservative to leave in the door area.

5.5   ESTIMATION USING MODELING

In cases that are more complicated or where a more precise estimate is required, mathematical models and statistics might be used. Sometimes dimensionless quantities are useful for characterizing systems, sometimes modeling the relationship of a small number of variables is needed, and at other times, extrapolating even a single variable from available data is all that is needed to make an estimate.

● EXAMPLE 5-6

You would like to enjoy a bowl of peas, but they are too hot to eat. Spreading them out on a plate allows them to cool faster. Describe why this happens and devise a model of how much faster the peas on the plate will cool. Mice have a harder time keeping warm compared to elephants. Explain how this is related to the bowl of peas. How does this relate to the fact that smaller animals have higher heart rates? Canaries and humming-birds can have heart rates of 1,200 beats per minute, whereas human heart rates should not exceed 150 beats per minute even during exercise.

The peas cool faster when spread out because of the increase in surface area. The ratio of surface area (proportional to cooling) to volume (proportional to the heat capacity for a particular substance) is therefore important. Similarly, smaller animals have a harder time staying warm because they have a higher ratio of surface area to volume. The higher heart rate is needed to keep their bodies warm. This also relates to why smaller animals consume a much larger amount of food compared to their body mass.

● **EXAMPLE 5-7**   A large sample of sunflower seeds is collected and their lengths are measured. Using that information, estimate the length of the longest sunflower seed you are likely to find if you measure one billion seeds.

Given a large sample, its average and standard deviation can be calculated. Assuming that the length of sunflower seeds is normally distributed, the one-in-a-billion largest sunflower seed would be expected to be six standard deviations greater than the sample average.

5.6 SIGNIFICANT FIGURES

Significant figures or "sig figs" are the digits considered reliable as a result of measurement or calculation. This is not to be confused with the number of digits or decimal places. The number of **decimal places** is simply the number of digits to the right of the decimal point. Example 5-8 illustrates these two concepts.

● **EXAMPLE 5-8**

NOTE

Decimal places is the number of digits to the right of the decimal point.

Significant figures are the digits considered reliable.

Mantissa: gives the numerical value of significant figures.

Exponent: specifies the location of the decimal point.

Number	Decimal Places	Significant Figures
376	0	3
376.0	1	4
376,908	0	6
3,760,000	0	3
3,760,000.	0	7
0.376	3	3
0.37600	5	5
0.0037600	7	5
376×10^{-6}	0*	3

* There is no universal agreement concerning whether numbers in scientific or engineering notation should be considered to have the number of decimal places indicated in the mantissa (as shown), or the number that would be present if the number were written out in standard decimal notation (6 in the last example above).

*For those who did not run across the term mantissa in high school (or have forgotten it)—the two parts of a number expressed in either scientific or engineering notation are the mantissa and the exponent. The **mantissa** is the part that gives the numerical values of the significant figures; the **exponent** specifies the location of the decimal point, thus the magnitude of the overall number. In the last row of the table above, the mantissa is 376, the exponent is −6. The mantissa can also contain a decimal point, for example, 3.76×10^{-4}: in this case the mantissa is 3.76 and the exponent is −4.*

The Meaning of "Significant"

All digits other than zero are automatically considered significant. Zero is significant when:

- It appears between two nonzero numbers
  - 306 has three significant figures
  - 5.006 has four significant figures
- It is a "terminal" zero in a number with a decimal point
  - 2.790 has four significant figures
  - 2000.0 has five significant figures

Zero is not significant when:

- It is used to fix a decimal place
  - 0.0456 has three significant figures
- It is used in integers without a decimal point that could be expressed in scientific notation without including that zero
  - 2000 has one significant figure (2×10^3)
  - 35,100 has three significant figures (3.51×10^4)

COMPREHENSION CHECK 5-1

Determine the number of significant figures and decimal places for each value.

- **(a)** 0.0050
- **(c)** 3.00
- **(d)** 447×10^9
- **(e)** 75×10^{-3}
- **(f)** 7,790,200
- **(h)** 20.000

Calculation Rules

As an engineer, you will likely find that your job involves the design and creation of a product. It is imperative that your calculations lead to the design being "reasonable." It is also important that you remember that others will use much of your work, including people with no technical training.

Engineers must not imply more accuracy in their calculations than is reasonable. To assist in this, there are many rules that pertain to using the proper number of "significant figures" in computations. These rules, however, are cumbersome and tedious. In your daily life as an engineer, you might use these rules only occasionally. The rules given below provide a reference if you ever need them; in this text, however, you are simply expected to be *reasonable,* the concept of which is discussed in Section 5.8. In general, asking yourself if the number of significant figures in your answer is reasonable is usually sufficient. However, it is a good idea to be familiar with the rules, or at least know how to find them and use them if the need ever arises.

Multiplication and Division

A quotient or product should contain the same number of significant figures as the number with the fewest significant figures. Exact conversions do not affect this rule.

● EXAMPLE 5-9

$(2.43)(17.675) = 42.95025 \cong 43.0$

- ■ *2.43 has three significant figures.*
- ■ *17.675 has five significant figures.*
- ■ *The answer (43.0) has three significant figures.*

● EXAMPLE 5-10

$(2.479\text{ h})(60\text{ min}/\text{h}) = 148.74 \cong 148.7\text{ min}$

- ■ *2.479 hours has four significant figures.*
- ■ *60 minutes/hour is an exact conversion.*
- ■ *The answer (148.7) has four significant figures.*

Addition and Subtraction

The answer resulting from an addition or subtraction should show significant figures only as far to the right as the least precise number in the calculation. For addition and subtraction operations, the "least precise" number should be that containing the lowest number of decimal places.

● EXAMPLE 5-11

$1725.463 + 489.2 + 16.73 = 1931.393$

- ■ *489.2 is the least precise.*
- ■ *The answer should contain one decimal place: 1931.4.*

● EXAMPLE 5-12

$903,000 + 59,600 + 104,470 = 1,067,070$

- ■ *903,000 is the least precise.*
- ■ *The answer should be carried to the thousands place: 1,067,000.*

Rounding

If the most significant figure dropped is 5 or greater, then increase the last digit retained by 1.

● EXAMPLE 5-13

Quantity	Rounded to	Appears as
43.48	3 significant figures	43.5
43.48	2 significant figures	43
0.0143	2 significant figures	0.014
0.0143	1 significant figures	0.01
1.555	3 significant figures	1.56
1.555	2 significant figures	0.6
1.555	1 significant figures	2

At what point in a calculation should I round my values?

Calculators are quite adept at keeping track of lots of digits—let them do what they are good at. In general, it is neither necessary nor desirable to round intermediate values in a calculation, and if you do, maintain at least two more significant figures for all intermediate values than the number you plan to use in the final result. The following example illustrates the risk of excessively rounding intermediate results.

$$\text{Evaluate } C = 10{,}000[0.6 - (5/9 + 0.044)]$$

- Using calculator with no intermediate rounding:

$$C = \textbf{4.4}$$

- Rounding value in inner parenthesis to two significant figures:
$$C = 10{,}000(0.6 - (0.599555)) = 10{,}000(0.6 - (0.60)) = \textbf{0}$$

- Rounding 9/5 to two significant figures:
$$C = 10{,}000(0.6 - (0.55555 + 0.044)) = 10{,}000(0.6 - (0.56 + 0.044))$$
$$= 10{,}000(0.6 - (0.604)) = \textbf{-40}$$

As you can see, rounding to two significant figures at different points in the calculation gives dramatically different results: 4.4, 0, and −40. **Be very sure you know what effect rounding of intermediate values will have if you choose to do so!**

Some numbers, such as certain unit conversions, are considered "exact" by definition. Do not consider them in the determination of significant figures. In calculations with a *known constant* (such as pi (π), which is defined to an infinite number of significant figures), *include at least two more significant figures* in the constant than are contained in the other values in the calculation.

COMPREHENSION CHECK 5-2

Express the answer to the following, using the correct number of significant digits.

(a) $102.345 + 7.8 - 169.05 =$
(b) $20. * 3.567 + 175.6 =$
(c) $(9.78 - 4.352)/2.20 =$
(d) $(783 + 8.98)/(2{,}980 - 1{,}387.2) =$

5.7 REASONABLENESS

In the preceding discussion of estimation, the word *reasonable* was mentioned in several places. We consider two types of reasonableness in answers to problems in this section.

- **Physically reasonable.** Does the answer make sense in light of our understanding of the physical situation being explored or the estimates that we can make?
- **Reasonable precision.** Is the number of digits in the answer commensurate with the level of accuracy and precision available to us in the parameters of the problem?

When Is Something Physically Reasonable?

Here are a few hints to help you determine if a solution to a problem is physically reasonable.

- First, ask yourself if the answer makes sense in the physical world.
  - You determine that the wingspan of a new airplane to carry 200 passengers should be 4 feet. This is obvious rubbish.
  - You determine that a sewage treatment plant for a community of 10,000 people must handle 100,000 pound-mass of sewage effluent per day. Since a gallon of water weighs about 8 pound-mass, this is about 1.25 gallons per person per day, which is far too low to be reasonable.
  - In an upper-level engineering course, you have to calculate the acceleration of a 1982 Volkswagen® Rabbit with a diesel engine. After performing your calculations, you find that the time required to accelerate from 0 to 60 miles per hour is 38 seconds. Although for a similarly sized gasoline engine, this is a rather low acceleration; for a small diesel engine, it is quite reasonable.
  - You are designing playground equipment, including a swing set. The top support (pivot point) for the swings is 10 feet above the ground. You calculate that a child using one of the swings will make one full swing (forward, then backward) in 3.6 seconds. This seems reasonable.
- If the final answer is in units for which you do not have an intuitive feel, convert to units for which you do have an intuitive feel.
  - You calculate the speed of a pitched baseball to be 2×10^{13} millimeters per year. Converting this to miles per hour gives over 1,400 miles per hour, obviously too fast for a pitched baseball.
  - You are interested in what angle a smooth steel ramp must have before a wooden block will begin to slide down it. Your calculations show that the value is 0.55 radians. Is this reasonable? If you have a better "feel" for degrees, you should convert the value in radians to degrees, which gives 32 degrees, this value seems reasonable.
  - You have measured the force of a hammer hitting a nail by using a brand-new sensor. The result is a value of 110 million dynes. Do you believe this value? Since few engineers work in dynes, it seems reasonable to convert this to units that are more familiar, such as pound-force. This conversion gives a value of 240 pound-force, which seems reasonable.
  - You are told by a colleague that a ¾-inch pipe supplying water to a chemical process delivers 10 cubic meters of water per day. Converting to gallons per minute gives 1.8 gallons per minute, which seems completely reasonable.
- If your solution is a mathematical model, consider the behavior of the model at very large and very small values.
  - You have determined that the temperature (T in degrees Fahrenheit) of a freshly forged steel ingot can be described as a function of time (t in minutes) by this expression: $T = 2,500 - 10t$. Using this equation to calculate the temperature of the ingot, you discover that after less than 300 minutes (6 hours), the temperature of the ingot will be less than absolute zero!
  - You have determined the temperature (T in degrees Celsius) of a small steel rod placed over a Bunsen burner with a flame temperature of 1,000 degrees Celsius is given by $T = 960 - 939e^{-0.002t}$, where t is the time in seconds from the first application of the flame to the rod. At time $t = 0$, $T = 21$ degree Celsius (since the exponential term will become $e^0 = 1$). This seems reasonable, since it implies that

- the temperature of the rod at the beginning of the experiment is 21 degrees Celsius, which is about room temperature. As the value of time increases, the temperature approaches 960 degrees Celsius (since $e^{-\infty} = 0$). This also seems reasonable since the ultimate temperature of the rod will probably be a bit less than the temperature of the flame heating, because of inefficiencies in the heat transfer process.

- A large tank is filled with water to a depth of 10 meters, and a drain in the bottom is opened so that the water begins to flow out. You determine that the depth (D) of water in the tank is given by $D = 5t^{-0.1}$, where t is the time in minutes after the drain was opened at $t = 0$. As t increases, D approaches zero, as we would expect since all of the water will eventually drain from the tank. As t approaches zero, however, D approaches infinity, an obviously ridiculous situation; thus, the model is probably incorrect.

When Is an Answer Reasonably Precise?

First, we need to differentiate between the two terms: *accurate* and *precise*. Although laypersons tend to use these words interchangeably, an aspiring engineer should understand the difference in meaning as applied to measured or calculated values.

Accuracy is a measure of how close a calculation or measurement (or an average of a group of measurements) is to the actual value. For measured data, if the average of all measurements of a specific parameter is close to the actual value, then the measurement is accurate, whether or not the individual measurements are close to each other. The difference between the measured value and the actual value is the error in the measurement. Errors come about due to lack of accuracy of measuring equipment, poor measurement techniques, misuse of equipment, and factors in the environment (e.g., temperature or vibration).

Repeatability is a measure of how close together multiple measurements of the same parameter are, whether or not they are close to the actual value.

Precision is a combination of accuracy and repeatability, and is reflected in the number of significant figures used to report a value. The more significant figures, the more precise the value is, assuming it is also accurate.

To illustrate these concepts, consider the distribution of hits on a standard "bulls-eye" target. The figure shows all four combinations of accuracy and repeatability, and is

- Neither repeatable nor accurate.
- Repeatable, but not accurate.
- Accurate, but not repeatable.
- Both repeatable and accurate. This is called precise.

When considering if the precision of a numeric value is reasonable, always ask yourself the following questions:

- How many significant figures do I need in my design parameters? The more precision you specify in a design, the more it will cost and the less competitive it will be unless the extra precision is really needed.

- You can buy a really nice 16-ounce hammer for about $20. If you wanted a 16 ± 0.0001-ounce hammer, it would probably cost well over a hundred dollars, possibly thousands.

NOTE

Most common measuring devices can reliably measure the parameter in question to only three or four significant figures at best, and sometimes less than that. To obtain a really repeatable measurement (e.g., to seven significant figures) in general requires sophisticated (and expensive) equipment.

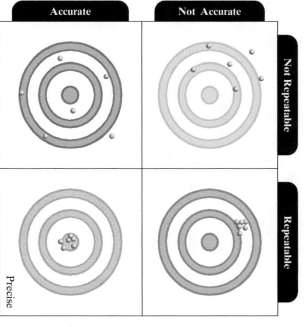

Not Accurate | Accurate
Not Repeatable
Repeatable
Precise

■ What are the inherent limitations of my measuring equipment? How much is the measurement affected by environmental factors, user error, etc.?

• The plastic ruler you buy at the discount store for considerably less than a dollar will measure lengths up to 12 inches with a precision of better than 0.1 inch, but not as good as 0.01 inch. On the other hand, you can spend a few hundred dollars for a high-quality micrometer and measure lengths up to perhaps 6 inches to a precision of 0.0001 inch.

• Pumps at gas stations all over the United States often display their gas price and the amount of gas pumped to three decimal places. When gas prices are high, it is extremely important to consumers that the pumps are correctly calibrated. The National Institute of Standards and Technology (NIST) requires that for every 5 gallons pumped, the amount must not be off by more than 6 cubic inches. To determine if a gas pump is calibrated correctly, you need to be able to see to three decimal places the amount pumped since 6 cubic inches is approximately 0.026 gallons.

You should report values in engineering calculations in a way that does not imply a higher level of accuracy than is known. Use the fewest number of decimal places without reducing the usefulness of the answer. Several examples, given below, illustrate this concept.

■ We want to compute the area (A) of a circle. We measure the diameter (D) as 2.63 centimeters. We calculate

$$A = \frac{1}{4}\pi D^2 = \frac{1}{4}\pi(2.63)^2 = 5.432521 \text{ cm}^2$$

The value of π is known to as many places as we desire, and ¼ is an exact number. It seems reasonable to give our answer as 5.4 or 5.43 square centimeters since the original data of diameter is given to two decimal places. Most of the time, reporting answers with two to four significant digits is acceptable and reasonable. We want to compute the area (A) of a circle. We measure the diameter (D) as 0.0024 centimeters. We calculate

$$A = \frac{1}{4}\pi D^2 = \frac{1}{4}\pi(0.0024)^2 = 0.0004446 \text{ cm}^2$$

If we keep only two decimal places, our answer would be 0.00 square centimeters, which has no meaning. Consequently, when reporting numerical results, particularly those with a magnitude much smaller than 1, we use significant figures, not decimal places. It would be reasonable to report our answer as 0.00044 or 4.4×10^{-4} square centimeters.

■ We want to determine a linear relationship for a set of data, using a standard software package such as Excel®. The program will automatically generate a linear relationship based on the data set. Suppose that the result of this exercise is

$$y = 0.50236x + 2.0378$$

While we do not necessarily have proof that the coefficients in this equation are nice simple numbers or even integers, a look at the equation above suggests that the linear relationship should probably be taken as

$$y = 0.5x + 2$$

■ If calculations and design procedures require a high level of precision, pay close attention to the established rules regarding significant digits. If the values you generate are small, you may need more significant digits. For example, if all the values are between 0.02 and 0.04 and you select one significant figure, *all* your values will read 0.02, 0.03, or 0.04; going to two significant figures gives values such as 0.026 or 0.021 or 0.034.

■ Calculators are often set to show eight or more decimal places.

● If you measure the size of a rectangle as 2¹¹⁄₁₆ inches by 5¹⁄₈ inches, then the area is calculated to be 6.4453125 square inches since the calculator does not care about how many significant digits result. It is unreasonable that we can determine the area of a rectangle to seven decimal places when we made two measurements, the most accurate of which was 0.0625 inches, or four decimal places.

● If a car has a mass of 1.5 tons, should we say it has a mass of 3010.29 pound-mass?

■ Worksheets in Excel often have a default of six to eight decimal places. Two important reasons to use fewer are that: (1) long decimal places are often unreasonable and (2) columns of numbers to this many decimal places make a worksheet difficult to read and unnecessarily cluttered.

COMPREHENSION CHECK 5-3

In each of the cases below, a value of the desired quantity has been determined in some way, resulting in a number displayed on a calculator or computer screen. Your task is to round each number to a *reasonable* number of significant digits—*up* if a higher value is conservative, *down* if a lower value is conservative, and to the *nearest* value if it does not make a difference. Specify why your assumption is conservative.

(a) The mass of an adult human riding on an elevator   178.8 pounds
(b) The amount of milk needed to fill a cereal bowl   1.25 cups
(c) The time it takes to sing *Happy Birthday*   32.67 seconds

Increasingly, engineers are working at smaller and smaller scales. On the left, a vascular clamp is compared to the tip of a match. The clamp is made from a bio-absorbable plastic through the process of injection molding.

Photo courtesy of E. Stephan

5.8 NOTATION

When discussing numerical values, there are several different ways to represent the values. To read, interpret, and discuss values between scientists and engineers, it is important to understand the different styles of notation. For example, in the United States a period is used as the decimal separator and a comma is used as a digit group separator, indicating groups of a thousand (such as 5,245.25). In some countries, however, this notation is reversed (5.245,25) and in other countries a space is used as the digit group separator (5 245.25). It is important to always consider the country of origin when interpreting written values. Several other types of notations are discussed below.

Engineering Notation Versus Scientific Notation

In high school, you probably learned to represent numbers in scientific notation, particularly when the numbers were very large or very small. Although this is indeed a useful means of representing numeric values, in engineering, a slight modification of this notation, called engineering notation, is often more useful. This is particularly true when the value of a parameter can vary over many orders of magnitude. For example, electrical engineers routinely deal with currents ranging from 10^{-15} amperes or less to 10^2 amperes or more.

Scientific notation is typically expressed in the form $\#.\#\#\# \times 10^N$, where the digit to the left of the decimal point is the most significant nonzero digit of the value being represented. Sometimes, the digit to the right of the decimal point is the most significant digit instead. The number of decimal places can vary, but is usually two to four. N is an integer, and multiplying by 10^N serves to locate the true position of the decimal point.

Engineering notation is expressed in the form $\#\#\#.\#\#\# \times 10^M$, where M is an integer multiple of 3, and the number of digits to the left of the decimal point is either 1, 2, or 3 as needed to yield a power of 10 that is indeed a multiple of 3. The number of digits to the right of the decimal point is typically between two and four.

NOTE

Scientific Notation:
$\#.\#\#\# \times 10^N$
N = integer

Engineering Notation:
$\#\#\#.\#\#\# \times 10^M$
M = integer multiple of 3

● **EXAMPLE 5-14**

Standard	Scientific	Engineering
43,480,000	4.348×10^7	43.48×10^6
0.0000003060	3.060×10^{-7}	306.0×10^{-9}
9,860,000,000	9.86×10^9	9.86×10^9
0.0351	3.51×10^{-2}	35.1×10^{-3}
0.0000000522	5.22×10^{-14}	52.2×10^{-15}
456200	4.562×10^8	456.2×10^6

COMPREHENSION CHECK 5-4

Express each of the following values in scientific and engineering notation.

(a) 58,093,099
(b) 0.00458097
(c) 42,677,000.99

Calculator E-notation

Most scientific calculators use the uppercase "E" as shorthand for both scientific and engineering notation when representing numbers. To state the meaning of the letter E in English, it is read as "times 10 raised to the ___." For example, 3.707 E –5 would be read as "3.707 times 10 to the negative 5." When transcribing numbers from your calculator, in general it is best *not* to use the E notation, showing the actual power of 10 instead. Thus 3.707 E –5 should be written as 3.707×10^{-5}.

Never use a lowercase "e" for transcribing these values from the calculator, such as $3.707\ e^{-5}$, since this looks like you are multiplying by the number e ($\cong 2.717$) raised to the negative 5. But if you do use a capital E (which is occasionally, though rarely, justifiable), *do not* superscript the number following the E (e.g., $3.707\ E^{-5}$) since this looks like you are raising some value E (whatever it may be) to a power.

Situations for Use of an Exponential Notation

In general, if the magnitude of a number is difficult to almost instantly determine when written in standard notation, use an exponential notation like scientific or engineering notation. Although there are no definite rules for this, if the magnitude is greater than 10,000 or less than 0.0001, you probably should consider using exponential notation. For larger numbers, using the comma notation can extend this range somewhat, for example, 85,048,900 is quickly seen to be 85 million plus a bit. However, there is no similar notation for very small numbers: 0.0000000483 is difficult to simply glance at and realize that it is about 48 billionths.

Note that it is never actually incorrect to use either exponential or standard notation; it is merely a matter of readability. To write 5×10^{20} as 500000000000000000000 is not wrong, but it may leave the readers' eyes vibrating trying to keep track of all the zeros. On the other hand, it is usually silly to write a number like 7 as 7×10^{0}.

Representation of Fractions and Use of Constants

Many of you have been previously taught that representing a numeric result exactly as a fraction is preferable to giving an approximate answer. This is seldom the preferred method of reporting values in engineering, for two reasons:

- Fractions are often difficult to glance at with instant comprehension of the actual value.
  - Quick! What does 727/41 equal? Did you immediately recognize that it is a little less than 18?
  - Is it easier to know the magnitude of 37/523 or 0.071?
- Seldom do engineers need a precision of more than three or four digits; thus, there is no need to try to represent values exactly by using the harder-to-read fractions.

Similarly, you may have learned earlier that when calculating with constants such as pi, it is better to leave answers in terms of that constant. For the same reasons cited above, it is generally better to express such values as a decimal number, for example, 27 instead of 8.6π.

There are, of course, exceptions to these rules, but in general, a simple decimal number is more useful to engineers.

In-Class Activities

ICA 5-1

With your team, you are to determine common, readily available or understood quantities to help you estimate a variety of parameters. For example, a 2-liter bottle of soda weighs about 4 pounds (this is an understood quantity since almost everyone has picked up one of these many times), or the end joint of your middle finger is about an inch long (this is a readily available quantity since it goes everywhere you do). To determine the benchmarks or "helpers," you may use whatever measuring tools are appropriate (rulers, scales, watches, etc.) to determine the values of the common objects or phenomena you choose. Try to determine at least two different estimation "helpers" for the following units:

- **Lengths:** millimeter, centimeter, inch (other than the example given above), foot, meter, kilometer
- **Areas:** square centimeter, square inch, square foot, square meter, acre
- **Volumes:** cubic centimeter, cubic inch, cubic foot, cubic meter, gallon
- **Weights and masses:** gram, newton, pound, kilogram, ton
- **Time:** second, minute, hour (the "helpers" you choose cannot be any form of device designed for measuring time).

ICA 5-2

Materials
Ruler
Tape measure
Calipers

Procedure

The following measurements and estimations are to be completed individually, not using one set of measurements per team. This activity is designed to help you learn the size of common items to help you with future estimates. Be sure give both the value and the unit for all measurements.

Measure the following:

(a) Your height in meters
(b) Your arm-span (left fingertip to right fingertip) in meters
(c) The length of your index finger, in centimeters
(d) The width of your thumb, in centimeters
(e) The width of the palm of your hand, in centimeters
(f) The length of your shoe, in feet
(g) The length of your "pace," in feet. A pace is considered as the distance between the toe of the rear shoe and the toe of the lead shoe during a normal step. Think about how to make this measurement before doing it.

Determine the following relationships:

(h) How does your arm span measurement compare to your height?
(i) How does your knee height compare to your overall height?
(j) How does the length of your index finger compare to the width of your thumb?

Determine through estimation:

(k) The height of a door in units of feet
(l) The length of a car in units of yards
(m) The area of the floor of the classroom in units of square meters
(n) The volume of your body in units of gallons

ICA 5-3

(a) Estimate by aggregation how many gallons of gasoline are used by cars each year in the United States.

(b) Estimate by aggregation the volume of a person. A rough approximation of the volume of a person would be a cylinder approximately 1.75 m tall with a radius of 0.25 m. How different was your estimate from the cylindrical approximation?

(c) At the time of publication, the website logging the progress of the Eagle Empowerment Youth Tour 2005 (http://www.eagle-empowerment.org/youthtour2005updates2.html) reported the height of the Empire State Building as 12,500 feet. Use estimation by analogy and estimation by aggregation to prove this is incorrect.

(d) Allow S to be the number of atoms along one edge of a cube of N total atoms. During X-ray diffraction, the scattering from each of those N atoms interacts with the scattering of every other atom. If a simulation of the diffraction from a cube with $S = 10$ takes 1 second to calculate, how long will a simulation a cube with $S = 100$ take to calculate?

(e) If you were leaving on a trip of 1,000 miles (1,600 kilometers), and you could not stop for money along the way, how much cash would you need to carry to be able to buy gas along the way? Estimate using upper and lower bounds.

ICA 5-4

(a) If estimating the amount of time to design a new product, should you err on the high side or the low side?

(b) If estimating the switching speed of the transistors for a faster computer, is it better to err on the low side (slower switching) or high side?

(c) How many square yards of fabric are needed to cover the seats in a typical minivan? Is it better to err on the high side or the low side?

(d) Estimate the dimensions of the classroom, in feet. Using these values and ignoring the fact that you would not paint over the windows and doors, estimate the gallons of paint required to paint the classroom. A gallon of paint covers 400 square feet. Would it be better to round the final answer up or down to the nearest gallon?

ICA 5-5

In each of the cases below, a value of some desired quantity has been determined in some way, resulting in a number displayed on a calculator or computer screen. Your task is to

■ Round each number to a *reasonable* number of significant digits—*up* if a higher value is conservative, *down* if a lower value is conservative, and to the *nearest* value if it does not make a difference.

■ Specify why your assumption is conservative.

(a) Paint needed to cover a single room   4.36 gallons

(b) Paint needed to paint all rooms in a given building   1,123.05 gallons

(c) The distance from Tampa to New York   1,484.2 miles

(d) The flight time from Charlotte to Atlanta   3 hours, 56 minutes

(e) The brightness of a light bulb   1,690 lumens

(f) The size of a bolt head   0.500 inch

(g) The mass of a typical paperclip   1.125 grams

ICA 5-6

(a) How many toothpicks can be made from an 8-foot long 2-inch by 4-inch board?

(b) Who travels farther: a star player during a college basketball game or a golfer playing 18 holes? By how much farther? State all estimations that determine your answer.

(c) Noah's ark has been described as having the following dimensions: 300 cubits long × 50 cubits wide × 30 cubits high. If a cubit is 18 inches, how many people could fit into the ark?

(d) Due to drought, the water level of a 10-acre pond is five feet below normal. If you wanted to fill the pond to normal capacity by using a hose connected to your kitchen faucet, how long would it take to fill the pond? Select an appropriate unit of time to report your answer.

(e) A cubic meter of air has a mass of about 1.2 kilograms. What is the total mass of air in your home or in a designated building?

(f) How many basketballs can be placed in the classroom?

(g) A portable device uses two D cells for power and can be operated for 50 hours before the batteries must be replaced. How long would the same device be able to operate if two AA cells were used for power instead of D cells?

(h) How many leaves are on the tree pointed out by the professor? What is the mass of that tree (above ground portion only)?

(i) How many carrots are used to make all of the canned soup consumed in the United States in 1 year? (Alternatively, how many acres are used to grow these carrots?)

(j) Estimate the mass of planet Earth.

Chapter 5 REVIEW QUESTIONS

1. How many cubic yards of concrete is required to construct 1 mile of interstate highway?
2. How many gallons of gasoline are burned when the students in this class leave for school break, assuming only one-way travel?
3. If all the land (both currently habituated and all the inhabitable land) were divided equally among all the people now living, how much land would each one have?
4. How many times do my rear tires rotate if I drive around the perimeter of campus?
5. A cubic meter of air has a mass of about 1.2 kilograms. What is the total mass of air within 1,000 feet of sea level on planet Earth?
6. How much water would be saved if everyone in the United States who does not turn off the faucet while they brush their teeth, did so?
7. In 1978, cars that got about 40 miles per gallon were readily available. If the average fuel economy of all cars sold since then was 40 miles per gallon (instead of the lower average mileage of the cars that were actually sold), how many billions of gallons of gas would have been saved in the United States since 1978?
8. If it is raining steadily at a rate of 1 inch per hour (a container with perpendicular sides and a flat bottom would accumulate water to a depth of 1 inch in 1 hour), how many raindrops are in each cubic yard of air approximately 10 feet above the ground in an open field at any given instant?

CHAPTER 6
SOLVEM

Everyone solves problems in different ways. There are, however, some procedures and techniques that can help in developing a generally successful problem-solving approach. Although it is not possible to write down a specific recipe that will always work, some broad approaches will help.

6.1   DEFINING SOLVEM

One problem-solving approach has been given the acronym **SOLVEM:**

Sketch
Observations or **O**bjectives
List
Variables and
Equations
Manipulation

Note that this approach is equally useful for problems involving estimation and more precise calculations. Each step is described below.

Sketch

Figure 6-1 illustrates how a drawing can help you visualize a problem. In sketching a problem, you are subconsciously thinking about it. Be sure to draw the diagram large enough so that everything is clear, and label the things that you know about the problem in the diagram. For some problems, a before-and-after set of diagrams may be helpful. In very complex problems, you can use intermediate diagrams or subdiagrams as well.

Figure 6-1 Sketches for seven problems.

Observations, Objectives

These can be in the form of simple statements, questions, or anything else that might acquaint you with the problem at hand. It often helps to divide your observations and objectives into several categories. Some of the easiest to remember are:

- Objective to be achieved
- Observations about the problem geometry (size, shape, etc.)
- Observations about materials and material properties (density, hardness, etc.)
- Observations about parameters not easily sketched (temperature, velocity, etc.)
- Other miscellaneous observations that might be pertinent

You will almost always find after writing down some observations that you actually know more about the problem than you originally thought.

Here are some typical examples:

Objectives

- Find the velocity, force, flow rate, time, pressure, etc., for a given situation.
- Profitably market the device for less than $25.
- Fit the device into a 12-cubic-inch box.

Observations

PROBLEM GEOMETRY

- The liquid has a free surface.
- The submerged plate is rectangular.
- The support is vertical.
- The tank is cylindrical.
- The cross-sectional area is octagonal.
- The orbit is elliptical.

MATERIALS AND MATERIAL PROPERTIES

- The gate is steel.
- The coefficient of static friction is 0.6.
- The specific gravity is 0.65.
- Ice will float in water.
- The alloy superconducts at 97 kelvin.
- The alloy melts at 543 degrees Fahrenheit.

OTHER PARAMETERS

- If depth increases, pressure increases.
- If temperature increases, resistance increases.
- The flow is steady.
- The fluid is a gas and is compressible.
- The pulley is frictionless.
- The magnetic field is decreasing.
- Temperature may not fall below 34 degrees Fahrenheit.

MISCELLANEOUS

- The force will act to the right.
- Gravity causes the ball to accelerate.
- The sphere is buoyant.
- Drag increases as the speed increases.

Remember to include those quantities whose value is zero! Often such quantities are hidden with terms such as:

- Constant (implies derivative = 0)
- Initially (at time = 0)
- At rest (no motion)
- Dropped (no initial velocity)
- At the origin (at zero position)
- Constant velocity (force = 0)
- Melts (changes phase, temperature is constant)

State the objective and any relevant observations for the following problem.

Calculate the mass in kilograms of gravel stored in a rectangular bin 18.5 feet by 25.0 feet. The depth of the gravel bin is 15 feet, and the density of the gravel is 97 pound-mass per cubic foot.

Finally, one of the most important reasons to make *many* observations is that you often will observe the "wrong" thing. For example, write down things as you read this:

A bus contains 13 passengers.

At the first stop, four get off and two get on.

At the next stop, six get off and one gets on.

At the next stop, nobody gets off and five get on.

At the next stop, eight get off and three get on.

At the next stop, one gets off.

At the last stop, four get off and four get on.

After putting your pencil down and without looking again at the list, answer the question given below textbox discussing "The Importance of Observations."

THE IMPORTANCE OF OBSERVATIONS

An excerpt adapted from The Crooked Man *by Sir Arthur Conan Doyle*

Dr. Watson writes: I looked at the clock. It was a quarter to twelve. This could not be a visitor at so late an hour. A patient, evidently, and possibly an all-night sitting. With a wry face I went out into the hall and opened the door. To my astonishment, it was Sherlock Holmes who stood upon my step.

"Ah, Watson, I hoped that I might not be too late to catch you."

"My dear fellow, pray come in."

"You look surprised, and no wonder! Relieved, too, I fancy! Hum! You still smoke the Arcadia mixture of your bachelor days, then! There's no mistaking that fluffy ash upon your coat. It's easy to tell that you've been accustomed to wear a uniform, Watson; you'll never pass as a pure-bred civilian as long as you keep that habit of carrying your handkerchief in your sleeve. Could you put me up for the night?"

"With pleasure."

"You told me that you had bachelor quarters for one, and I see that you have no gentleman visitor at present. Your hat-stand proclaims as much."

"I shall be delighted if you will stay."

"Thank you. I'll find a vacant peg, then. Sorry to see that you've had the British workman in the house. He's a token of evil. Not the drains, I hope?"

"No, the gas."

"Ah! He has left two nail marks from his boot upon your linoleum just where the light strikes it. No, thank you, I had some supper at Waterloo, but I'll smoke a pipe with you with pleasure."

I handed him my pouch, and he seated himself opposite to me, and smoked for some time in silence. I was well aware that nothing but business of importance could have brought him to me at such an hour, so I waited patiently until he should come round to it.

"I see that you are professionally rather busy just now."

"Yes, I've had a busy day. It may seem very foolish in your eyes, but I really don't know how you deduced it."

"I have the advantage of knowing your habits, my dear Watson. When your round is a short one you walk, and when it is a long one you use a hansom (a carriage). As I perceive that your boots, although used, are by no means dirty, I cannot doubt that you are at present busy enough to justify the hansom."

"Excellent!"

"Elementary. It is one of those instances where the reason can produce an effect which seems remarkable to his neighbor, because the latter has missed the one little point which is the basis of the deduction."

While we cannot all be as observant as Sherlock Holmes, we can improve our powers of observation through practice. This will pay dividends as we seek to be engineers with high levels of analytical skills.

QUESTION: For the bus problem, how many stops did the bus make? *The lesson here is that often we may be observing the wrong thing.*

List of Variables and Constants

Go over the observations previously determined and list the variables that are important. It may help to divide the list into several broad categories—those related to the geometry of the problem, those related to the materials, and a properties category—although for some types of problems those categories may not be appropriate. Include in your list the written name of the variable, the symbol used to represent the quantity, and, if the value of the variable is known, list the numeric value, including units. If a value is a constant you had to look up, record where you found the information.

INITIAL AND FINAL CONDITIONS

- Initial temperature (T_0) 60 [°F]
- Initial radius (r_i) 5 [cm]
- Mass of the object (m) 23 [kg]

CONSTANTS

- Acceleration of gravity (g) 32.2 [ft/s^2]
- Ideal gas constant (R) 8,314 [(Pa L)/(mol K)]

GEOMETRY

- Length of beam (L) [m]
- Cross-sectional area of a pipe (A) [cm^2]
- Volume of a reactor vessel (V) [gal]

MATERIALS

- Steel
- Polyvinyl chloride (PVC)
- Plasma
- Gallium arsenide
- Medium-density balsa wood

PROPERTIES

- Dynamic viscosity of honey (μ) 2,500 [cP]
- Density of PVC (ρ) 1,380 [kg/m³]
- Spring constant (k) 0.05 [N/m]
- Specific gravity   (SG)   1.34

Create a list of variables and constants for the following problem.

Calculate the mass in kilograms of gravel stored in a rectangular bin 18.5 feet by 25.0 feet. The depth of the gravel bin is 15 feet, and the density of the gravel is 97 pound-mass per cubic foot.

Equations

Only after completing the steps above (S-O-L-V) should you begin to think about the equations that might govern the problem. It is useful to make a list of the pertinent equations in a broad sense before listing specific expressions. For example:

- Conservation of energy
- Conservation of mass
- Conservation of momentum
- Frequency equations
- Ideal gas law

- Newton's laws of motion
- Stress–strain relations
- Surface areas of geometric solids
- Volumes of geometric solids
- Work, energy relations

You may need "subequations" such as:

- Distance = (velocity)(time)
- Energy = (power)(time)
- Force = (pressure)(area)

- Mass = (density)(volume)
- Voltage = (current)(resistance)
- Weight = (mass)(gravity)

For an equation, list the broad category of the equation (Hooke's law) and then the actual expression ($F = kx$) to help with problem recognition.

Do not substitute numerical values of the parameters into the equation right away. Instead, manipulate the equation algebraically to the desired form.

Create a list of equations for the following problem.

Calculate the mass in kilograms of gravel stored in a rectangular bin 18.5 feet by 25.0 feet. The depth of the gravel bin is 15 feet, and the density of the gravel is 97 pound-mass per cubic foot.

Manipulation

Most of the time, you need to manipulate pertinent equations before you can obtain a final solution. ***Do not substitute numerical values of the parameters into the equation right away.*** Instead, manipulate the equation algebraically to the desired form. Often you will discover terms that will cancel, giving you a simpler expression to deal with. By doing this, you will:

- Obtain general expressions useful for solving other problems of this type
- Be less likely to make math errors
- Be able to judge whether your final equation is dimensionally consistent
- Better understand the final result

The SOLVEM acronym does not contain a word or step for "numerical solution." In fact, this process helps you analyze the problem and obtain an expression or procedure so that you can find a numerical answer. The thought here is that engineers need training to be able to analyze and solve problems. If you can do everything except "substitute numbers" you are essentially finished—as an engineer, you will "be paid the big bucks" for analysis, not for punching a calculator.

NOTE
Don't plug values into the equation until the final step.

6.2 REPRESENTING FINAL RESULTS

When you have completed all the steps to SOLVEM, plug in values for the variables and constants and solve for a final answer. Be sure to use reasonableness. The final answer should include both a numeric value and its unit. In addition, it is often useful to write a sentence describing how the answer meets the objectives. Box your final answer for easy identification.

Repeated use of SOLVEM can help you develop a better "gut-level understanding" about the analysis of problems by forcing you to talk and think about the generalities of the problem before jumping in and searching for an equation into which you can immediately substitute numbers.

**COMPREHENSION
CHECK 6-5**

Manipulate and solve for the following problem, using the information from Comprehension Checks 1–4.

Calculate the mass in kilograms of gravel stored in a rectangular bin 18.5 feet by 25.0 feet. The depth of the gravel bin is 15 feet, and the density of the gravel is 97 pound-mass per cubic foot.

6.3 AVOIDING COMMON MISTAKES

Erroneous or argumentative thinking can lead to problem-solving errors. For example,

- **I can probably find a good equation in the next few pages.** Perhaps you read a problem and rifle through the chapter to find the proper equation so that you can start substituting numbers. You find one that looks good. You do not worry about whether the equation is the right one or whether the assumptions you made in committing to the equation apply to the present problem. You whip out your calculator and produce an answer. *Don't do this!*

NOTE
Be sure your equation is the right one for the problem you are solving.

■ **I hate algebra, or I cannot do algebra, or I have got the numbers, so let us substitute the values right in.** Many problems become much simpler if you are willing to do a little algebra before trying to find a numerical solution. Also, by doing some manipulation first, you often obtain a general expression that is easy to apply to another problem when a variable is given a new value. By doing a little algebra, you can also often circumvent problems with different sets of units. *Do some algebra!*

■ **It is a simple problem, so why do I need a sketch?** Even if you have a photographic memory, you will need to communicate with people who do not. It is usually much simpler to sort out the various parts of a problem if a picture is staring you right in the face. *Draw pictures!*

■ **I do not have time to think about the problem, I need to get this stuff finished.** Well, most often, if you take a deep breath and jot down several important aspects of the problem, you will find the problem much easier to solve and will solve it correctly. *Take your time!*

● **EXAMPLE 6-1**

Estimate how many miles of wire stock are needed to make 1 million standard paper clips.

Sketch:

See the adjacent diagram.

Objective:

Determine the amount of wire needed to manufacture a million paper clips.

Observations:

■ Paper clips come in a variety of sizes
■ There are four straight segments and three semicircular sections in one clip
■ The three semicircular sections have slightly different diameters
■ The four straight sections have slightly different lengths

List of Variables and Constants:

■ L Overall length of clip
■ W Overall width of clip
■ L_1, L_2, L_3, L_4 Lengths of four straight sections
■ D_1, D_2, D_3 Diameters of three semicircular sections
■ P_1, P_2, P_3 Lengths of three semicircular sections
■ A Total amount (length) of wire per clip

Estimations and Assumptions:

■ Length of clip: $L = 1.5$ in
■ Width of clip: $W = 3/8$ in
■ Diameters from largest to smallest
  • $D_1 = W = 3/8$ in
  • $D_2 = 5/16$ in
  • $D_3 = 1/4$ in

- Lengths from left to right in sketch
  - L_1 = To be calculated
  ,
  - L_2 = 0.8 in
  - $L_3 \approx L_4 = 1$ in

Equations:

- Perimeter of semicircle: $P = \pi D / 2$ (half of circumference of circle)
- $L_1 = L - D_1/2 - D_2/2$
- Total length of wire in clip: $A = L_1 + L_2 + L_3 + L_4 + P_1 + P_2 + P_3$

Manipulation:

In this case, none of the equations need to be manipulated into another form.

Length of longest straight side:	$L_1 = 1.5 - \frac{3}{16} - \frac{5}{32} \approx 1.2$ in
Lengths of semicircular sections:	$P_1 = \pi^{3}/_{16} \approx 0.6$ in
	$P_2 = \pi^{5}/_{32} \approx 0.5$ in
	$P_3 = \pi^{1}/_{8} \approx 0.4$ in
Overall length for one clip:	$A = 1.2 + 0.8 + 1 + 1 + 0.6$
	$+ 0.5 + 0.4 = 5.5$ in/clip
Length of wire for 1 million clips:	$(5.5 \text{ in/clip}) (1 \times 10^6 \text{ clips}) = 5.5 \times 10^6$ in
Convert from inches to miles:	$(5.5 \times 10^6 \text{ in}) (1 \text{ ft}/12 \text{ in})$
	$(1 \text{ mile}/5{,}280 \text{ ft}) \approx 86.8$ miles

One million, 1.5-inch paper clips require about 87 miles of wire stock.

● EXAMPLE 6-2

A spherical balloon has an initial radius of 5 inches. Air is pumped in at a rate of 10 cubic inches per second, and the balloon expands. Assuming that the pressure and temperature of the air in the balloon remain constant, how long will it take for the surface area to reach 1,000 square inches?

Sketch:

Objective:

Determine how long it will take for the surface area of the balloon to reach 1,000 in^2

Observations:

- The balloon is spherical
- The balloon, thus its volume and surface area, gets larger as more air is pumped in
- The faster air is pumped in, the more rapidly the balloon expands

List of Variables and Constants:

- Initial radius: R_i = 5 in
- Final radius: R_f [in]
- Initial surface area: A_i [in²]
- Final surface area: A_f [in²]
- Change in volume: ΔV [in³]
- Initial volume: V_i [in³]
- Final volume: V_f [in³]
- Fill rate: Q = 10 [in³/s]
- Time since initial size: t [s]

Equations:

- Surface area of sphere: $A = 4\pi R^2$
- Volume of sphere: $V = 4\pi R^3/3$
- Change in volume: $\Delta V = Qt$

Manipulation:

There are a few different ways to proceed. The plan used here is to determine how much the balloon volume changes as air is blown into the balloon and to equate this to an expression for the volume change in terms of the balloon geometry (actually the radius of the balloon).

Radius of balloon in terms of surface area:

$$R = \left(\frac{A}{4\pi}\right)^{1/2}$$

Final balloon radius in terms of surface area:

$$R_f = \left(\frac{A_f}{4\pi}\right)^{1/2}$$

Final volume of balloon in terms of surface area:

$$V_f = \left(\frac{4\pi}{3}\right)\left(\frac{A_f}{4\pi}\right)^{3/2}$$

Volume change in terms of air blown in:

$$\Delta V = V_f - V_i = Qt$$

Volume change in terms of geometry:

$$V_f - V_i = \left(\frac{4\pi}{3}\right)\left(\frac{A_f}{4\pi}\right)^{3/2} - \left(\frac{4\pi}{3}\right)R_i^3 = Qt$$

Solve for time to blow up balloon:

$$t = \left(\frac{4\pi}{3Q}\right)\left(\frac{A_f}{4\pi}\right)^{3/2} - \left(\frac{4\pi}{3Q}\right)R_i^3$$

And simplifying:

$$t = \left(\frac{4\pi}{3Q}\right)\left\{\left(\frac{A_f}{4\pi}\right)^{3/2} - R_i^3\right\}$$

It takes just over 4 minutes to increase the volume to 1,000 cubic inches.

NOTE

Whenever you obtain a result in equation form, you should check to see if the dimensions match in each term.

IMPORTANT

Recall that you should manipulate the equations before inserting known values. Note that the final expression for elapsed time is given in terms of initial radius (R_i), flow rate (Q), and final surface area (A_f). So you now have a general equation that can be solved for any values of these three parameters. If you had begun substituting numbers into equations at the beginning and then wanted to obtain the same result for different starting values, you would have to resolve the entire problem.

In-Class Activities

ICA 6-1

Each of these items should be addressed by a team. List as many things about the specified items as you can determine by observation. One way to do this is to let each team member make one observation, write it down, and iteratively canvass the team until nobody can think of any more additions (it is fine to pass). Remember that you have five senses. Also note that observations are things you can actually detect during the experiment, *not* things you already know or deduce that cannot be observed.

To help, Examples A and B are given here before you do one activity (or more) on your own. Remember that not all observations will be important for a particular problem, but write them down anyway – they may trigger an observation that is important.

Example A: A loudspeaker reproducing music

- Electrical signal is sent to speaker.
- Speaker vibrates from electrical signal.
- Speaker motion imparts kinetic energy to the air.
- Diaphragm accelerates.
- Speaker is gray.
- A magnet is involved.
- Speaker is circular.
- Speaker is about 10 inches in diameter.
- Speaker diaphragm is made of paper; vibrating air creates sound.
- Gravity acts on speaker.
- Speaker is in a "box."

Example B: Drinking a soft drink in a can through a straw

- Liquid is cold.
- Straw is cylindrical.
- Can is cylindrical.
- Low pressure in your mouth draws the liquid up.
- Liquid assumes the shape of the container.
- Gravity opposes the rise of the liquid.
- Moving liquid has kinetic energy.
- As the liquid rises, it gains potential energy.
- Table supports the weight of the can, liquid, and straw.
- Can is opaque.
- Liquid is brown.
- Liquid is carbonated (carbonic acid).
- Liquid contains caffeine.
- Friction between straw and lips allows you to hold it.
- Plan view of the can is a circle.
- Silhouette of the can is the same from any direction.
- Silhouette of the can is a rectangle.
- Can is painted.
- Can is metal.
- Liquid surface is horizontal.
- Liquid surface is circular.

From the list below or others as selected by the instructor, list as many observations as you can about the following topic:

(a) An object provided by the professor (placed on the desk)
(b) Candle placed on the desk and lit
(c) Ball dropped from several feet, allowed to bounce and come to rest
(d) A weight on a string pulled to one side and released; watched until it comes to rest
(e) Coin spinning on the desk
(f) Cup of hot coffee placed on desk
(g) A glass of cold water placed on desk
(h) Book pushed across the desk

(i) Large container guided smoothly up a ramp
(j) Ruler hanging over the desk
(k) Your computer (when turned off)
(l) Your chair
(m) Your classroom
(n) A weight tied on a string and twirled

Final Assignment of this ICA: You have done several observation exercises. In these, you thought of observation as just a "stream of consciousness" with no regard to organization of your efforts. With your previous observation as a basis, generalize the search for observations into several (three to six or so) categories. The use of these categories should make the construction of a list of observations easier in the future.

ICA 6-2

What diameter will produce a maximum discharge velocity of a liquid through an orifice on the side at the bottom of the cylindrical container? Consider diameters ranging from 0.2 to 2 meters.

Use the SOLVEM method to determine the answer.

ICA 6-3

A hungry bookworm bores through a complete set of encyclopedias consisting of n volumes stacked in numerical order on a library shelf. The bookworm starts inside the front cover of volume 1, bores from page 1 of volume 1 to the last page of the last volume, and stops inside the back cover of the last volume. Note that the book worm starts inside the front cover of volume 1 and ends inside the back cover of volume n.

Assume that each volume has the same number of pages. For each book, assume that you know how thick the cover is, and that the thickness of a front cover is equal to the thickness of a back cover; assume also that you know the total thickness of all the pages in the book. How far does the bookworm travel? How far will it travel if there are 13 volumes in the set and each book has 2 inches of pages and a $\frac{1}{8}$-inch thick cover?

Use the SOLVEM method to determine the answer.

ICA 6-4

Two cargo trains each leave their respective stations at 1:00 p.m. and approach each other, one traveling west at 10 miles per hour and the other on separate tracks traveling east at 15 miles per hour. The stations are 100 miles apart. Find the time when the trains meet and determine how far the eastbound train has traveled.

Use the SOLVEM method to determine the answer.

ICA 6-5

Water drips from a faucet at the rate of three drops per second. What distance separates one drop from the following drop 0.65 seconds after the leading drop leaves the faucet? How much time elapses between impacts of the two drops if they fall onto a surface that is 6 feet below the lip of the faucet?

Your sketch should include the faucet, the two water drops of interest, and the impact surface. Annotate the sketch, labeling the each item shown and denote the relevant distances in symbolic form, for example, you might use d_1 to represent the distance from the faucet to the first drop.

Use the SOLVEM method to determine the answer.

ICA 6-6

During rush hour, cars back up when the traffic signal turns red. When cars line up at a traffic signal, assume that they are equally spaced (Δx) and that all the cars are the same length (L). You do not begin to move until the car in front of you begins to move, creating a reaction time (Δt) between the time the car in front begins to move and the time you start moving. To keep things simple, assume that when you start to move, you immediately move at a constant speed (v). If the traffic signal stays green for some time (t_g), how many cars (N) will make it through the light?

After you have analyzed this problem with SOLVEM, answer the following:

(a) If the light remains green for twice the time, how many more cars will get through the light?

(b) If the speed of each car is doubled when it begins to move, will twice as many cars get through the light? If not, what variable would have to go to zero for this to be true?

(c) For a reaction time of zero and no space between cars, find an expression for the number of cars that will pass through the light. Does this make sense?

ICA 6-7

Suppose that the earth were a smooth sphere and you could wrap a 25,000-mile-long band snugly around it. Now let us say that you lengthen the band by 10 feet, loosening it just a little. What would be the largest thing that could slither under the new band (assume that it is now raised above the earth's surface equally all the way around so that it doesn't touch anywhere): an amoeba, a snake, or an alligator?

Use the SOLVEM method to determine the answer.

Chapter 6 REVIEW QUESTIONS

1. A motorcycle weighing 500 pounds-mass plus a rider weighing 300 pounds-mass produces the following chart. Predict a similar table if a 50-pound-mass dog is added as a passenger. Use SOLVEM.

Velocity (v) [mi/h]	Time (t) [s]
0	0.0
10	2.3
20	4.6
30	6.9
40	9.2

2. A circus performer jumps from a platform onto one end of a seesaw, while his or her partner, a child of age 12, stands on the other end. How high will the child "fly"? Analyze this problem with SOLVEM.

3. Your college quadrangle is 85 meters long and 66 meters wide. When you are late for class, you can walk (well, run) at 7 miles per hour. You are at one corner of the quad and your class is at the directly opposite corner. How much time can you save by cutting across the quad rather than walking around the edge? Analyze this problem with SOLVEM.

4. I am standing on the upper deck of the football stadium. I have an egg in my hand. I am going to drop it and you are going to try to catch it. You are standing on the ground. Apparently, you do not want to stand directly under me; in fact, you would like to stand as far to one side as you can so that if I accidentally release it, it won't hit you on the head. If you can run at 20 feet per second and I am at a height of 100 feet, how far away can you stand and still catch the egg if you start running when I let go? Analyze this problem with SOLVEM.

5. A 1-kilogram mass has just been dropped from the roof of a building. I need to catch it after it has fallen exactly 100 meters. If I weigh 80 kilograms and start running at 7 meters per second as soon as the object is released, how far away can I stand and still catch the object? Analyze this problem using SOLVEM.

6. Neglect the weight of the drum in the following problem. A sealed cylindrical drum has a diameter of 6 feet and a length of 12 feet. The drum is filled exactly half-full of a liquid having a density of 90 pound-mass per cubic foot. It is resting on its side at the bottom of a 10-foot deep drainage channel that is empty. Suppose a flash flood suddenly raises the water level in the channel to a depth of 10 feet. Determine if the drum will float. The density of water is 62 pound-mass per cubic foot. Analyze this problem with SOLVEM.

Part 2

UBIQUITOUS UNITS

You may not be sure what the word "ubiquitous" means ... we suggest you look it up!

Ubiquitous: **yoo·bik·we·teous** ~ adjective; definition

LEARNING OBJECTIVES

The overall learning objectives for this unit include:

- Apply basic principles from mathematical and physical sciences, such as trigonometry, Hooke's law, and the ideal gas law, to solve engineering problems.

- Convert units for physical and chemical parameters such as density, energy, pressure, and power as required for different systems of units,

- Identify basic and derived dimensions and units; accurately express relevant observations and parameters such as distance, force, and temperature in appropriate units.

- Use "practical" skills, such as visualizing common units and conducting simple measurements, calculations, and comparisons to make estimations.

Imagine you are in a small boat with a large stone in the bottom of the boat. The boat is floating in the swimming pool in the campus recreation center. What happens to the level of water in the pool if you throw the stone overboard? Assume no water splashes out of the pool or into the boat.

Archimedes was a Greek scientist and mathematician. Most people know Archimedes for his discovery of buoyancy. According to legend, the king asked Archimedes to determine if his new crown was made of pure gold. Before this, no method had been developed for measuring the density of irregularly shaped objects. While taking a bath, Archimedes noted that the water rose in proportion to the amount of his body in the tub. He shouted "Eureka (I have found it)!" and ran though the streets naked because he was so excited he forgot to get dressed. While Archimedes never recounts this tale himself, he does outline Archimedes' principle in his treatise *On Floating Bodies: A body immersed in a fluid is buoyed up by a force equal to the weight of the displaced fluid.* Before we can begin to answer the question of the boat and the stone (the answer is found on the final page of Chapter 8), we need to understand the principles of dimensions and units.

HOW I STUDY

The Myers–Briggs Type Indicator, often referred to as the MBTI, is a method for assessing individuals—their attitudes and modes of actions, learning, and interacting with others. By answering a series of questions, an individual is categorized according to four dichotomies. You can think of these as preferences for particular ways of conducting your life. This brief introduction is by no means intended to acquaint you with the intricacies of the MBTI, but simply to help you gain insight that will help you study, learn, and interact with others more effectively. An individual's preference relative to each of the four dichotomies is indicated by a single letter. When combined, these create a four-letter code that describes your preferences. The four dichotomies are as follows:

Cognitive Attitude:	Extrovert or Introvert	E vs. I
Mode of Data Gathering:	Sensing or Intuition	S vs. N
Mode of Decision Making:	Thinking or Feeling	T vs. F
Lifestyle Preference:	Judging or Perceiving	J vs. P

Cognitive Attitude (or how one directs one's energy)

- The Extrovert (E) prefers action, and focuses on people and objects.
- The Introvert (I) prefers reflection, and focuses on concepts and ideas.

Mode of Data Gathering (or how one perceives things)

- The Sensing (S) individual tends to trust data gathered by the five senses and is most interested in details and facts.
- The Intuitive (N) individual tends to trust information that is theoretical or abstract and is most interested in how data fit a theory or a pattern.

Mode of Decision Making (or how one judges things)

- The Thinking (T) person makes decisions with an emotionally detached attitude, being concerned with what is most logical and what established rules dictate.
- The Feeling (F) person makes decisions by empathizing with the situation, being concerned with what will promote the most harmonious outcome.

Lifestyle Preference (or how one relates to the outside world)

- The Judging (J) individual prefers making decisions to obtaining information, whether gathering that information by thinking or feeling.
- The Perceiving (P) individual prefers gathering data to making decisions, whether gathering that information by sensing or intuition.

The Myers Briggs Type Index is based on Dr. Carl Jung's original work on Personality types and results in the individual being identified as a single type as represented by the 4 letters. However, we aren't the same in all situations, and the MBTI fails to show any information as to degree of preference. Dr. Lois Breur Krause did further research on applying Dr. Jung's work specifically to learning and studying. The resulting material on learning and studying specific to the individual learner's profile is found in the book *"How We Learn and Why We Don't."* Before proceeding further, it would be helpful for you to take the inventory yourself. It may be done online at http://www.CognitiveProfile.com.

Engraving from Mechanics Magazine published in London in 1824

HOW ATTITUDES ARE ASSESSED: YOUR FULL PROFILE

Dr. Krause's Cognitive Profile Inventory uses two of Jung's four bipolar descriptors and results in a Profile that describes your proportion of strength in each of 4 quadrants, ST, SF, NT and NF. It does not include the Judger/Perceiver or Introvert/Extrovert bipolar descriptors as they were found to be less critical to learning and studying. This allows the model to be reduced to a more manageable size, and is actually more complete in its application. It shows where you are strongest or most comfortable, and identifies where you can build skills to strengthen proportionally weaker areas. By using study techniques that complement the way your brain wants to learn, you can make your study time more productive and more efficient, and probably improve your grades. By identifying and building skills in your weaker areas, you will be more able to tackle previously difficult types of tasks.

Knowing your profile and being able to recognize characteristics in others will help you in your studies, your interactions with our professors and fellow students and eventually with your coworkers on the job.

Typical Characteristics

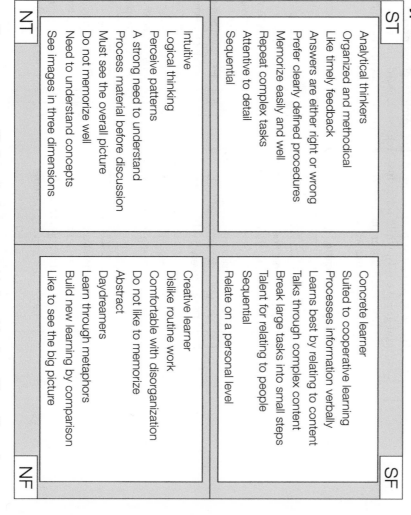

ST

- Analytical thinkers
- Organized and methodical
- Like timely feedback
- Answers are either right or wrong
- Prefer clearly defined procedures
- Memorize easily and well
- Repeat complex tasks
- Attentive to detail
- Sequential

SF

- Concrete learner
- Suited to cooperative learning
- Processes information verbally
- Learns best by relating to content
- Talks through complex content
- Break large tasks into small steps
- Talent for relating to people
- Sequential
- Relate on a personal level

NT

- Intuitive
- Logical thinking
- Perceive patterns
- A strong need to understand
- Process material before discussion
- Must see the overall picture
- Do not memorize well
- Need to understand concepts
- See images in three dimensions

NF

- Creative learner
- Dislike routine work
- Comfortable with disorganization
- Do not like to memorize
- Abstract
- Daydreamers
- Learn through metaphors
- Build new learning by comparison
- Like to see the big picture

Compare your profile from the inventory with the table above. You will see that you have greater or lesser areas in each quadrant. The quadrant in which you have the greatest area is your dominant quadrant, where you are most comfortable, most fluent, and most efficient. You may or may not have a second quadrant that is nearly as strong, or runs a close second. You will also see that you probably have a quadrant or two that have considerably less area. That identifies what skills you may need to build in order to accomplish some types of tasks, or where you may need to find ways to adapt material to better fit your dominant quadrant. If you have what is called a "kite shaped" profile, where your two strongest quadrants are opposite one another, it is likely that you have already developed strong coping skills to balance your natural abilities. This is frequently found in strong creative, NF dominant individuals who find that ST skills of organization work well to bring success. It doesn't mean your ST is native to you, but that you have learned that concrete, methodical organization works when you need it and have come to trust and rely on those skills.

To simplify things a little, we focus here on only two of the dichotomies: how you gather information (sensing or intuition) and how you make decisions (thinking or feeling). This limitation reduces the number of possible dichotomy combinations to 4 instead of 16, which we will call profiles: ST, SF, NT, and NF.

Remember that people who are dominant in a particular quadrant will certainly have talents that draw from the other quadrants as well, since essentially everyone has some of the characteristics of the other types. It is critical that you recognize that you do not act, think, and learn solely within your dominant quadrant. The dominant quadrant is likely, however, to describe the areas in which you are most comfortable and talented.

Study Strategies for Each of the Four Profiles

By now, you must have realized that some teachers present information in ways that you grasp easily, while other instructors are hard for you to follow. In college, you can get lost much faster because the pace and expectations are considerably higher than in high school. One way to prevent this is to know how you learn.

Study Strategies

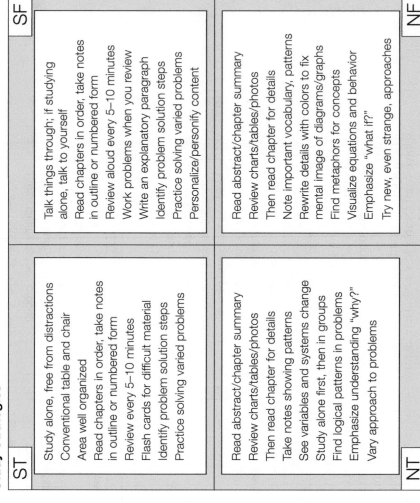

ST
- Study alone, free from distractions
- Conventional table and chair
- Area well organized
- Read chapters in order, take notes in outline or numbered form
- Review every 5–10 minutes
- Flash cards for difficult material
- Identify problem solution steps
- Practice solving varied problems

SF
- Talk things through; if studying alone, talk to yourself
- Read chapters in order, take notes in outline or numbered form
- Review aloud every 5–10 minutes
- Work problems when you review
- Write an explanatory paragraph
- Identify problem solution steps
- Practice solving varied problems
- Personalize/personify content

NT
- Read abstract/chapter summary
- Review charts/tables/photos
- Then read chapter for details
- Take notes showing patterns
- See variables and systems change
- Study alone first, then in groups
- Find logical patterns in problems
- Emphasize understanding "why?"
- Vary approach to problems

NF
- Read abstract/chapter summary
- Review charts/tables/photos
- Then read chapter for details
- Note important vocabulary, patterns
- Rewrite details with colors to fix mental image of diagrams/graphs
- Find metaphors for concepts
- Visualize equations and behavior
- Emphasize "what if?"
- Try new, even strange, approaches

The Cognitive Profile Inventory is specifically designed help you determine the combination of study strategies that will work best for you personally. It determines your complete profile, showing both your strengths and areas where you are less strong and emphasizes that you have some area in each quadrant, a profile, not just a single type. The book and associated website specifically discuss the following topics:

- Successful study strategies by quadrant.
- Working with faculty whose teaching style does not match your learning style.
- How to deal with and benefit from students whose profiles are different from yours.
- How to use knowledge of your profile to inform your career direction decisions.

It is critical to recognize that you do not act, think, and learn solely within your dominant quadrant. The dominant quadrant is likely, however, to describe the areas in which you are most comfortable and talented. The table below summarizes the learning strategies for each type.

Contributions to Engineering and Science from Each of the Four Profiles

This section lists typical contributions to engineering and science made by workers in each of the four quadrants. Engineers and scientists, like other professionals, need to develop skills in all four quadrants. You may find that you are most strongly drawn to work that is in your dominant quadrant.

Team Contributions and Careers

ST	SF
Memorization is good for legal and medical careers—good partners to engineering/science Skill at complex, repetitive tasks; make good experimentalists Construction is sequential	People skills lend themselves to careers in consulting, teaching, and technical sales These interpersonal skills are also powerful assets in leadership and teamwork Ability to personalize knowledge; relate technical subjects to the general public
NT	**NF**
Seeing all sides of an issue is a management skill; seeing all sides of a problem is a design and development skill Pattern recognition is a powerful research skill Visualization skills are an asset to three-dimensional design work	Emotional awareness results in a heightened social consciousness—particularly useful in work that affects politics and the public Creativity and passion are well suited to entrepreneurs and inventors

HOW KNOWING YOUR MBTI TYPE OR COGNITIVE PROFILE HELPS INDIVIDUAL AND TEAM INTERACTIONS

When you are working with a team or group or even with another individual student it helps to know their profile, to see their strengths, and then to take advantage of the strengths in the group. An ST will keep track of materials, details and tasks to be accomplished. An SF will see that everyone is participating and being listened to, the NT will determine the best way to accomplish the assigned task without getting bogged down or off track, and the NF will find a creative approach to the results, pulling all the details from different directions together to make a cohesive presentation in the required format.

In real life, this is how it worked out for two of the authors.

We—Dr. Stephan and Dr. Park—are complete MBTI opposites. I, Dr. Stephan, am ESTJ and he, Dr. Park, is INFP—notice no letters in common. Our first few years together at Clemson University, we very nearly came to blows. We each thought the other was "so smart they were stupid," mentally ill, or probably both. However, we have learned to work together quite effectively, and we each value what the other brings to the team. Admittedly, we frequently have difficulty understanding what the other is saying, occasionally even having to ask someone else to translate English to English for us. (And no, this is not an exaggeration!) At this point, we laugh about it a fair amount.

The moral of our little tale is this: just because a colleague makes little sense to you does not necessarily means that he or she is not firing on all thrusters—it may simply be a difference in personality types. You should try to understand how your fellow students or coworkers think and act, not simply immediately condemn them. As always, there are exceptions to every rule and you will indeed sometimes stumble on others that really are not an asset to the team in any way, but you will have to deal with that by other methods. In general, everyone on a team brings their own unique skills to the table. The best teams, in fact, have a variety of personality types.

As a point of interest, each of the four two-letter profiles mentioned earlier is represented among the authors of this text. Hopefully, our melding of the various ways the five of us perceive the world and communicate our knowledge into one unified presentation will make sense to most of our readers.

The information below may help to illustrate how each of us uniquely developed different strategies for success in college.

How I Study

by Dr. Beth Stephan

Two weeks before the exam:

- **Review all book and lecture materials.** Take notes on important formulas and concepts as you reread the text (assuming you have already read it once). This will become the foundation of a note sheet. Work the example questions on your own, and compare the answers. Determine how the lectures were different from the book (different examples, different equation derivations). Determine if particular topics were emphasized more than others.
- **Reexamine assignments.** Determine if there was a recurring type of question. Does this match the emphasis areas given in the lecture materials? Decide if there are concepts you did not understand. Work these questions again, and determine if you now understand the concept or need to ask for help.
- **Divide the studying over several days.** Create a list of materials to review each day. Study in small chunks, not hours at a time on one subject. If you become tired—stop! Get something to eat, take a walk, or work on a different subject. You will not absorb the material well if you cannot focus.

One week before the exam:

- **Figure out the exam structure.** If you do not already know what will be covered on the exam, ask the professor. Determine the material covered on the exam, the type and number of questions, and review problems if available. Note any special things to bring (e.g., calculator, extra batteries, laptop, note sheet, or textbook).

- **Attend any review session.** This is a good place to cover the text examples or assignment questions you still do not understand. Be specific—come prepared with a list of things to ask. Do not worry about your class image. If it is "uncool" to ask questions, imagine how "uncool" it will be when you fail an exam because you failed to ask.

Three days before:

- **Create a "brain dump" sheet.** The basic idea is you, your memory, alone, pencil, paper; fill it up with everything you can remember. Compare with book review notes sheet. Review any concepts you incorrectly listed or omitted on the brain dump sheet.

- **Make a notes sheet (see below for more information).**

- **Take a sample exam.** Create a sample exam and put it away, and then take it a few days later under actual exam conditions (time, materials allowed—not in front of the television). This is a great place to use a study group to generate questions and check your answers.

The night before and day of:

- **Pack all materials needed for exam before going to sleep.**

- **Get a good night's sleep.**

- **Get up early.** You do not want to be in a rush or panic to get to class.

- **Take a shower and get dressed up.** Confidence comes from knowing the material and feeling good about yourself. Do not wear a suit, but wear something you would wear to dinner with friends. Jeans and a tucked-in shirt improve your mood compared to sleep pants and shower shoes.

- **Eat some good food.** It is impossible to ignore a growling stomach during an exam.

Notice here it does not say "Study," "Cram," or "Pull an All Nighter." At this point, you will do better if you get a good night's sleep rather than studying all night. A rested brain can pull up information far better and faster than a tired one.

On the exam:

- **Read the directions and questions carefully.** Look over the whole exam before beginning to answer any questions. Be sure you are answering the right question. Watch for details of how the answer should be presented and what to include in your solution. But do not overanalyze—go with your instincts.

- **Answer the easy questions first.** Skip what you do not know—maximize your points! Exams are not always ordered easy to hard, so there may be some simple questions on page 5 buried behind several pages of derivations.

- **Try to answer all questions, even if you are unsure of what you are doing.** Sometimes in trying to work out a problem, the solution will become clear to you. Start by writing down what you know or equations you think may apply. If you get stuck, move on. You may answer a few more questions and the solution to the "stuck" question will come to you subconsciously.

- **Ask the instructor to explain unclear points.**

- **Use all of the time allotted for the test.** Go back and review that your answers match the question asked. Be sure you have used consistent unit systems. Double-check your calculations. Take the exam twice if time permits. It is difficult to find a mistake when checking over your own work, especially under stress conditions. Think of it as proofreading: it is always better to have someone else check it for you or to read it out loud. By working the problem all over again, you may write something differently and be able to compare it to find your mistake.

- **Relax!** Have confidence to know you are prepared, and do your best. At this point, that is all you can do, so do not fret about the outcome!

What goes on a note sheet?

- **Important formulas and definitions.** Determine if any will be given to you during the exam. If they will be provided (such as a conversion table), do not waste the time and effort to put them on your note sheet and risk writing them incorrectly. Check your note sheet carefully against the text and lecture materials. Make sure the formulas are written correctly.

- **Procedures.** Write general steps that can be followed for any problem. Do *not* include example problems. You will not have time on an exam to figure them out if you have not already done so.

- **Reminders.** Include tips to yourself on things you have made mistakes on during the assignments, such as "Do not forget to convert 1 atm = 101,325 Pa" or "Check to make sure input power is always greater than output power." Be sure to write down important facts, such as "The density of water = 1 g/cc" even if you have this memorized. Under pressure, it becomes harder to recall small details.

Tips and Techniques

- **Be sure you can read it!** Often, symbols have two or three different meanings. Be sure you can decipher what you write. Write neatly. If you cannot read it on the exam, it will not help! Do not copy old exams. Most professors are not lazy enough to give you the exact same question from the text all over again on the exam, but will alter it to stretch your mind.

- **Be sure it is your own work.** Each student understands the material in a unique way. Things you struggle with may be easy for your neighbor, and chances are your neighbor organizes material differently than you do. Do *not* copy anyone else's note sheet. Sometimes, students find it helpful to write encouraging meditative thoughts, such as "Remain CALM" or "You can do this!" or an inspirational quote. Write something that will ground you, and if you begin to panic, you can read your notes to yourself and try to relax.

- **Create a note sheet even if you cannot use it on the exam.** A note sheet is a great organizational tool to make sure you have the important stuff all in one place. It makes a great last-minute review paper to look over those last 10 minutes before the exam. Since you composed it, you should (in theory) understand everything on it. Flipping through the text at the last minute often causes panic if you come across a topic you are unsure of.

How I Study

by Dr. Bill Park

Engineering is about solving problems. I did not learn to solve the problems in my field (electrical engineering, EE) by reading books, or highlighting stuff, or listening to professors rattle on interminably; *I slogged through lots and lots of problems!* If you look at my old textbooks, you will find no handwritten notes, no highlighting, no dog-eared corners. By the way, I kept *all* of my texts, and I am very glad I did. Even today, decades later, I not infrequently look something up in them.

This is not to say that I did not go to class every day (unless I was deathly ill) and take detailed notes—I absolutely did. The professor's explanations or examples frequently proved invaluable in helping me solve the problems later. My first rule for success in college was *never* cut class unless absolutely necessary. You never know when the professor will say the one thing that will make everything fall into place in your brain. This happened to me many times during my formal education.

As an EE, I never had to do much unit conversion to a large extent; EEs just have to move the decimal place around efficiently and correctly using appropriate metric prefixes; because everything is in SI units. However, I would have studied the units material in this book the same way I studied electronics, communication theory, or digital signal processing.

When learning new material, I would look at the first problem at the end of the chapter being studied. Note that I did *not* say the first problem the professor assigned. It would be obvious that I knew how to work the problem, probably because I had worked a few similar exercise problems, or I thought I could work the problem but was not sure about all of the details, or I was totally clueless.

If the solution and all of the steps necessary was obvious, I would move on to the next problem. There is little to be gained from working problems with which you are already proficient, except possibly self-esteem. However, I promise you that there is more self-esteem to be had by conquering a new type of problem than by being bored to tears working the same old problems a zillion times.

As I read through the problems, eventually I would find one I was not certain about, so I would have a go at it. If I figured it out, I would move on to the next. If I got stuck, was uncertain, or came upon a problem that I had no idea how to approach, I would try to find an example problem that was similar, whether in the text or in my class notes. Working through a solved example or two (or ten) would usually give me the insight I needed to solve the problem at hand.

Some of you are thinking at this point, "This guy is insane. I do not have time to work that many problems!" Well, sorry folks. Engineering school is *far* more than a full-time job, at least if you wish to live up to your potential. Unless you have an IQ of about 175 or higher, you will need to spend far more than 40 hours per week to *excel* in a curriculum as difficult as engineering. There is nothing anyone can do to change that.

If working through the available examples failed, then, *and only then*, would I resort to reading the book, and even then I would try to isolate the sections that had bearing on the problem I was trying to work. Many engineering books are deadly dull (in my opinion) and are excellent cures for insomnia!

Sometimes, particularly if I had to resort to the book, things were still not clear. Time to go see the professor!

You will find that if you ask professors for help, most of them will quickly know whether or not you have put an appropriate amount of effort into learning on your own, or whether you tried for a few minutes and gave up. Professors' time is a limited commodity, and if you have obviously done your part, they are generally far more willing to help you. I *never* went to a professor about a problem unless I had beaten my head against the wall to the point where a few more blows would gelatinize my brain. All of this effort almost always paid off, because invariably I could articulate exactly where my comprehension failed and more often than not the professor could clear up my misunderstanding within 1–5 minutes—my brain was primed for the answer.

If you say to a professor, "I do not understand this problem about power," then the professor will have to start asking questions to try to find exactly where your problem is. If, on the other hand, you say "I understand how to get the total amount of energy required to lift the load, and I understand how to get the power since I know how long it takes, but I am confused about the relationship between input power, output power, and efficiency," then the professor immediately knows which part of the problem to explain, using less professorial time, and keeping her or him happy. Do you want a happy professor or an irritable professor? (No-brainer!)

Another issue: note sheets. I do not believe I ever made out a note sheet for a test, even when it was allowed. I recall in first semester calculus, we were allowed to have a note sheet on tests. For the first test, I showed up with no notes. The student next to me leaned over, almost aghast, just before the test was handed out: "Where is your note sheet?!?" My reply was, "What in the world would I put on the note sheet? That the derivative of x with respect to x is 1? If you had done enough problems, you'd know all this stuff!"

Another time, in second semester electronics, we had open-book tests. One of the problems required an equation I did not recall. Rather than waste my time flipping frantically through the book, I derived the necessary formula from fundamental principles — much quicker than finding it in the book. This is the level of understanding for which I strove.

More germane to the topic of units, when I teach this material, it is sometimes necessary to express a complex unit, like Pascal, in terms of base SI units. I *do not* have this stuff memorized, but I can easily derive it from my understanding of what pressure and force are. Pressure is force per area, and by Newton's second law, force is mass times acceleration. Stuffing in the base units gives:

$$(kg\,m/s^2)/m^2 = kg/(m\,s^2)$$

I do not use this frequently enough to have it memorized, but I can derive it in just a few seconds. Things I use frequently I memorize without trying; things I only use occasionally are not worth cluttering up my brain with.

To summarize my approach to studying engineering:

■ The focus is on solving problems, not on reading books and notes. I work problems until the solutions to similar problems are almost blindingly obvious.

■ I strive to understand concepts and the overall picture, not memorize formulae and details — the details I can fill in later. To me, memorization (at least in engineering) is double-plus unclever.

■ I do my work before seeking help. Not only is this more effective for me, it uses less time on the part of the person from whom I seek help.

With all of this said, you need to tailor your study methods to the subject. I have taken courses (e.g., plant taxonomy and Chinese) that require rather prodigious feats of memorization. However, for me, engineering is not something to be memorized, but mastered by understanding concepts.

CHAPTER 7
FUNDAMENTAL DIMENSIONS AND BASE UNITS

As aspiring engineers you must learn to distinguish among many terms that laymen tend to use interchangeably. You must also understand the technical meaning of terms that are misunderstood by those untrained in science or engineering. One term that is often misunderstood is "dimension." To most people, a dimension refers to a straight line (length, one dimension), a flat surface (area, two dimensions), or a solid object (volume, three dimensions). Some slightly more educated folks might include time as a fourth dimension. The number of concepts classified as dimensions is far broader.

A **dimension** is a measurable physical idea; it generally consists solely of a word description with no numbers. A **unit** allows us to quantify a dimension—to state a number describing how much of that dimension exists in a specific situation. Units are defined by convention and related to an accepted standard.

- Length is a dimension. There are many units for length, such as mile, foot, meter, light-year, and fathom.
- Time is a dimension. There are many units for time, such as second, minute, hour, day, fortnight, year, and century.
- Temperature is a dimension. There are many units for temperature, such as Celsius, Fahrenheit, and kelvin.

The dimensions of length, time, and temperature are familiar to us, but in reality, we do not often use these words since they are fairly vague.

We do not say . . .	We do say . . .
It is really a long **length** to Lumberton.	Lumberton is about 175 **miles** away.
Bake the cake for a **time**.	Bake the cake for 35 **minutes**.
Set the oven to a high **temperature**.	Set the oven to 450 **degrees Fahrenheit**.

The difference between the left and the right columns is that the statements on the left refer to dimensions and those on the right refer to established standards or units.

7.1 THE METRIC SYSTEM

NOTE

Within this text, dimensions are shown in braces {} and units in brackets [].

The SI system (Le Système International d'Unités), commonly known as the metric system, is the standard set of units for most of the world. Originally developed by French scientists under King Louis XVI, the SI system was finalized by the international scientific community as the standard unit system in 1971. This system defines seven base units, from which all others are derived. Table 7-1 shows the seven base units and their corresponding fundamental dimensions.

Table 7-1 Fundamental dimensions and base units

Dimension	Symbol	Unit	Symbol
Length	L	meter	m
Mass	M	kilogram	kg
Time	T	second	s
Temperature	Θ	kelvin	K
Amount of substance	N	mole	mol
Light intensity	J	candela	cd
Electric current	I	ampere	A

SI Prefixes

The SI system is based upon multiples of 10. By using an **SI prefix** when reporting numbers, we avoid scientific notation or long strings of zeros. For example, instead of saying, "The distance to Atlanta is 198,000 meters," we would say, "The distance to Atlanta is 198 kilometers."

For a list of SI prefixes, refer to the inside cover of this book or to Table 7-2. Note that the abbreviations for all SI prefixes from kilo- down to yocto- are lower case, whereas from Mega- up to Yotta- are upper case.

Table 7-2 SI prefixes (example: 1 millimeter [mm] = 1 × 10^{-3} meters [m])

Numbers Less than One			Numbers Greater than One		
Power of 10	Prefix	Abbreviation	Power of 10	Prefix	Abbreviation
10^{-1}	deci-	d	10^{1}	deca-	da
10^{-2}	centi-	c	10^{2}	hecto-	h
10^{-3}	milli-	m	10^{3}	kilo-	k
10^{-6}	micro-	μ	10^{6}	Mega-	M
10^{-9}	nano-	n	10^{9}	Giga-	G
10^{-12}	pico-	p	10^{12}	Tera-	T
10^{-15}	femto-	f	10^{15}	Peta-	P
10^{-18}	atto-	a	10^{18}	Exa-	E
10^{-21}	zepto-	z	10^{21}	Zetta-	Z
10^{-24}	yocto-	y	10^{24}	Yotta-	Y

● EXAMPLE 7-1

Express the following values using the correct SI prefix.

Quantity		SI Prefix	SI Abbreviation
(a) 3,100 joules		3.1 kilojoules	3.1 kJ
(b) 2.51×10^6 watts		2.51 megawatts	2.51 MW
(c) 4×10^{-18} seconds		4 attoseconds	4 as
(d) 3×10^{-6} grams		3 micrograms	3 μg

Determining the appropriate SI prefix to use becomes simple when the number is placed in engineering notation; just examine the exponent.

As a reminder, scientific and engineering notation are defined as follows:

Scientific notation is typically expressed in the form $\#.\#\#\# \times 10^N$, where the digit to the left of the decimal point is the most significant nonzero digit of the value being represented. Sometimes, the digit to the right of the decimal point is the most significant digit instead. The number of decimal places can vary, but is usually two to four. N is an integer, and multiplying by 10^N serves to locate the true position of the decimal point.

Engineering notation is expressed in the form $\#\#\#.\#\#\# \times 10^M$, where M is an integer multiple of 3, and the number of digits to the left of the decimal point is 1, 2, or 3 as needed to yield a power of 10 that is indeed a multiple of 3. The number of digits to the right of the decimal point is typically between two and four.

● EXAMPLE 7-2

Express the following values using scientific notation, engineering notation, or with the correct SI prefix.

Standard	Scientific	Engineering	With Prefix
(a) 43,480,000 m	4.348×10^7 m	43.48×10^6 m	43.48 Mm
(b) 0.0000003060 V	3.060×10^{-7} V	306.0×10^{-9} V	306.0 nV
(c) 9,860,000,000 J	9.86×10^9 J	9.86×10^9 J	9.86 GJ
(d) 0.0351 s	3.51×10^{-2} s	35.1×10^{-3} s	35.1 ms
(e) 0.0000000522 μA	5.22×10^{-14} A	52.2×10^{-15} A	52.2 fA
(f) 456200 kW	4.562×10^8 W	456.2×10^6 W	456.2 MW

Note that the numeric values of the mantissa are the same in the last two columns, and the exponent in engineering notation specifies the metric prefix.

Official SI Rules

When reporting units using the SI system, follow these official rules.

■ **If a unit abbreviation appears as a capital letter, it has been named after a person; all other abbreviations appear as lowercase letters.** For example, the abbreviation "N" stands for "newton," the SI unit of force named after Isaac Newton.

Correct: The book weighs 5 N.   Incorrect: The book weighs 5 n.
Correct: The rod is 5 m long.   Incorrect: The rod is 5 M long.

The one exception to this rule is the volumetric unit of liter. The abbreviation is shown as L, since a lowercase l can be confused with both the number 1 and the uppercase letter I.

■ **Symbols of units are not shown as plural.**

Correct: 10 centimeters = 10 cm   Incorrect: 10 centimeters ≠ 10 cms

■ **Symbols are not shown with a period unless they appear at the end of a sentence.**

Correct: The rod is 5 mm long.   Incorrect: The rod is 5 mm. long.

■ **Symbols are written in upright Roman type (m, k, L) to distinguish them from mathematical variables (*m*, *k*, *l*), which are indicated by italics.**

■ **One space separates the number and symbol, except with the degree symbol referring to an angle.**

Correct: 5 mm or 5 °   Incorrect: 5mm or 5 °

■ **Spaces or commas may be used to group digits by threes.**

Correct: 1 000 000 or 1,000,000

■ **Symbols for derived units formed by multiple units are joined by a space or center dot. Care must be taken to avoid confusing SI prefixes with units.**

Correct: kg m or kg · m   Incorrect: kgm or mkg

This is particularly important when confusion might arise. For example, "ms" stands for millisecond, but "m s" stands for meter second. In cases like this, using a center dot is preferable since it is less likely to be misunderstood.

■ **Symbols for derived units formed by dividing units are joined by a virgule (the "slash" /) or shown with a negative exponent. Care must be taken to appropriately display the entire denominator.**

Correct: N/(m s²) or N m⁻¹ s⁻²   Incorrect: N/m s²

■ **Do not combine prefixes to form compound prefixes. Use the single correct prefix.**

Correct: picojoules (pJ)   Incorrect: millinanojoules (mnJ)
Correct: Gigaseconds (Gs)   Incorrect: kiloMegaseconds (kMs)

Indicate if the following units are correctly expressed according to the official SI rules. If the unit is incorrectly displayed, show the correction.

(a) Reading this sentence took 5 Secs.
(b) The average person's pupils are 60mms. apart.
(c) One gallon is the same as 380 microkiloliters.

7.2 OTHER UNIT SYSTEMS

Prior to the adoption of the SI unit system by the scientific community, several other systems of units were used and are still used today, particularly in the United States. The other countries that use non-SI units are Liberia and Myanmar. Great Britain officially converted to metric in 1965, but it is still common there to see nonmetric units used in communications for the general public.

It is important to know how to convert between all unit systems. Table 7-3 compares several systems. The system listed as AES (American Engineering System) is in common use by the general public in the United States. The USCS (United States Customary System) is commonly called "English" units.

Table 7-3 Comparison of unit system, with corresponding abbreviations

Dimension	SI (MKS)	AES	USCS
Length {L}	meter [m]	foot [ft]	foot [ft]
Mass {M}	kilogram [kg]	pound-mass [lb$_m$]	slug
Time {T}	second [s]	second [s]	second [s]
Relative temperature {Θ}	Celsius [°C]	Fahrenheit [°F]	Fahrenheit [°F]
Absolute temperature {Θ}	kelvin [K]	Rankine [°R]	Rankine [°R]

Accepted Non-SI Units

The units in Table 7-4 are not technically in the SI system, but due to their common usage, are acceptable for use in combination with the base SI units.

Table 7-4 Acceptable non-SI units

Unit	Equivalent SI	Unit	Equivalent SI
Astronomical unit [AU]	1 AU = 1.4959787 × 10^{11} m	day [d]	1 d = 86,400 s
Atomic mass unit [amu]	1 amu = 1.6605402 × 10^{-24} g	hour [h]	1 h = 3,600 s
Electronvolt [eV]	1 eV = 1.6021773 × 10^{-19} J	minute [min]	1 min = 60 s
Liter [L]	1 L = 0.001 m^3	year [yr]	1 yr = 3.16 × 10^7 s
		degree [°]	1° = 0.0175 rad or 1 rad = 57.3°

NOTE
1 liter does not equal
1 cubic meter!

7.3 CONVERSION PROCEDURE FOR UNITS

We use conversion factors to translate from one set of units to another. This must be done correctly and consistently to obtain the right answers. Some common conversion factors can be found inside the cover of this book, categorized by dimension. Although many more conversions are available, all the work for a typical engineering class can be accomplished using the conversions found in this table.

LENGTH

1 m = 3.28 ft
1 km = 0.621 mi
1 in = 2.54 cm
1 mi = 5,280 ft
1 yd = 3 ft

NOTE

Place the units you are converting TO in the NUMERATOR; place the units you are converting FROM in the DENOMINATOR.

Let us examine the conversions found for the dimension of length, as shown in the box, beginning with the conversion: 1 meter [m] = 3.28 feet [ft]. By dividing both sides of this equation by 3.28 feet, we obtain

$$\frac{1 \text{ m}}{3.28 \text{ ft}} = 1$$

or in other words, "There is 1 meter per 3.28 feet." If we divide both sides of the original expression by 1 meter, we obtain

$$1 = \frac{3.28 \text{ ft}}{1 \text{ m}}$$

or in other words, "In every 3.28 feet there is 1 meter."

The number 1 is dimensionless, a pure number. *We can multiply any expression by 1 without changing the expression.* We do this so as to change the units to the standard we desire.

For example, on a trip we note that the distance to Atlanta is 123 miles [mi]. How many kilometers [km] is it to Atlanta? From the conversion table, we can find that 1 kilometer [km] = 0.621 miles [mi], or

$$1 = \frac{1 \text{ km}}{0.621 \text{ mi}}$$

By multiplying the original quantity of 123 miles by 1, we can say

$$(123 \text{ mi})(1) = (123 \text{ mi})\left(\frac{1 \text{ km}}{0.621 \text{ mi}}\right) = 198 \text{ km}$$

Note that we could have multiplied by the following relationship:

$$1 = \frac{0.621 \text{ mi}}{1 \text{ km}}$$

We would still have multiplied the original answer by 1, but the units would not cancel and we would be left with an awkward, meaningless answer.

$$(123 \text{ mi})(1) = (123 \text{ mi})\left(\frac{0.621 \text{ mi}}{1 \text{ km}}\right) = 76 \frac{\text{mi}^2}{\text{km}}$$

As a second example, we are designing a reactor system using 2-inch [in] diameter plastic pipe. The design office in Germany would like the pipe specifications in units of centimeters [cm]. From the conversion table, we find that 1 inch [in] = 2.54 centimeters [cm], or

$$1 = \frac{1 \text{ in}}{2.54 \text{ cm}}$$

By multiplying the original quantity of 2 inches by 1, we can say

$$(2 \text{ in})(1) = (2 \text{ in})\left(\frac{2.54 \text{ cm}}{1 \text{ in}}\right) = 5 \text{ cm}$$

In a final example, suppose a car travels at 40 miles per hour (abbreviated mph). Stated in words, "a car traveling at a rate of 40 mph will take 1 hour to travel 40 miles if the velocity remains constant." By simple arithmetic this means that the car will travel 80 miles in 2 hours or 120 miles in 3 hours. In general,

$$\text{Distance} = (\text{velocity})(\text{time elapsed at that velocity})$$

Suppose the car is traveling at 40 mph for 6 minutes. How far does the car travel? Simple calculation shows

$$\text{Distance} = (40)(6) = 240$$

Without considering units, the preceding example implies that if we drive our car at 40 mph, we can cover the distance from Charlotte, North Carolina, to Atlanta, Georgia, in 6 minutes! What is wrong? Note that the velocity is given in miles per hour, and the time is given in minutes. If the equation is written with consistent units attached, we get

$$\text{Distance} = \left(\frac{40 \text{ mi}}{h}\right)\left(\frac{6 \text{ min}}{1} \middle| \frac{1 \text{ h}}{60 \text{ min}}\right) = 4 \text{ mi}$$

It seems more reasonable to say "traveling at a rate of 40 miles per hour for a time period of 6 minutes will allow us to go 4 miles."

To convert between any set of units, the following method demonstrated in Examples 7-3 to 7-6 is very helpful. This procedure is easy to use, but take care to avoid mistakes. If you use one of the conversion factors incorrectly, say, with 3 in the numerator instead of the denominator, your answer will be in error by a factor of 9.

● **EXAMPLE 7-3**

Convert the length 40 yards [yd] into units of feet [ft].

Method	Steps
(1) Term to be converted	40 yd
(2) Conversion formula	1 yd = 3 ft
(3) Make a fraction (equal to one)	$\frac{3 \text{ ft}}{1 \text{ yd}}$
(4) Multiply	$\frac{40 \text{ yd}}{} \middle| \frac{3 \text{ ft}}{1 \text{ yd}}$
(5) Cancel, calculate, be reasonable	120 ft

COMPREHENSION CHECK 7-3

The highest mountain in the world is Mount Everest in Nepal. The peak of Mount Everest is 29,029 feet above sea level. Convert the height from feet to miles.

COMPREHENSION CHECK 7-4

In North America, the greatest depth of snow on the ground was recorded at 1,145.5 centimeters at Tamarack, California. Convert the depth from centimeters to inches.

COMPREHENSION CHECK 7-5

The shortest race in the Olympics is the 100-meter dash. Convert the length from meters to feet.

7.4 CONVERSIONS INVOLVING MULTIPLE STEPS

Sometimes, more than one conversion factor is needed. We can multiply by several conversion factors, each one of which is the same as multiplying by 1, as many times as needed to reach the desired result. For example, suppose we determined that the distance to Atlanta is 123 miles [mi]. How many yards [yd] is it to Atlanta? From the conversion table, we do not have a direct conversion between miles and yards, but we see that both can be related to feet. We can find that 1 mile [mi] = 5,280 feet [ft], or

$$1 = \frac{5,280 \text{ ft}}{1 \text{ mi}}$$

We can also find that 1 yard [yd] = 3 feet [ft], or

$$1 = \frac{1 \text{ yd}}{3 \text{ ft}}$$

By multiplying the original quantity of 123 miles by 1 using the first set of conversion factors, we can say:

$$(123 \text{ mi})\,(1) = (123 \text{ mi})\left(\frac{5,280 \text{ ft}}{1 \text{ mi}}\right) = 649,440 \text{ ft}$$

If we multiply by 1 again, using the second set of conversion factors and applying reasonableness:

$$(649,440 \text{ ft})\,(1) = (649,440 \text{ ft})\left(\frac{1 \text{ yd}}{3 \text{ ft}}\right) = 216,000 \text{ yd}$$

This is usually shown as a single step:

$$(123 \text{ mi})\left(\frac{5,280 \text{ ft}}{1 \text{ mi}}\right)\left(\frac{1 \text{ yd}}{3 \text{ ft}}\right) = 216,000 \text{ yd}$$

Unit Conversion Procedure

1. Write the value and unit to be converted.
2. Write the conversion formula between the given unit and the desired unit.
3. Make a fraction, equal to 1, of the conversion formula in Step 2, such that the original unit in Step 1 is located either in the denominator or in the numerator, depending on where it must reside so that the original unit will cancel.
4. Multiply the term from Step 1 by the fractions developed in Step 3.
5. Cancel units, perform mathematical calculations, and express the answer in "reasonable" terms (i.e., not too many decimal places).

● EXAMPLE 7-4

Convert the length 40 yards [yd] into units of millimeters [mm].

Method	**Steps**
(1) Term to be converted	40 yd
(2) Conversion formula	1 yd = 3 ft 1 ft = 12 in 1 in = 2.54 cm 1 cm = 10 mm
(3) Make fractions (equal to one)	$\dfrac{3\text{ ft}}{1\text{ yd}}$ $\dfrac{12\text{ in}}{1\text{ ft}}$ $\dfrac{2.54\text{ cm}}{1\text{ in}}$ $\dfrac{10\text{ mm}}{1\text{ cm}}$
(4) Multiply	$\dfrac{40\text{ yd}}{}\bigg|\dfrac{3\text{ ft}}{1\text{ yd}}\bigg|\dfrac{12\text{ in}}{1\text{ ft}}\bigg|\dfrac{2.54\text{ cm}}{1\text{ in}}\bigg|\dfrac{10\text{ mm}}{1\text{ cm}}$
(5) Cancel, calculate, be reasonable	37,000 mm

● EXAMPLE 7-5

Convert 55 miles per hour [mph] to units of meters per second [m/s].

Note that we have two units to convert here, miles to meters, and hours to seconds.

Method	**Steps**
(1) Term to be converted	55 mph
(2) Conversion formula	1 km = 0.621 mi 1 km = 1,000 m 1 h = 60 min 1 min = 60 s
(3) Make fractions (equal to one)	
(4) Multiply	$\dfrac{55\text{ mi}}{\text{h}}\bigg|\dfrac{1\text{ km}}{0.621\text{ mi}}\bigg|\dfrac{1,000\text{ m}}{1\text{ km}}\bigg|\dfrac{1\text{ h}}{60\text{ min}}\bigg|\dfrac{1\text{ min}}{60\text{ s}}$
(5) Cancel, calculate, be reasonable	24.6 m/s

TIME

1 d = 24 h
1 h = 60 min
1 min = 60 s
1 yr = 365 d

● EXAMPLE 7-6

Convert the volume of 40 gallons [gal] into units of cubic feet [ft³].

By examining the *"Volume"* box in the conversion table, we see that the following facts are available for use:

$$1\text{ L} = 0.264\text{ gal} \quad \text{and} \quad 1\text{ L} = 0.0353\text{ ft}^3$$

By the transitive property, *if a = b and a = c, then b = c. Therefore, we can directly write*

$$0.264\text{ gal} = 0.0353\text{ ft}^3$$

Method	**Steps**
(1) Term to be converted	40 gal
(2) Conversion formula	0.264 gal = 0.0353 ft³
(3) Make a fraction (equal to one)	$\dfrac{0.0353\text{ ft}^3}{0.264\text{ gal}}$
(4) Multiply	$\dfrac{40\text{ gal}}{}\bigg|\dfrac{0.0353\text{ ft}^3}{0.264\text{ gal}}$
(5) Cancel, calculate, be reasonable	5.3 ft³

VOLUME

1 L = 0.264 gal
1 L = 0.0353 ft³
1 L = 33.8 fl oz
1 mL = 1 cm³

This picture shows 5-gallon water bottles made from polycarbonate. Millions of these bottles are made each year around the world to transport clean water to remote locations.

The use of polycarbonate to contain products for consumption has raised safety concerns because bisphenol A is leached from the plastic into the stored liquid. As of March 2009, six U.S. manufacturers have stopped using polycarbonate in bottles and cups used by infants and small children.

Photo courtesy of Kautex Machines

One frequently needs to convert a value that has some unit or units raised to a power, for example, converting a volume given in cubic feet to cubic meters. It is critical in this case that the power involved be applied to the *entire* conversion factor, both the numerical values and the units.

● **EXAMPLE 7-7**

Convert 35 cubic inches [in³] to cubic centimeters [cm³ or cc].

Method	Steps
(1) Term to be converted	35 in^3
(2) Conversion formula	$1 \text{ in} = 2.54 \text{ cm}$
(3) Make fractions (equal to one)	$35 \text{ in}^3 \left\| \dfrac{(2.54 \text{ cm})^3}{(1 \text{ in})^3} \right.$
(4) Multiply	$35 \text{ in}^3 \left\| \dfrac{(2.54)^3 \text{ cm}^3}{1 \text{ in}^3} \right.$
(5) Cancel, calculate, be reasonable	574 cm^3

NOTE

When raising a quantity to a power, be sure to apply the power to both the value and the units.

Note that in some cases, a unit that is raised to a power is being converted to another unit that has been defined to have the same dimension as the one raised to a power. This is difficult to say in words, but a couple of examples should clarify it.

If one is converting square meters [m²] to acres, the conversion factor is *not* squared, since the conversion provided is already in terms of length squared: 1 acre = 4,047 m².

If one is converting cubic feet [ft³] to liters [L], the conversion factor is *not* cubed, since the conversion provided is already in terms of length cubed: 1 L = 0.0353 ft³.

Convert a velocity of 250 kilometers per second [km/s] to units of millimeters per picosecond [mm/ps].

Method

	Steps
(1) Term to be converted	250 km/s
(2) Conversion formula	1 km = 10^3 m 1 mm = 10^{-3} m 1 ps = 10^{-12} s
(3) Make fractions (equal to one) (4) Multiply	$\dfrac{250 \text{ km}}{\text{s}} \left\| \dfrac{10^3 \text{ m}}{1 \text{ km}} \right\| \dfrac{1 \text{ mm}}{10^{-3} \text{ m}} \left\| \dfrac{10^{-12} \text{ s}}{1 \text{ ps}} \right.$
(5) Cancel, calculate, be reasonable	250×10^{-6} mm/ps

- *Comment:* Following the rules for use of prefixes given earlier would indicate that the term in the denominator should not have a prefix at all, and it should be transferred to the numerator, giving 250×10^6 mm/s. Beyond that, it was earlier stated that in general, the prefix should be adjusted to give one, two, or three digits to the left of the decimal place (with no power of 10). This would yield 250 km/s, right back where we started.

- *Moral:* **specific instructions** (such as "convert to mm/ps") **usually override the general rules.** *In this case, perhaps we are studying the velocity of protons in a particle accelerator, and for comparison with other experiments, we need to know how many millimeters the particles go in one picosecond, rather than ending up with the units the general rules would dictate.*

Officially, a hurricane is a tropical storm with sustained winds of at least 74 miles per hour. Convert this speed into units of kilometers per minute.

Many toilets in commercial establishments have a value printed on them stating the amount of water consumed per flush. For example, a label of 2 Lpf indicates the consumption of 2 liters per flush. If a toilet is rated at 3 Lpf, how many flushes are required to consume 20 gallons of water?

RULES OF THUMB

1 quart ≈ 1 liter
1 cubic meter ≈ 250 gallons
1 cup ≈ 250 milliliters

1 cubic foot ≈ 7.5 gallons
1 cubic meter ≈ 5, 55-gallon drums
1 golf ball ≈ 1 cubic inch

LESSONS OF THE MARS CLIMATE ORBITER

Some of you may have heard that the loss of the Mars Climate Orbiter (MCO) spacecraft in 1999 was due to a unit conversion error. The complete story is rather more complicated and illustrates a valuable lesson in engineering design. Most engineering failures are not due to a single mistake, since built-in redundancies and anticipation of failure modes make this unlikely. Three primary factors (plus bad luck) conspired to send the MCO off course.

First, the spacecraft was asymmetrical, with the body of the spacecraft on one side and a large solar panel on the other. You might think shape is not an issue in the vacuum of space, but in fact it is, and the NASA engineers were well aware of the potential problems. The panel acted like a sail, causing the craft to slowly change its orientation and requiring the MCO to make occasional small corrections by firing thrusters onboard the craft. This was a perfectly manageable "problem."

Second, the software on the spacecraft expected thruster data in SI units, requiring the force expressed in newtons. On the Earth, a separate system calculated and sent instructions to the MCO concerning when and how long to fire its thrusters. The Earth-based system relied on software from an earlier Mars mission, and the thruster equations had to be modified to correct for the thrusters used on the new spacecraft. The original software had been written correctly, with the conversion factor from pound-force to new-tons included. However, this conversion was neither documented nor obvious from the code, being buried in the equations. When the equations were rewritten, the programmers were unaware of the conversion factor and it was left out of the new code. This sent incorrect thruster-firing data to the MCO, specifically being too small by a factor of 4.45. This problem alone was manageable by comparing the calculated trajectory with tracking data.

Finally, after the third trajectory correction, the MCO entered "safe mode" while adjusting the solar panel, indicating a fault on the craft. At about the same time, the preliminary indications that the spacecraft trajectory was flawed began to come in. Unfortunately, the engineers spent the next several weeks trying to determine what caused the craft to enter safe mode, falsely assuming the preliminary trajectory data was in error and waiting for longer-term tracking to give a better estimate. In the end, the spacecraft arrived at Mars about 100 kilometers off course.

Here is where the bad luck comes in. Other configurations of the craft or trajectory might have caused the 100 kilometer error to be away from Mars or parallel to the surface, in which case the trajectory could have been corrected later. Unfortunately, the trajectory was 100 kilometers lower than expected, and the MCO was probably destroyed by heating and stresses as it plunged through the Martian atmosphere. Cost: well over $100 million.

7.5 CONVERSIONS INVOLVING "NEW" UNITS

In the past, many units were derived from common physical objects. The "inch" was the width of man's thumb, and the "foot" was the heel-to-toe length of a king's shoe. Obviously, when one king died or was deposed and another took over, the unit of "foot" changed, too. Over time, these units were standardized and have become common terminology.

New units are added as technology evolves; for example, in 1999 the unit of katal was added as an **SI** derived unit of catalytic activity used in biochemistry. As you proceed in your engineering field, you will be introduced to many "new" units. The procedures discussed here apply to *any* unit in *any* engineering field.

● **EXAMPLE 7-9**

According to the U.S. Food and Drug Administration (21CFR101.9), the following definition applies for nutritional labeling:

1 fluid ounce means 30 milliliters

Using this definition, how many fluid ounces [fl oz] are in a "U.S. standard" beverage can of 355 milliliters [mL]?

Method	Steps
(1) Term to be converted	355 mL
(2) Conversion formula	1 fl oz = 30 mL
(3) Make a fraction (equal to one) (4) Multiply	$\dfrac{355 \text{ mL}}{} \Bigg| \dfrac{1 \text{ fl oz}}{30 \text{ mL}}$
(5) Cancel, calculate, be reasonable	11.8 fl oz

● **EXAMPLE 7-10**

The volume of water in a reservoir or aquifer is often expressed using the unit of acre-foot. A volume of 1 acre-foot is the amount of water covering an area of 1 acre to a depth of 1 foot.

Lake Mead, located 30 miles southeast of Las Vegas, Nevada, is the largest man-made lake in the United States. It holds approximately 28.5 million acre-feet of water behind the Hoover Dam. Convert this volume to units of gallons.

Method	Steps				
(1) Term to be converted	28.5×10^6 acre feet				
(2) Conversion formula	1 acre = 4,047 m² 1 m = 3.28 ft 1 m³ = 100³cm³ 1,000 cm³ = 0.264 gal				
(3) Make a fraction (4) Multiply	$\dfrac{28.5 \times 10^6 \text{ acre ft}}{}$	$\dfrac{4,047 \text{ m}^2}{1 \text{ acre}}$	$\dfrac{1 \text{ m}}{3.28 \text{ ft}}$	$\dfrac{100^3 \text{ cm}^3}{1 \text{ m}^3}$	$\dfrac{0.264 \text{ gal}}{1,000 \text{ cm}^3}$
(5) Cancel, calculate, be reasonable	9.3×10^{12} gal				

COMPREHENSION CHECK 7-8

A hogshead is a unit of volume describing a large barrel of liquid. Convert 10 hogsheads into units of cubic feet. Conversion factor: 1 hogshead = 63 gallons.

A barrel in petroleum engineering is a unit of volume describing a measure of crude oil. Convert 1 barrel into units of cubic meters. Conversion factor: 1 barrel = 42 gallons.

A drum is a shipping container used to transport liquids. Convert 5 drums into units of liters. Conversion factor: 1 drum = 55 gallons.

7.6 DERIVED DIMENSIONS AND UNITS

With only the seven base dimensions in the metric system, all measurable things in the known universe can be expressed by various combinations of these concepts. These are called **derived dimensions**. As simple examples, area is length squared, volume is length cubed, and velocity is length divided by time.

As we explore more complex parameters, the dimensions become more complex. For example, the concept of force is derived from Newton's second law, which states that force is equal to mass times acceleration. Force is then used to define more complex dimensions such as pressure, which is force acting over an area, or work, which is force acting over a distance. As we introduce new concepts, we introduce the dimensions and units for each parameter.

Sometimes, the derived dimensions become quite complicated. For example, electrical resistance is mass times length squared divided by both time cubed and current squared. Particularly in the more complicated cases like this, a **derived unit** is defined to avoid having to say things like "The resistance is 15 kilogram-meters squared divided by second cubed ampere squared." It is much easier to say "The resistance is 15 ohms," where the derived unit "ohm" equals one (kg m²)/(s³ A²).

Within this text, dimensions are presented in exponential notation rather than fractional notation. If a dimension is not present in the quantity, it is noted by a zero exponent.

Quantity	Fractional Notation	Exponential Notation
Velocity	$\dfrac{L}{T}$	$M^0\,L^1\,T^{-1}\,\Theta^0$
Acceleration	$\dfrac{L}{T^2}$	$M^0\,L^1\,T^{-2}\,\Theta^0$

Currently, there are officially 22 named derived units in the SI system. All are named after famous scientists or engineers who are deceased. Five of the most common derived units can be found in Table 7.5. It is worth noting that numerous named derived dimensions do not have a corresponding named derived SI unit. For example, there is no named derived SI unit for the derived dimension velocity as there is for force (newton) or electrical resistance (ohm).

Table 7.5 **Common derived units in the SI system**

Dimension	SI Unit	Base SI Units	Derived from
Force (F)	newton [N]	$1\ N = 1\dfrac{kg\ m}{s^2}$	$F = ma$ Force = mass times acceleration
Energy (E)	joule [J]	$1\ J = 1\ N\ m = 1\dfrac{kg\ m^2}{s^2}$	$E = Fd$ Energy = force times distance
Power (P)	watt [W]	$1\ W = 1\dfrac{J}{s} = 1\dfrac{kg\ m^2}{s^3}$	$P = E/t$ Power = energy per time
Pressure (P)	pascal [Pa]	$1\ Pa = 1\dfrac{N}{m^2} = 1\dfrac{kg}{m\ s^2}$	$P = F/A$ Pressure = force per area
Voltage (V)	volt [V]	$1\ V = 1\dfrac{W}{A} = 1\dfrac{kg\ m^2}{s^3\ A}$	$V = P/I$ Voltage = power per current

- A note of caution: One letter can represent several quantities in various engineering disciplines. For example, the letter "P" can indicate pressure, power, or vertical load on a beam. It is important to examine and determine the nomenclature in terms of the context of the problem presented.
- Always remember to use the units and the symbol in calculations.

COMPREHENSION CHECK 7-11

Complete Table 7-6 by finding the exponents to express the parameters in the form $\{=\}\ M^a\ L^b\ T^c\ \Theta^d$.

Table 7-6 **Dimensions of some common parameters**

Quantity	Common Units	Exponents M	L	T	Θ
Fundamental Quantities					
Mass	kg	1	0	0	0
Length	m	0	1	0	0
Time	s	0	0	1	0
Temperature	K	0	0	0	1
Geometric Quantities					
Area	ft²				
	acre	0	2	0	0
Volume	gal				
	L				
Rate Quantities					
Velocity	mi/h	0	1	−1	0
Acceleration	ft/s²	0	1	−2	0
Flowrate	gal/min				
Evaporation	kg/h				

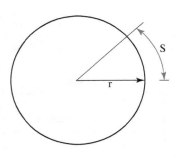

Special Unit: Radian

The derived unit of **radian** is defined as the angle at the center of a circle formed by an arc (S) equal in length to the radius (r) of that circle. In a complete circle there are 2π radians. Since by definition a radian is a length (S) divided by a length (r), it is a dimensionless ratio.

$$1 \text{ radian } [\text{rad}] = S/r$$

Thus, an angle has units, but is dimensionless! In addition to radians, another common unit used for angle is the degree [°]. There are 360° in a complete circle.

$$360° = 2\pi \text{ radians}$$

7.7 EQUATION LAWS

Equations are mathematical "sentences" composed of "words" (terms) that are strung together with "punctuation marks" (mathematical symbols, such as $+$, $-$, $\times$, $\div$, and $=$). Just as there are rules in the English language that govern how a sentence is structured, there exists a set of "rules" for equations.

Addition and Subtraction

Suppose we are interested in the manufacture and use of sandpaper for furniture construction. We think for a while and then develop a list of the important quantities that affect the final product, along with their respective units and dimensions:

W	Wood removed	[in]	L
R	Roughness diameter	[mm]	L
D	Density of grains	[kg/m³]	$\dfrac{M}{L^3}$
A	Adhesive thickness	[mm]	L
H	How heavy the paper is	[N]	$\dfrac{ML}{T^2}$
O	Operation stroke length	[cm]	L
K	Kernel (grain) spacing	[mm]	L

Let us propose a simple equation with only plus and minus signs that could possibly relate several of these parameters. If we are interested in how heavy the product would be, we might assume this would depend on the thickness of the adhesive, the diameter of the roughness, and the grain density. We will try

$$H = A + R + D$$

Each of these terms represents something "real," and consequently we expect that each term can be expressed in terms of fundamental dimensions. Writing the equation in terms of dimensions given:

$$\frac{ML}{T^2} = L + L + \frac{M}{L^3}$$

IMPORTANT CONCEPT: PLUS LAW

Every term being added or subtracted in an equation must have the same dimension.

It is obvious that this is just terrible! We cannot add length and mass or time; as the adage goes, "You can't add apples and oranges!" The same holds true for dimensions. As a result of this observation, we see that this cannot possibly be a valid equation. This gives one important "law" governing equations, the **Plus law**.

Let us try this again with another equation to see if we can determine how effective the sandpaper will be, or how much wood will be removed after each stroke. We might assume this depends on the operation stroke length, the roughness diameter, and the spacing of the grains.

$$W = O + R + K$$

Substituting dimensions,

$$L = L + L + L$$

We see that at least dimensionally, this can be a valid equation, based on the Plus law. Next, units can be inserted to give

$$\text{inches} = \text{centimeters} + \text{millimeters} + \text{millimeters}$$

IMPORTANT CONCEPT: UNIT LAW

Every term in an equation must have the same units so that the arithmetic operations of addition and subtraction can be carried out.

Dimensionally, this equation is fine, but from the perspective of units, we cannot carry out the arithmetic above without first converting all the length dimensions into the same units, such as millimeters. We can state an important result from this observation as well, forming the **Unit law**.

It is important to state a corollary to this observation. If two parameters have the same dimensions and units, it is not always meaningful to add or subtract them. Two examples show this.

COROLLARY TO UNIT LAW

A dimensionally consistent and unit consistent equation is not necessarily a valid equation in terms of physical meaning.

1. If Student A has a mass m_A [kilograms] and Student B a mass m_B [kilograms], then the total mass of both students [kilograms] is the sum of the two masses. This is correct and meaningful in both dimensions and units.
2. Suppose we assume that an equation to predict the mass of a car is this: mass of the car in kilograms = mass of an oak tree in kilograms + mass of an opossum in kilograms. This equation has three terms; all with the dimension of mass and units of kilograms; thus, the terms can be added, although the equation itself is nonsense.

Consequently, the requirement that each term must have the same dimensions and units is a necessary, but not a sufficient, condition for a satisfactory equation.

Multiplication and Division

There are many ways to express the rate at which things are done. Much of our daily life is conducted on a "*per*" or rate basis. We eat 3 meals *per* day, have 5 fingers *per* hand, there are 11 players *per* team in football, 3 feet *per* yard, 4 tires *per* car, 12 fluid ounces *per* canned drink, and 4 people *per* quartet.

IMPORTANT CONCEPT: PER LAW

When parameters are multiplied or divided, the dimensions and units are treated with the same operation rules as numerical values.

Although it is incorrect to add or subtract parameters with different dimensions, it is perfectly permissible to divide or multiply two or more parameters with different dimensions. This is another law of dimensions, the **Per law**.

When we say 65 miles *per* hour, we mean that we travel 65 miles in 1 hour. We could say we travel at 130 miles per 2 hours, and it would mean the same thing. Either way, this rate is expressed by the "*per*" ratio, distance per time.

One of the most useful applications of your knowledge of dimensions is in helping to determine if an equation is dimensionally correct. This is easy to do and only involves the substitution of the dimensions of every parameter into the equation and simplifying the resulting expressions. A simple application will demonstrate this process.

● EXAMPLE 7-11

Is the following equation dimensionally correct?

$$t = \sqrt{\frac{d_{final} - d_{initial}}{0.5a}}$$

where
t is time
d is distance
a is acceleration
0.5 is unitless

Determine the dimensions of each parameter:

Acceleration	(a)	$\{=\}\ L^1\ T^{-2}$
Distance	(d)	$\{=\}\ L$
Time	(t)	$\{=\}\ T$

Substitute into the equation:
$$T = \sqrt{[L - L]\left|\frac{T^2}{L}\right|}$$

Simplifying
$$T = \sqrt{L\left|\frac{T^2}{L}\right|} = \sqrt{T^2} = T$$

Yes, the equation is dimensionally correct. Both sides of the equation have the same dimensions.

● EXAMPLE 7-12

We can use dimensional arguments to help remember formulas. We are interested in the acceleration of a body swung in a circle of radius (r), at a constant velocity (v). We remember that acceleration depends on r and v, and one is divided by the other, but cannot quite remember how. Is the acceleration (a) given by one of the following?

$$a = \frac{v}{r} \quad \text{or} \quad a = \frac{v}{r^2} \quad \text{or} \quad a = \frac{v^2}{r} \quad \text{or} \quad a = \frac{r}{v} \quad \text{or} \quad a = \frac{r}{v^2} \quad \text{or} \quad a = \frac{r^2}{v}$$

Determine the dimensions of each parameter:

Acceleration	(a)	$\{=\}\ L^1\ T^{-2}$
Radius	(r)	$\{=\}\ L$
Velocity	(v)	$\{=\}\ L^1\ T^{-1}$

Original Equation	Substituting into the Equation	Simplify	Correct?
$a = v/r$	$LT^{-2} = (LT^{-1})\ L^{-1}$	$LT^{-2} = T^{-1}$	No
$a = v/r^2$	$LT^{-2} = (LT^{-1})\ L^{-2}$	$LT^{-2} = L^{-1}\ T^{-1}$	No
$a = v^2/r$	$LT^{-2} = (LT^{-1})^2\ L^{-1}$	$LT^{-2} = LT^{-2}$	Yes
$a = r/v$	$LT^{-2} = L\ (LT^{-1})^{-1}$	$LT^{-2} = T$	No
$a = r/v^2$	$LT^{-2} = L\ (LT^{-1})^{-2}$	$LT^{-2} = L^{-1}\ T^2$	No
$a = r^2/v$	$LT^{-2} = L^2\ (LT^{-1})^{-1}$	$LT^{-2} = LT$	No

COMPREHENSION CHECK 7-12

The power absorbed by a resistor can be given by $P = I^2R$, where P is power in units of watts [W], I is electric current in amperes [A], and R is resistance in ohms [Ω]. Express the unit of ohms in terms of fundamental dimensions.

Weirs are typically installed in open channels such as streams to determine discharge (flow rate). A Cipoletti weir is described by the following equation, where Q is flow rate [gallons per minute, or gpm], L is length [cm], and H is height [cm]. For the following equation to be dimensionally correct, what are the dimensions on the constant value of 3.37?

$$Q = 3.37\, LH^{3/2}$$

7.8 CONVERSION INVOLVING EQUATIONS

Engineering problems are rarely as simple as converting from one set of units to another. Normally, an equation is involved in the problem solution. To minimize the likelihood of mistakes, we adopt the following procedure for all problems. While this procedure may seem to overanalyze simple problems, it is relatively foolproof and will become more and more useful as the material progresses in difficulty.

Equation Procedure

1. Given a problem, first convert all parameters into base SI units, combinations of these units, or accepted non-SI units. Use the five-step conversion procedure previously described.
2. Perform all necessary calculations, as follows:
   (a) Determine the appropriate equation.
   (b) Insert the known quantities and units. Be sure to carry the units through until the end!
   (c) Calculate the desired quantity and express the answer in "reasonable" terms. This gives the answer in SI units.
3. Convert the final answer to the required units and express the answer in "reasonable" terms.

On a trip from Alphaville to Betaville, you can take two main routes. Route 1, which goes through Gammatown, is 50 kilometers [km] long; however, you can only drive an average speed of 36 miles per hour [mph]. Route 2 travels along the freeway, at an average speed of 50 mph, but it is 65 km long. How long does it take to complete each route? State the time for each route in minutes [min].

Step One: Convert to Base SI Units		
Method	**Route 1**	**Route 2**
(1) Term to be converted	36 mph	50 mph
(2) Conversion formula (3) Make a fraction (equal to one) (4) Multiply	$\dfrac{36\text{ mi}}{\text{h}}\left\|\dfrac{1\text{ km}}{0.621\text{ mi}}\right.$	$\dfrac{50\text{ mi}}{\text{h}}\left\|\dfrac{1\text{ km}}{0.621\text{ mi}}\right.$
(5) Cancel, calculate, be reasonable	58 km/h	81 km/h
Step Two: Calculate		
Method	**Route 1**	**Route 2**
(1) Determine appropriate equation	Distance = (velocity) (time) which can be rewritten as . . . Time = distance/velocity	
(2) Insert known quantities	$\text{Time} = \dfrac{50\text{ km}}{58\,\frac{\text{km}}{\text{h}}}$	$\text{Time} = \dfrac{65\text{ km}}{81\,\frac{\text{km}}{\text{h}}}$
(3) Calculate, be reasonable	Time = 0.86 h	Time = 0.8 h
Step Three: Convert from Base SI Units to Desired Units		
Method	**Route 1**	**Route 2**
(1) Term to be converted	0.86 h	0.8 h
(2) Conversion formula (3) Make a fraction (equal to one) (4) Multiply	$\dfrac{0.86\text{ h}}{}\left\|\dfrac{60\text{ min}}{1\text{ h}}\right.$	$\dfrac{0.8\text{ h}}{}\left\|\dfrac{60\text{ min}}{1\text{ h}}\right.$
(5) Cancel, calculate, be reasonable	52 min	48 min

RULE OF THUMB

$$\dfrac{\text{km}}{\frac{\text{km}}{\text{h}}} = \dfrac{\text{km h}}{\text{km}}$$

COMPREHENSION CHECK 7-14

Eclipses, both solar and lunar, follow a cycle of just over 18 years, specifically 6585.32 days. This is called the Saros Cycle. One Saros Cycle after any given eclipse an almost identical eclipse will occur due to fact that the Earth, the Moon, and the Sun are in essentially the same positions relative to each other. The Sun, and the entire solar system, is moving relative to the Cosmic Microwave Background Radiation (the largest detectable frame of reference) at roughly 370 kilometers per second. How far does our solar system travel through the universe in one Saros Cycle? Express your answer in the following units:

(a) meters, with an appropriately chosen prefix;
(b) miles;
(c) astronomical units. Check Table 7-4 for the definition of an AU;
(d) light-years. One light year $= 9.46 \times 10^{15}$ meters.

COMPREHENSION CHECK 7-15

A basketball has a diameter of approximately 27 centimeters. Find the volume of the basketball in units of gallons.

In-Class Activities

ICA 7-1

Complete the following table:

	Meters	Centimeters	Millimeters	Micrometers	Nanometers
Abbreviation	[m]				
Example	9E-08	9E-06	9E-05	0.09	90
(a)		50			
(b)				5	
(c)			300		

ICA 7-2

Complete the following table:

	Grams	Milligrams	Micrograms	Nanograms	Kilograms
Abbreviation	[g]				
(a)					0.4
(b)		20			
(c)				800	
(d)			3		

ICA 7-3

Complete the following table:

	Inches	Feet	Yards	Meters	Miles
Abbreviation	[in]				
(a)		90			
(b)					2
(c)				52	
(d)			53.5		

ICA 7-4

Complete the following table:

	Kilograms	Grams	Pound-Mass	Slugs	Ton
Abbreviation	[kg]				
(a)		700			
(b)					1.5
(c)				75	
(d)			150		

ICA 7-5

Complete the following table:

	Cubic Inch	Fluid Ounces	Gallon	Liter	Cubic Foot
Abbreviation	[in³]				
Example	716	400	3.12	11.8	0.414
(a)					3
(b)				5	
(c)			42		

ICA 7-6

Complete the following table:

	Square Feet	Square Meter	Acre	Square Inch	Square Mile
Abbreviation	[ft²]				
(a)		0.06			
(b)					3
(c)				500	
(d)			1.5		

ICA 7-7

Complete the following table:

	Miles per Hour	Kilometers per Hour	Yards per Minute	Feet per Second
Abbreviation	[mph] or [mi/h]			
(a)		100		
(b)	55			
(c)				110
(d)			2.25	

ICA 7-8

Complete the following table:

	Gallons per Minute	Cubic Feet per Hour	Liters per Second	Fluid Ounces per Day
Abbreviation	[gpm] or [gal/min]			
(a)		15		
(b)	20			
(c)				64
(d)			8	

ICA 7-9

In China, one "bu" is 1.66 meters. A "league" is defined as 3 miles. Convert 2 leagues to units of bu.

ICA 7-10

In China, one "bu" is 1.66 meters. The average height of a human is 5 feet, 7 inches. Convert this height to units of bu.

ICA 7-11

In China, one "cun" is 3.5 centimeters. A "cubit" is defined as 18 inches. Convert 50 cubits to units of cun.

ICA 7-12

In China, one "fen" is defined as 3.3 millimeters. Ten nanometers is the thickness of a cell membrane. Convert 10 nanometers to units of fen.

ICA 7-13

A blink of a human eye takes approximately 300–400 milliseconds. Convert 350 milliseconds to units of shake. One "shake" is equal to 10 nanoseconds.

ICA 7-14

As we all know, everyone gets their fifteen minutes of fame. Convert your 15 minutes of fame to units of shake. One "shake" is equal to 10 nanoseconds.

ICA 7-15

If the SI prefix system was expanded to other units, there would be such definitions as a "millihour," meaning 1/1,000 of an hour. Convert 1 millihour to units of shake. One "shake" is equal to 10 nanoseconds.

ICA 7-16

A "jiffy" is defined as 1/60 of a second. Convert 20 jiffys to units of shake. One "shake" is equal to 10 nanoseconds.

ICA 7-17

A football field is 120 yards long by 53.5 yards wide. Rather than using the traditional MKS (meter–kilogram–second) unit system, an unusual unit system is the FFF system: furlong–firkin–fortnight. One furlong is equal to 201 meters. Calculate the area of the football field, and convert this area into units of furlong squared.

ICA 7-18

A "knot" is a unit of speed in marine travel. One knot is 1.852 kilometers per hour. Rather than using the traditional MKS (meter–kilogram–second) unit system, an unusual unit system is the FFF system: furlong–firkin–fortnight. One furlong is equal to 201 meters and one fortnight is 14 days. Convert the speed of 20 knots to units of furlong per fortnight.

ICA 7-19

The Earth's escape velocity is 7 miles per second. Rather than using the traditional MKS (meter–kilogram–second) unit system, an unusual unit system is the FFF system: furlong–firkin–fortnight. One furlong is equal to 201 meters and one fortnight is 14 days. Convert this to units of furlong per fortnight.

ICA 7-20

A manufacturing process uses 10 pound-mass of plastic resin per hour. Rather than using the traditional MKS (meter–kilogram–second) unit system, an unusual unit system is the FFF system: furlong–firkin–fortnight. One firkin is equal to 40 kilograms and one fortnight is 14 days. Convert this rate to units of firkin per fortnight.

ICA 7-21

A "pinch" is defined as ⅛ of a teaspoon, or 0.616 milliliters [mL]. Convert 1 pinch to units of drops. One "metric drop" is equal to 5 microliters [μL].

ICA 7-22

One metric teaspoon is defined as 5 milliliters [mL]. Convert 2 teaspoons to units of drops. One "metric drop" is equal to 5 microliters [μL].

ICA 7-23

One cup is 250 milliliters [mL]. Convert ½ cup to units of drops. One "metric drop" is equal to 5 microliters [μL].

ICA 7-24

A standard can of soda is 355 milliliters [mL]. Convert 355 milliliters to units of drops. One "metric drop" is equal to 5 microliters [μL].

ICA 7-25

A category F5 tornado can have wind speeds of 300 miles per hour [mph]. What is this velocity in units of meters per second?

ICA 7-26

A new hybrid automobile with regenerative braking has a fuel economy of 55 miles per gallon [mpg] in city driving. What is this fuel economy expressed in units of feet per milliliter?

ICA 7-27

The AbioCor™ artificial heart pumps at a rate of 10 liters per minute. Express this rate in units of gallons per second.

ICA 7-28

If a pump moves water at 2 cubic feet per hour, what is this rate in units of cubic centimeters per second?

ICA 7-29

A circular window has a 10-inch radius. What is the surface area of one side of the window in units of square centimeters?

ICA 7-30

When shipping freight around the world, most companies use a standardized set of containers to make transportation and handling easier. The 40-foot container is the most popular container worldwide. If the container is 2.4 meters wide and has an enclosed volume of 2,385 cubic feet, what is the height of the container in units of inches?

ICA 7-31

A body traveling in a circle experiences an acceleration (a) of $a = v^2/r$, where v is the speed of the body and r is the radius of the circle. We are tasked with designing a large centrifuge to allow astronauts to experience a high "g" forces similar to those encountered on takeoff. One "g" is defined as 9.8 meters per second squared. Design specifications indicate that our design must create at least 5 "g"s. If we use a radius of 30 feet, what is the required speed of the rotating capsule at the end of the arm?

ICA 7-32

We have constructed a model car that can accelerate (a) over time (t) and travel a distance (d). A friend who is knowledgeable in physics tells us that we can compute the distance traveled with the equation $d = \frac{1}{2} at^2$. Given the following values, compute the distance traveled in units of miles: $a = 6.5$ feet per second squared, and $t = 0.25$ hour.

ICA 7-33

Complete the following table, expressing each unit in terms of fundamental dimensions:

	Quantity and/or Unit	Symbol	Exponents			
			M	L	T	Θ
	acre	acre	0	2	0	0
	atmospheres	atm	1	−1	−2	0
(a)	calorie	cal				
(b)	calories per minute	cal/min				
(c)	cubic feet	ft³				
(d)	day	d				
(e)	degrees Fahrenheit	°F				
(f)	foot pound-force	ft lb$_f$				
(g)	gallon	gal				
(h)	horsepower	hp				
(i)	inches of mercury	in Hg				
(j)	joule	J				
(k)	kelvin	K				
(l)	kilogram	kg				
(m)	liter	L				
(n)	mile	mi				
(o)	newton	N				
(p)	pascal	Pa				
(q)	pound-force	lb$_f$				
(r)	pound-force per square inch	psi				
(s)	pound-mass	lb$_m$				
(t)	slug					
(u)	square feet	ft²				
(v)	watt	W				

ICA 7-34

For each equation listed, indicate if the equation is a correct mathematical expression based on dimensional considerations. You must show you work to receive credit.

(a) Volume = (mass)/(density)
(b) Area = (acceleration)^2 (time)^3
(c) Speed = (time)^2 (acceleration)
(d) Speed = (mass)$^{1/3}$ ((time) (density)$^{1/3}$)
(e) Acceleration = (velocity)^2/(area)$^{1/2}$
(f) Energy = (mass) (speed) (area)$^{1/2}$
(g) Energy = (pressure) (volume)
(h) Power = (mass) (velocity)/(time)
(i) Time = (area)$^{1/2}$/(velocity)

ICA 7–35

Identify the following quantities through the use of fundamental dimensions. Choose from the multiple list shown below:

(a) Acceleration   (d) Power
(b) Energy   (e) Pressure
(c) Force   (f) Velocity

Quantity
(a) mgH where: m = mass [kg] g = gravity [m/s^2] H = height [m]
(b) $P/(mg)$ where: m = mass [kg] g = gravity [m/s^2] P = power [W]
(c) ρQgH where: ρ = density [kg/m^3] Q = volumetric flowrate [m^3/s] g = gravity [m/s^2] H = height [m]
(d) $\sqrt{\dfrac{E}{H_\rho}}$ where: ρ = density [kg/m^3] E = energy [J] H = height [m]
(e) mgv where: m = mass [kg] g = gravity [m/s^2] v = velocity [m/s]
(f) nRT where: n = amount [mol] R = ideal gas constant [atm L/(mol K)] T = temperature [K]
(g) PV where: P = pressure [Pa] V = volume [m^3]

CHAPTER 7 REVIEW QUESTIONS

1. The Whos Horton heard down in Who-ville love basketball. A regulation Who-ville basketball court is 6 picometers by 10 picometers. What is the area of a regulation Who-ville basketball court in units of square nanometers?
2. The largest hailstone is the United States was 44.5 centimeters in circumference in Coffeyville, Kansas. What is the diameter of the hailstone in units of inches?
3. The largest hailstone is the United States was 44.5 centimeters in circumference in Coffeyville, Kansas. What is the volume of the hailstone in units of liters?
4. How large a surface area in units of square feet will 1 gallon of paint cover if we apply a coat of paint that is 0.1 centimeter thick?
5. How large a surface area in units of square feet will 1 gallon of paint cover if we apply a coat of paint that is 0.1 inches thick?
6. An unmanned X-43A scramjet test vehicle has achieved a maximum speed of Mach number = 9.68 in a test flight over the Pacific Ocean. Mach number is defined as the speed of an object divided by the speed of sound. Assuming the speed of sound is 343 meters per second, what is this record speed expressed in units of miles per hour?
7. One of the National Academy of Engineering Grand Challenges for Engineering is **Provide Access to Clean Water.** Only 5% of water is used for households—the majority is used for agriculture and industry. It takes 240 gallons of water to produce one pound of rice. How many liters of water are needed to produce one kilogram of rice?
8. One of the National Academy of Engineering Grand Challenges for Engineering is **Provide Access to Clean Water.** Only 5% of water is used for households—the majority is used for agriculture and industry. It takes 1,680 gallons of water to produce one pound of grain-fed beef. How many cubic feet of water are needed to produce one kilogram of beef?
9. One of the National Academy of Engineering Grand Challenges for Engineering is **Provide Access to Clean Water.** Only 5% of water is used for households—the majority is used for agriculture and industry. It is estimated that 528 gallons of water are required to produce food for one person for one day. How many liters per year are required to feed one person?
10. A common unit of volume for large water bodies is acre-foot, which is the product of the area of 1 acre multiplied by a depth of 1 foot. If a lake contains 43 million cubic feet of water, what is the volume of the lake expressed in units of acre-foot?
11. New plastic fuel tanks for cars can be molded to many shapes, an advantage over the current metal tanks, allowing manufacturers to increase the tank capacity from 77 liters to 82 liters. What is this increase in gallons?
12. If a liquid evaporates at a rate of 50 kilograms per minute, what is this evaporation rate in units of pounds-mass per second?
13. If a liquid evaporates at a rate of 50 kilograms per minute, what is this evaporation rate in units of slugs per hour?
14. If a liquid evaporates at a rate of 50 kilograms per minute, what is this evaporation rate in units of grams per second?
15. If a pump moves water at 70 gallons per minute, what is the volumetric flow rate in units of cubic inches per second?
16. If a pump moves water at 70 gallons per minute, what is the volumetric flow rate in units of cubic feet per hour?
17. If a pump moves water at 70 gallons per minute, what is the volumetric flow rate in units of liters per day?
18. In an attempt to convert the United States to the metric system, a proposal is introduced to force all car manufacturers to report engine power in units of kilowatts. Convert a 250 horsepower motor rating into kilowatts.
19. The oxgang is unit of area equal to 20 acres. Express an area of 12 oxgangs in units of square meters.

20. The distance travelled in an experimental spacecraft depends on several parameters:
    - The initial position from the starting point: x_0
    - The initial velocity: v_i
    - The rate of acceleration: a
    - The time of travel: t

    The equation that governs the location of the spacecraft is $x = x_0 + v_i t + 1/2\, at^2$.

      If an experimental spacecraft has a head start of 0.3 miles from the starting point, has an initial speed of 50 miles per hour, and accelerates at a constant rate of 10 feet per second squared, how far is it from the starting point after 1.5 hours? Express your answer in units of feet.

21. We know a speed boat can travel at 30 knots. How long (in minutes) will it take to cross the Chesapeake Bay at a place where the bay is 24 miles across? 1 knot = 1 nautical mile per hour; 1 nautical mile = 6,076 feet.

22. In an effort to modernize the United States interstate system, the Department of Transportation proposes to change speed limits from miles per hour to "flashes." A flash is equal to 10 feet per second. On a car speedometer, what will the new range be in units of "flashes" if the old scale was set to a maximum of 120 miles per hour?

23. In many engineering uses, the value of "g," the acceleration due to gravity, is taken as a constant. However, g is actually dependent upon the distance from the center of the Earth. A more accurate expression for g is:

$$g = g_0 \left(\frac{R_e}{R_e + A} \right)^2$$

    Here, g_0 is the acceleration of gravity at the surface of the Earth, A is the altitude, and R_e is the radius of the Earth, approximately 6,380 kilometers. What is the value of g at an altitude of 20 miles in units of meters per second squared?

24. In many engineering uses, the value of "g," the acceleration due to gravity, is taken as a constant. However, g is actually dependent upon the distance from the center of the Earth. A more accurate expression for g is:

$$g = g_0 \left(\frac{R_e}{R_e + A} \right)^2$$

    Here, g_0 is the acceleration of gravity at the surface of the Earth, A is the altitude, and R_e is the radius of the Earth, approximately 6,380 kilometers. If the value of g is 9 meters per second squared, what is the altitude in units of miles?

25. The Units Society Empire (USE) had defined the following set of "new" units: 1 foot = 10 toes. Convert 45 toes to units of meters.

26. The Units Society Empire (USE) had defined the following set of "new" units: 1 mile = 50 yonders. Convert 500 yards to units of yonders.

27. The Units Society Empire (USE) had defined the following set of "new" units: 1 leap = 4 years. Convert 64 leaps to units of months.

28. The Units Society Empire (USE) had defined the following set of "new" units:

Length	1 car = 20 feet
Time	1 class = 50 minutes

    Determine X in the following expression: speed limit, 60 miles per hour = X cars per class.

29. The Units Society Empire (USE) had defined the following set of "new" units:

Length	1 stride = 1.5 meters
Time	1 blink = 0.3 second

    Determine X in the following expression: Boeing 747 cruising speed, 550 miles per hour = X strides per blink.

30. The Units Society Empire (USE) had defined the following set of "new" units:

Length   1 stride = 1.5 meters
Time   1 blink = 0.3 second
Mass   1 heavy = 5 kilograms

Determine X in the following expression: force, 1 newton = X heavy stride per blink squared.

31. The Units Society Empire (USE) had defined the following set of "new" units:

Length   1 car = 20 feet
Time   1 class = 50 minutes
Mass   1 light = 2 pound-mass

Determine X in the following expression: force, 1 pound-force = X light car per class squared.

32. A box has a volume of 10 gallons. If two sides of the box measure 2.4 meters × 2.4 feet, what is the length of the third side of the box in units of inches?

33. We turn on our garden hose and point it straight up. It seems reasonable to assume that the height (H) to which the jet of water rises depends on the initial velocity of the water (v_0) and the acceleration due to gravity (g) as expressed by the relationship

$$H = K\frac{v_0^2}{g}$$

The constant (K) is unitless. If the value of K is 25, what initial velocity, in units of meters per second, will give a water height of 0.5 meters?

CHAPTER 8
UNIVERSAL UNITS

In Chapter 7, the concepts of derived dimensions and units were introduced. Five of the most common named units were given in Table 7-5, which is so critical it is repeated here as Table 8-1. Recall that numerous common derived dimensions do not have a corresponding derived SI unit. For example, there is no named SI unit for the derived dimension velocity as there is for force (newton) or electrical resistance (ohm).

The conversion table inside the front cover of this book groups unit conversion factors by dimension. Several fundamental dimensions, such as length and time, were previously discussed in Chapter 7. The remaining derived dimensions shown in the table are discussed below, such as force, along with several named derived dimensions that do not have corresponding simple unit conversions, such as density.

Table 8-1 Common derived units in the SI system

Dimension	SI Unit	Base SI Units	Derived from
Force (F)	newton [N]	$1\,\text{N} = 1\dfrac{\text{kg m}}{\text{s}^2}$	$F = ma$ Force = mass times acceleration
Energy (E)	joule [J]	$1\,\text{J} = 1\,\text{N m} = 1\dfrac{\text{kg m}^2}{\text{s}^2}$	$E = Fd$ Energy = force times distance
Power (P)	watt [W]	$1\,\text{W} = 1\dfrac{\text{J}}{\text{s}} = 1\dfrac{\text{kg m}^2}{\text{s}^3}$	$P = E/t$ Power = energy per time
Pressure (P)	pascal [Pa]	$1\,\text{Pa} = 1\dfrac{\text{N}}{\text{m}^2} = 1\dfrac{\text{kg}}{\text{m s}^2}$	$P = F/A$ Pressure = force per area
Voltage (V)	volt [V]	$1\,\text{V} = 1\dfrac{\text{W}}{\text{A}} = 1\dfrac{\text{kg m}^2}{\text{s}^3\,\text{A}}$	$V = P/I$ Voltage = power per current

8.1 FORCE

When you push a grocery cart, it moves. If you keep pushing, it keeps moving. The longer you push, the faster it goes; the velocity increases over time, meaning that it accelerates. If you push a full grocery cart that has a high mass, it does not speed up as much, meaning it accelerates less than a cart with low mass. Simply put, the acceleration (a) of a body depends on the force (F) exerted on it and its mass (m). This is a simple form of "Newton's second law of motion" and is usually written as $F = ma$.

Table 8-2 **Dimensions of force**

Quantity	Common Units	Exponents			
		M	L	T	Θ
Force	N	1	1	–2	0

The SI unit of force, the **newton** [N], is defined as the force required to accelerate a mass of one kilogram at a rate of one meter per second squared (see Table 8-2). It is named for Sir Isaac Newton (1643–1727). Newton's *Principia* is considered one of the world's greatest scientific writings, explaining the law of universal gravitation and the three laws of motion. Newton also developed the law of conservation of momentum, the law of cooling, and the reflecting telescope. He shares credit for the development of calculus with Gottfried Leibniz.

In the SI system, mass, length, and time are base units and force is a derived unit; force is found from combining mass, length, and time using Newton's second law. The SI system is called "coherent," because the derived unit is set at one by combing base units. The AES system is considered non-coherent as it uses units that do not work together in the same fashion as the SI units do. There are two uses of the term "pound" in the AES system, which occurred in common usage long before Newton discovered gravity. To distinguish mass in pounds and force in pounds, the unit of mass is given as pound-mass (lb_m) and the unit of force is given as pound-force (lb_f). One pound-force is the amount of force needed to accelerate one pound-mass at a rate of 32.2 feet per second squared. Since this relationship is not easy to remember or use in conversions, we will stick with SI units for problem solving, following the procedure discussed in Chapter 7.

● **EXAMPLE 8-1**

A professional archer is designing a new longbow with a full draw weight of 63 pounds-force [lb_f]. The draw weight is the amount of force needed to hold the bowstring at a given amount of draw, or the distance the string has been pulled back from the rest position. What is the full draw weight of this bow in units of newtons [N]?

Method	Steps
(1) Convert term	63 lb_f
(2) Apply conversion formula	1 N = 0.225 lb_f
(3) Make a fraction	$\dfrac{63\ lb_f}{} \bigg| \dfrac{1\ N}{0.225\ lb_f}$
(4) Multiply	
(5) Cancel, calculate, be reasonable	280 N

8.2 WEIGHT

The **mass** of an object is a fundamental dimension. Mass is a quantitative measure of how much of an object there is, or in other words, how much matter it contains. The **weight** (*w*) of an object is a force equal to the mass of the object (*m*) times the acceleration of **gravity** (*g*).

While mass is independent of location in the universe, weight is dependent upon both mass and gravity (Table 8-3).

On the Earth, the pull of gravity is approximately 9.8 meters per second squared [m/s²]. On the moon, gravity is approximately one-sixth this value, or 1.6 m/s². A one kilogram [kg] object acted on by Earth's gravity would have a weight of 9.8 N, but on the moon it would have a weight of 1.6 N. Unless otherwise stated, assume all examples take place on the Earth.

Table 8-3 Dimensions of weight

Quantity	Common Units	Exponents			
		M	L	T	Θ
Weight	N	1	1	−2	0

DEVILISH DERIVATION

- **Mass of an object:** A quantitative measure of how much of an object there is.
- **Weight of an object:** A quantitative measure of the force exerted on the object due to gravity; we are concerned about the force between the Earth (subscript e) and a body on the Earth (or another planet).

Newton's law of universal gravitation

$$F = G\frac{mm_e}{R^2}$$

where:

   G is universal gravitational constant

$$G = 6.673 \times 10^{-11} (\text{N m}^2)/\text{kg}^2$$

   m is the mass
   R is the distance between the centers of mass of the two bodies

On the Earth, the distance between the center of a body and the center of the earth is approximately the radius of the Earth, R_e.

The mass of one of the bodies (Earth) is the mass of the Earth (with an "e" subscript). Rewrite the equation:

$$F = m\left[G\frac{m_e}{R_e^2}\right]$$

The quantity in square brackets is a constant (call it "g"). We call the force "the weight (w) of the body." So,

$$w = mg$$

This is the common equation that relates weight and mass. The value for g is calculated to be 9.8 meters per second squared [m/s²], or 32.2 feet per second squared [ft/s²]. Note that g has the units of acceleration.

● EXAMPLE 8-2

What is the weight of a 225-kilogram [kg] bag of birdseed in units of newtons [N]?

Step One: Convert to Base SI Units	
No conversion necessary	

Step Two: Calculate	
Method	**Steps**
(1) Determine appropriate equation	$w = mg$
(2) Insert known quantities	$w = \dfrac{225 \text{ kg}}{} \dfrac{9.8 \text{ m}}{\text{s}^2}$
(3) Calculate, be reasonable	$w = 2{,}205 \dfrac{\text{kg m}}{\text{s}^2}$

This is apparently our final answer, but the units are puzzling. If the unit of force is the newton, and if this is a valid equation, then our final result for force should be newtons. If we consider the dimensions of force:

Quantity	Common Units	Exponents			
		M	**L**	**T**	**Θ**
Force	N	1	1	−2	0

A unit of force has dimensions F{=}ML/T², which in terms of base SI units would be F[=]kg m/s². As this term occurs so frequently it is given the special name "newton" (see Table 8-1). Anytime we see the term [kg m/s²], we know we are dealing with a force equal to a newton.

(3) Calculate, be reasonable	$w = 2{,}205 \dfrac{\text{kg m}}{\text{s}^2} \left| \dfrac{1 \text{ N}}{\frac{1 \text{ kg m}}{\text{s}^2}} \right. = 2{,}205 \text{ N}$

Step Three: Convert from Base SI Units to Desired Units	
No conversion necessary	

COMPREHENSION CHECK 8-1

The mass of the human brain is 1,360 grams. State the weight of the human brain in units of newtons on the Earth.

COMPREHENSION CHECK 8-2

The mass of the human brain is 1,360 grams. State the weight of the human brain in units of newtons on the moon. The gravity on the moon is 1.6 meters per second squared.

COMPREHENSION CHECK 8-3	What is the weight of a 5-kilogram bowling ball in units of pounds-force?

8.3 DENSITY

IMPORTANT CONCEPT

Density is shown as ρ

$\rho = m/V$

SI unit $= kg/m^3$

Specific weight is shown as γ

$\gamma = w/V$

SI unit $= N/m^3$

Density (ρ, Greek letter rho) is the mass of an object (m) divided by the volume the object occupies (V). Density should not be confused with weight—think of the old riddle: which weighs more, a pound of feathers or a pound of bricks? The answer is they both weigh the same amount, one pound, but the density of each is different. The bricks have a higher density than the feathers, since the same mass takes up less space.

Specific weight (γ, Greek letter gamma) is the weight of an object (w) divided by the volume the object occupies (V) (Table 8-4).

Table 8-4 Dimensions of density and specific weight

Quantity	Common Units	Exponents			
		M	L	T	(-)
Density	kg/m^3	1	−3	0	0
Specific weight	N/m^3	1	2	2	0

● **EXAMPLE 8-3**

The density of sugar is 1.61 grams per cubic centimeter [g/cm^3]. What is the density of sugar in units of pound-mass per cubic foot [lb_m/ft^3]?

NOTE

Upon conversion from units of grams per cubic centimeter to pound-mass per cubic foot, the answer should be ≈ 60 times larger.

Method	Steps
(1) Term to be converted	1.61 g/cm^3
(2) Conversion formula	
(3) Make fractions	$1.61\dfrac{g}{cm^3}\left\lvert\dfrac{2.205\ lb_m}{1,000\ g}\right\rvert\dfrac{1,000\ cm^3}{0.0353\ ft^3}$
(4) Multiply	
(5) Cancel, calculate, be reasonable	101 lb_m/ft^3

● **EXAMPLE 8-4**

The density of a biofuel blend is 0.72 grams per cubic centimeter [g/cm^3]. What is the density of the biofuel in units of kilograms per cubic meter [kg/m^3]?

NOTE

Upon conversion from units of grams per cubic centimeter to kilograms per cubic meter, the answer should be 1,000 times larger.

Method	Steps
(1) Term to be converted	0.72 g/cm^3
(2) Conversion formula	
(3) Make fractions	$0.72\dfrac{g}{cm^3}\left\lvert\dfrac{1\ kg}{1,000\ g}\right\rvert\dfrac{(100\ cm)^3}{1\ m^3}$
(4) Multiply	
(5) Cancel, calculate, be reasonable	720 kg/m^3

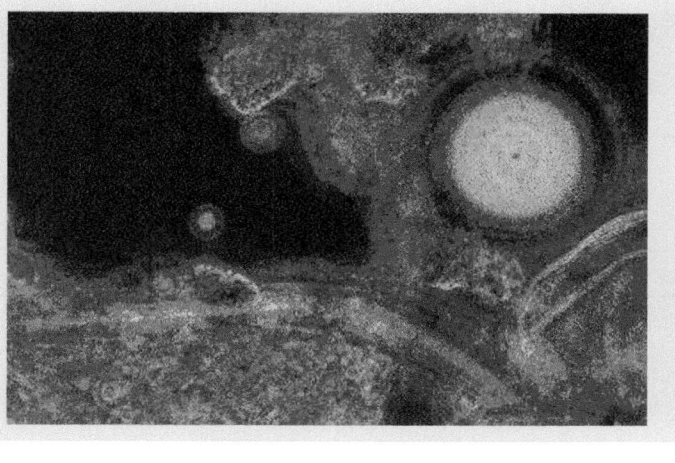

A vast array of valuable compounds can be formed by microbial cultures. Oil produced by the fungi *Pythium irregulare* can be extracted and used for biofuels or pharmaceutical compounds. Biosystems engineers culture the microorganism, design the bioreactor, and extract the valuable compounds using sustainable, ecoprocessing techniques.

Photo courtesy of C. Drapcho

● EXAMPLE 8-5

What is the weight of water, in units of pounds-force [lb_f], in a 55-gallon drum completely full? Assume the density of water to be 1 gram per cubic centimeter. Ignore the weight of the drum.

Step One: Convert to Base SI Units		
Method	**Steps**	
(1) Term to be converted	55 gal	1 g/cm^3
(2) Conversion formula (3) Make fractions (4) Multiply	$\dfrac{55 \text{ gal}}{} \left\| \dfrac{1{,}000 \text{ cm}^3}{0.264 \text{ gal}} \right\| \dfrac{1 \text{ m}^3}{100^3 \text{ cm}^3}$	$\dfrac{1 \text{ g}}{\text{cm}^3} \left\| \dfrac{1 \text{ kg}}{1{,}000 \text{ g}} \right\| \dfrac{100^3 \text{ cm}^3}{1 \text{ m}^3}$
(5) Cancel, calculate, be reasonable	0.208 m^3	1,000 kg/m^3
Step Two: Calculate		
Method	**Steps**	
(1) Determine appropriate equation	$w = mg$	
(2) Insert known quantities	$w = \dfrac{m}{} \left\| \dfrac{9.8 \text{ m}}{\text{s}^2} \right.$	
For Unknown Quantities, Repeat the Process		
Method	**Steps**	
(1) Determine appropriate equation	$m = \rho V$	
(2) Insert known quantities	$m = \dfrac{1{,}000 \text{ kg}}{\text{m}^3} \left\| 0.208 \text{ m}^3 \right.$	
(3) Calculate, be reasonable	$m = 208 \text{ kg}$	
(2) Insert known quantities	$w = \dfrac{208 \text{ kg}}{} \left\| \dfrac{9.8 \text{ m}}{\text{s}^2} \right.$	
(3) Calculate, be reasonable	$w = 2{,}038 \dfrac{\text{kg m}}{\text{s}^2} \left\| \dfrac{1 \text{ N}}{\frac{1 \text{ kg m}}{\text{s}^2}} \right. = 2{,}038 \text{ N}$	

Step Three: Convert from Base SI Units to Desired Units	
Method	**Steps**
(1) Term to be converted	2,038 N
(2) Conversion formula	
(3) Make a fraction	$\dfrac{2{,}038 \text{ N}}{} \bigg| \dfrac{0.225 \text{ lb}_f}{1 \text{ N}}$
(4) Multiply	
(5) Cancel, calculate, be reasonable	460 lb$_f$

Specific Gravity

IMPORTANT CONCEPT

$$SG = \frac{\rho_{object}}{\rho_{water}}$$

In technical literature, density is rarely given; instead, the **specific gravity** is reported. The specific gravity (SG) of an object is a dimensionless ratio of the density of the object to the density of water (see Table 8-5). It is convenient to list density in this fashion so *any* unit system may be applied by our choice of the units of the density of water. The specific gravities of several common substances are listed in Table 8-6.

Table 8-5 Dimensions of specific gravity

Quantity	Common Units	Exponents			
		M	**L**	**T**	**Θ**
Specific gravity	–	0	0	0	0

IMPORTANT CONCEPT

Density of water

$= 1 \text{ g/cm}^3$

$= 1 \text{ kg/L}$

$= 1{,}000 \text{ kg/m}^3$

$= 62.4 \text{ lb}_m/\text{ft}^3$

$= 1.94 \text{ slug/ft}^3$

Table 8-6 Specific gravity values for common substances

Liquids	SG		Solids	SG
Acetone	0.785		Aluminum	2.70
Benzene	0.876		Baking soda	0.689
Citric acid	1.67		Brass	8.40–8.75
Gasoline	0.739		Concrete	2.30
Glycerin	1.26		Copper	8.96
Iodine	4.93		Gallium	5.91
Mercury	13.6		Gold	19.3
Mineral oil	0.900		Graphite	2.20
Olive oil	0.703		Iron	7.87
Propane	0.806		Lead	11.4
Sea water	1.03		Polyvinyl chloride (PVC)	1.38
Toluene	0.865		Silicon	2.33
Water	1.00		Zinc oxide	5.60

When calculating or considering specific gravities, it is helpful to keep in mind the range of values that you are likely to have.

The densest naturally occurring elements at normal temperature and pressure are osmium and iridium, both with a specific gravity close to 22.6. The *densest substances that a normal person is likely to encounter are platinum (SG = 21.5) and gold (SG = 19.3).* Thus, if you calculate a specific gravity to be higher than about 23, you have almost certainly made an error.

Most liquids are similar to water, with a specific gravity around 1. One notable exception is mercury, with a specific gravity of 13.

On the lower end of the scale, the *specific gravity of air is about 0.001*, whereas hydrogen has a specific gravity of slightly less than 0.0001.

Therefore, if you get a specific gravity value less than about 10^{-4}, you need to check your work very carefully.

● **EXAMPLE 8-6**

The specific gravity of butane is 0.599. What is the density of butane in units of kilograms per cubic meter?

Step One: Convert to Base SI Units	
No conversion needed	
Step Two: Calculate	
Method	**Steps**
(1) Determine appropriate equation	$\rho_{object} = (SG)(\rho_{water})$
(2) Insert known quantities	$\rho_{object} = (0.599)\left(1{,}000 \dfrac{kg}{m^3}\right)$
(3) Calculate, be reasonable	$\rho_{object} = 599 \dfrac{kg}{m^3}$
Step Three: Convert from Base SI Units to Desired Units	
No conversion needed	

● **EXAMPLE 8-7**

Mercury has a specific gravity of 13.6. What is the density of mercury in units of slugs per cubic foot?

Step One: Convert to Base SI Units	
No conversion needed	
Step Two: Calculate	
Method	**Steps**
(1) Determine appropriate equation	$\rho_{object} = (SG)(\rho_{water})$
(2) Insert known quantities	$\rho_{object} = (13.6)\left(62.4 \dfrac{lb_m}{ft^3}\right)$
(3) Calculate, be reasonable	$\rho_{object} = 848.64 \dfrac{lb_m}{ft^3}$

Step Three: Convert from Base SI Units to Desired Units	
Method	**Steps**
(1) Term to be converted	848.64 lb_m/ft^3
(2) Conversion formula	
(3) Make a fraction	$\dfrac{848.64\ lb_m}{ft^3} \left\lvert \dfrac{1\ slug}{32.2\ lb_m} \right.$
(4) Multiply	
(5) Cancel, calculate, be reasonable	26.4 slug/ft^3

COMPREHENSION CHECK 8-4

Convert 50 grams per cubic centimeter into units of pounds-mass per cubic foot.

COMPREHENSION CHECK 8-5

A 75-gram cylindrical rod is measured to be 10 centimeters long and 2.5 centimeters in diameter. What is the specific gravity of the material?

8.4 AMOUNT

Some things are really very large and some are very small. Stellar distances are so large that it becomes inconvenient to report values such as 235 trillion miles, or 6.4×10^{21} feet when we are interested in the distance between two stars or two galaxies. To make things better, we use a new unit of length that itself is large—the distance that light goes in a year; this is a very long way, 3.1×10^{16} feet. As a result, we do not have to say that the distance between two stars is 620,000,000,000,000,000 feet, we can just say that they are 2 light-years apart.

This same logic holds when we want to discuss very small things such as molecules or atoms. Most often we use a constant that has been named after Amedeo Avogadro, an Italian scientist (1777–1856) who first proposed the idea of a fixed ratio between the amount of substance and the number of elementary particles. The Avogadro constant has a value of 6.022×10^{23} particles per mole. If we have 12 of something, we call it a dozen. If we have 20, it is a score. If we have 6.022×10^{23} of anything, we have a mole. If we have 6.022×10^{23} baseballs, we have a mole of baseballs. If we have 6.022×10^{23} elephants, we have a mole of elephants, and if we have 6.022×10^{23} molecules, we have a mole of molecules. Of course, the mole is never used to define amounts of macroscopic things like elephants or baseballs, being relegated to the realm of the extremely tiny. In the paragraphs below we will see how this rather odd value originated and how this concept simplifies our calculations.

The mass of a nucleon (neutron or proton) is about 1.66×10^{-24} grams. To avoid having to use such tiny numeric values when dealing with nucleons, physicists defined the **atomic mass unit** [amu] to be approximately the mass of one nucleon. Technically, it is defined as one-twelfth of the mass of a carbon twelve atom. In other words, 1 amu = 1.66×10^{-24} g. The symbol "u" is often used for amu, which is also known as a **Dalton** [Da].

If there is $(1.66 \times 10^{-24}$ g)/(1 amu), then there is (1 amu)/$(1.66 \times 10^{-24}$ g). Dividing this out gives 6.022×10^{23} amu/g. This numeric value is used to define the **mole** [mol]. One mole of a substance (usually an element or compound) contains exactly 6.022×10^{23} fundamental units (atoms or molecules) of that substance. In other words, there are 6.022×10^{23} fundamental units per mole. This is often written as

$$N_A = 6.022 \times 10^{23} \text{ mol}^{-1}$$

As mentioned above, this is called Avogadro's constant or **Avogadro's number**, symbolized by N_A. So why is this important? Consider combining hydrogen and oxygen to get water (H_2O). We need twice as many atoms of hydrogen as atoms of oxygen for this reaction; thus, for every mole of oxygen, we need two moles of hydrogen, since one mole of anything contains the same number of fundamental units, atoms in this case.

The problem is that it is difficult to measure a substance directly in moles, but it is easy to measure its mass. *Avogadro's number affords a conversion path between moles and mass.* Consider hydrogen and oxygen in the above. The atomic mass of an atom in **atomic mass units** [amu] is approximately equal to the number of nucleons it contains. Hydrogen contains one proton, and thus has an atomic mass of 1 amu. We can also say that there is 1 amu per hydrogen atom. Oxygen has an atomic mass of 16; thus, there are 16 amu per oxygen atom. Since atomic mass refers to an individual specific atom, the term **atomic weight** is used, representing the average value of all isotopes of the element. This is the value commonly listed on periodic tables.

Let us use this information, along with Avogadro's number, to determine the mass of one mole of each of these two elements.

$$\text{Hydrogen:} \quad \frac{1 \text{ amu}}{\text{H atom}} \left| \frac{1 \text{ g}}{6.022 \times 10^{23} \text{ amu}} \right| \frac{6.022 \times 10^{23} \text{atom}}{1 \text{ mol}} = \frac{1 \text{ g}}{1 \text{ mol H}}$$

$$\text{Oxygen:} \quad \frac{16 \text{ amu}}{\text{O atom}} \left| \frac{1 \text{ g}}{6.022 \times 10^{23} \text{ amu}} \right| \frac{6.022 \times 10^{23} \text{ atom}}{1 \text{ mol}} = \frac{16 \text{ g}}{1 \text{ mol O}}$$

The numerical value for the atomic mass of a substance is the same as the number of grams in one mole of that substance, often called the **molar mass**.

Atomic weight = molar mass

Avogadro's number is the link between the two. Hydrogen has a molar mass of 1 gram per mole; oxygen has a molar mass of 16 grams per mole.

When groups of atoms react together, they form molecules. Consider combining hydrogen and oxygen to get water (H_2O). Two atoms of hydrogen combine with one atom of oxygen, so 2 * 1 amu H + 16 amu O = 18 amu H_2O. The **molecular mass** of water is 18 amu. By an extension of the example above, we can also state that one mole of water has a mass of 18 grams, called the **formula weight**.

molecular weight = formula weight

The difference between these ideas is summarized in Table 8-7.

This text assumes that you have been exposed to these ideas in an introductory chemistry class and so does not cover them in any detail. In all problems presented, you will be given the atomic weight of the elements or the formula weight of the molecule, depending on the question asked. This topic is briefly introduced because Avogadro's number (N_A) is important in the relationship between several constants, including the following:

- The gas constant (R [=] J/(mol K)) and the Boltzmann constant (k [=] J/K), which relates energy to temperature: $R = kN_A$.

- The elementary charge (e [=] C) and the Faraday constant (F [=] C/mol), which is the electric charge contained in one mole of electrons: $F = eN_A$.
- An electron volt [eV] is a unit of energy describing the amount of energy gained by one electron accelerating through an electrostatic potential difference of one volt: $1\ eV = 1.602 \times 10^{-19}$ J.

Table 8-7 Definitions of "amount" of substance

The quantity . . .	measures the . . .	in units of . . .	and is found by . . .
Atomic mass	Mass of one atom of an individual isotope of an element	[amu]	Direct laboratory measurement
Atomic weight	Average mass of all isotopes of an element	[amu]	Listed on Periodic Table
Molar mass	Mass of one mole of the atom	[g/mol]	Listed on Periodic Table
Molecular mass or molecular weight	Sum of average weight of isotopes in molecule	[amu]	Combining atomic weights of individual atoms represented in the molecule
Formula weight	Mass of one mole of the molecule	[g/mol]	Combining molar mass of individual atoms represented in the molecule

● EXAMPLE 8-8

Let us return to the problem of combining hydrogen and oxygen to get water. Assume you have 50 grams of oxygen with which you want to combine the proper mass of hydrogen to convert it completely to water. The atomic weight of hydrogen is 1 and the atomic weight of oxygen is 16.

First determine how many moles of oxygen are present.

$$\frac{50\ g\ O}{} \left| \frac{1\ mol\ O}{16\ g\ O} \right. = 3.125\ mol\ O$$

We need twice as many moles of hydrogen as oxygen (H_2O), so we need 6.25 moles of hydrogen. Converting to mass gives

$$\frac{6.25\ mol\ H}{} \left| \frac{1\ g\ H}{1\ mol\ H} \right. = 6.25\ g\ H$$

● EXAMPLE 8-9

Acetylsalicylic acid (aspirin) has the chemical formula $C_9H_8O_4$. How many moles of aspirin are in a 1-gram dose? Use the following facts:

- Atomic weight of carbon = 12
- Atomic weight of hydrogen = 1
- Atomic weight of oxygen = 16

First, determine how many grams are in 1 mole of aspirin (determine formula weight).

$$\text{FW of aspirin} = \left[\frac{12\frac{g}{mole}}{1 \text{ molecule C}}\Big|9 \text{ C molecules}\right] + \left[\frac{1\frac{g}{mole}}{1 \text{ molecule H}}\Big|8 \text{ H molecules}\right]$$

$$+ \left[\frac{16\frac{g}{mole}}{1 \text{ molecule O}}\Big|4 \text{ O molecules}\right] = 180\frac{g}{mole}$$

Finally, convert to moles per dose.

$$\frac{1 \text{ g aspirin}}{\text{dose}}\Big|\frac{1 \text{ mol aspirin}}{180 \text{ g aspirin}} = 5.56 \times 10^{-3}\frac{\text{mol aspirin}}{\text{dose}}$$

● **EXAMPLE 8-10**

Many gases exist as diatomic compounds in nature, meaning two of the atoms are attached to form a molecule. Hydrogen, oxygen, and nitrogen all exist in a gaseous diatomic state under standard conditions.

Assume there are 100 grams of nitrogen gas in a container. How many moles of nitrogen (N_2) are in the container? Atomic weight of nitrogen = 14.

First, determine how many grams are in 1 mole of nitrogen (determine the formula weight).

$$\text{FW of } N_2 = \frac{14\frac{g}{mol}}{1 \text{ mol N}}\Big|2 \text{ mol N} = 28\frac{g}{mol}$$

Next, convert mass to moles.

$$\frac{100 \text{ grams of } N_2}{}\Big|\frac{\text{mole}}{28 \text{ gram}} = 3.57 \text{ moles } N_2$$

8.5 TEMPERATURE

Temperature was originally conceived as a description of energy: heat (thermal energy) flows spontaneously from "hot" to "cold." But how hot is "hot"? The thermometer was devised as a way to measure the "hotness" of an object. As an object gets warmer, it usually expands. In a thermometer, a temperature is a level of hotness that corresponds to the length of the liquid in the tube. As the liquid gets warmer, it expands and moves up the tube. To give temperature a quantitative meaning, numerous temperature scales have been developed.

Many scientists, including Isaac Newton, have proposed temperature scales. Two scales were originally developed about the same time—**Fahrenheit** [°F] and **Celsius** [°C]—and have become widely accepted in laymen use. These are the most frequently used temperature scales by the general public. Gabriel Fahrenheit (1686–1736), a German physicist and engineer, developed the Fahrenheit scale in 1708. Anders Celsius (1701–1744), a Swedish astronomer, developed the Celsius scale in 1742. The properties of each scale are in Table 8-8.

You may wonder why the Celsius scale seems so reasonable, and the Fahrenheit scale so random. Actually, Mr. Fahrenheit was just as reasonable as Mr. Celsius. Mr. Celsius set the freezing point of water to be 0 and the boiling point to be 100. Mr. Fahrenheit took as 0 a freezing mixture of salt and ice, and as 100 body temperature. With this scale, it just so happens that the freezing and boiling points of water work out to be odd numbers.

Table 8-8 Properties of water

Scale	Freezing Point	Boiling Point	Divisions Between Freezing and Boiling
Fahrenheit [°F]	32	212	180
Celsius [°C]	0	100	100
Kelvin [K]	273	373	100
Rankine [°R]	492	672	180

Some units can cause confusion in conversion. One of those is temperature. One reason for this is that we use temperature in two different ways: (1) reporting an actual temperature value and (2) discussing the way a change in temperature affects a material property. To clarify, we resort to examples.

Conversion Between Temperature Values

IMPORTANT CONCEPT

When actual temperature readings are converted:

$$\frac{T[°F] - 32}{180} = \frac{T[°C] - 0}{100}$$

$$T[K] = T[°C] + 273$$

$$T[°R] = T[°F] + 460$$

When an actual temperature reading is reported, such as "the temperature in this room is 70°F," how do we convert from one temperature unit to another? The scales have different zero points, so they cannot be converted with a single conversion factor as done previously but require a conversion formula. Most of you are familiar with the conversion between Fahrenheit and Celsius, but this equation is cumbersome to remember.

$$T[°F] = \frac{9}{5} T[°C] + 32$$

Let us imagine we have two thermometers, one with the Fahrenheit scale and the other with the Celsius scale. We set two thermometers side by side so that the freezing point and the boiling point of water are at the same location on both thermometers. We are interested in the relationship between these two scales. From this figure we see that the fraction of the distance from the freezing point to the boiling point in both scales is the same. This means that we can write

$$\frac{T[°F] - 32}{212 - 32} = \frac{T[°C] - 0}{100 - 0}$$

This relationship is really all we need to know to relate a temperature in degrees Fahrenheit to one in degrees Celsius. You can easily do the algebra to convert from Fahrenheit to Celsius, or vice versa. By remembering this form, you do not have to remember if the conversion is 9/5 or 5/9, or to add or subtract 32. This formula is determined by the method of interpolation.

There are numerous other temperature scales, but two are worth mentioning: **kelvin** [K] and **degrees rankine** [°R]. The kelvin scale is named for First Baron William Thomson Kelvin (1824–1907), an English mathematician and physicist. Kelvin first proposed the idea of "infinite cold," or absolute zero, in 1848, using the Celsius scale for comparison. The Rankine scale is named for William J. M. Rankine (1820–1872), a Scottish engineer and physicist, who proposed an analogy to the kelvin scale, using the Fahrenheit scale. Both men made significant contributions to the field of thermodynamics.

The kelvin and Rankine scales are "absolute," which means that at absolute zero, the temperature at which molecules have minimum possible motion, the temperature is zero. Absolute temperature scales therefore have no negative values. In the kelvin scale, the degree sign is not used; it is simply referred to as "kelvin," not "degrees kelvin." It is the base SI unit for temperature and the most frequently used temperature unit in the scientific community.

IMPORTANT CONCEPT

Absolute temperature scales are never negative.

● **EXAMPLE 8-11**

The hottest temperature in the United States ever recorded by the National Weather Service, 56.7 degrees Celsius [°C], occurred in Death Valley, California, on July 10, 1913. State this value in units of degrees Fahrenheit [°F].

Step One: Convert to Base SI Units	
No conversion needed	
Step Two: Calculate	
Method	**Steps**
(1) Determine appropriate equation	$\dfrac{T[°F] - 32}{212 - 32} = \dfrac{T[°C] - 0}{100 - 0}$
(2) Insert known quantities	$\dfrac{T[°F] - 32}{180} = \dfrac{56.7}{100}$
(3) Calculate, be reasonable	$T = 134°F$
Step Three: Convert from Base SI Units to Desired Units	
No conversion needed	

Conversions Involving Temperature Within a Material Property

IMPORTANT CONCEPT

When properties that contain temperature are converted:

$$\frac{1°C}{1.8°F} \quad \frac{1K}{1°C} \quad \frac{1°R}{1°F}$$

For this type of conversion, we read the units under consideration as "*per* degree Fahrenheit," with the clue being the word "*per.*"

When considering how a change in temperature affects a material property, we use a scalar conversion factor. In general, we encounter this in sets of units relating to the property of the material; for example, the units of the thermal conductivity are given by W/m K, which is read as "watts per meter kelvin." When this is the case, we are referring to the size of the degree, not the actual temperature.

To find this relationship, remember that between the freezing point and the boiling point of pure water, the Celsius scale contains 100 divisions, whereas the Fahrenheit scale contains 180 divisions. The conversion factor between Celsius and Fahrenheit is $100°C \equiv 180°F$, or $1°C \equiv 1.8°F$.

● **EXAMPLE 8-12**

The specific heat (C_p) is the ability of an object to store heat. Specific heat is a material property, and values are available in technical literature. The specific heat of copper is 0.385 J/(g °C), which is read as "joules per gram degree Celsius." Convert this to units of J/(lb$_m$°F), which reads "joules per pound-mass degree Fahrenheit."

Method	Steps
(1) Term to be converted	$0.385 \dfrac{J}{g\,°C}$
(2) Conversion formula	
(3) Make a fraction	$\dfrac{0.385\ J}{g\,°C} \left\lvert \dfrac{1{,}000\ g}{2.205\ lb_m} \right\rvert \dfrac{1°C}{1.8°F}$
(4) Multiply	
(5) Cancel, calculate, be reasonable	$97 \dfrac{J}{lb_m\,°F}$

A note of clarification about the term "PER": When reading the sentence: "Gravity on earth is commonly assumed to be 9.8 meters per second squared," there is often little confusion in translating the words to symbols: $g = 9.8$ m/s^2. For a more complex unit however, this can present a challenge. For example, the sentence "The thermal conductivity of aluminum is 237 calories per hour meter degree Celsius," can be confusing because it can be interpreted as:

$$k = 237 \frac{cal}{h\,m\,°C} \quad \text{or} \quad k = 237 \frac{cal}{h}(m\,°C) \quad \text{or} \quad k = 237 \frac{cal}{h\,m}°C$$

Officially, according to SI rules, when writing out unit names anything following the word "per" appears in the denominator of the expression. This implies the first example listed is correct.

COMPREHENSION CHECK 8-6

The temperature of dry ice is –109.3 degrees Fahrenheit [°F]. Convert this temperature into units of kelvin [K].

COMPREHENSION CHECK 8-7

The specific heat capacity of copper is 0.09 British thermal units per pound-mass degree Fahrenheit [BTU/(lb$_m$ °F)]. Convert into units of British thermal units per gram kelvin $\left[\text{BTU}/(\text{g K})\right]$.

8.6 PRESSURE

IMPORTANT CONCEPT

Pressure = force/area

$Pa = \dfrac{N}{m^2}$

SI unit of pressure = Pascal

Pressure is defined as force acting over an area, where the force is perpendicular to the area. In SI units, a **pascal** [Pa] is the unit of pressure, defined as one newton of force acting on an area of one square meter (Table 8-9). The unit pascal is named after Blaise Pascal (1623–1662), a French mathematician and physicist who made great contributions to the study of fluids, pressure, and vacuums. His contributions with Pierre de Fermat on the theory of probability were the groundwork for calculus.

Table 8-9 **Dimensions of pressure**

Quantity	Common Units	Exponents			
		M	**L**	**T**	**Θ**
Pressure	Pa	1	−1	−2	0

● EXAMPLE 8-13

An automobile tire is pressurized to a 40 pound-force per square inch [psi or lb_f/in^2]. State this pressure in units of atmospheres [atm].

By examining the "Pressure" box in the conversion table on the inside front cover, we see that the following facts are available for use: 1 atm = 14.7 psi.

Method	Steps
(1) Term to be converted	40 psi
(2) Conversion formula	1 atm = 14.7 psi
(3) Make a fraction	$\dfrac{40\ psi}{}\ \dfrac{1\ atm}{14.7\ psi}$
(4) Multiply	
(5) Cancel, calculate, be reasonable	2.7 atm

PRESSURE

1 atm = 1.01325 bar
  = 33.9 ft H_2O
  = 29.92 in Hg
  = 760 mm Hg
  = 101,325 Pa
  = 14.7 psi

COMPREHENSION CHECK 8-8

If the pressure is 250 feet of water [ft H_2O], what is the pressure in units of inches of mercury [in Hg]?

In this chapter, we consider four forms of pressure, all involving fluids. The general term **fluid** applies to a gas, such as helium or air, or a liquid, such as water or honey.

■ **Atmospheric pressure**—the pressure created by the weight of air above us.
■ **Hydrostatic pressure**—the pressure exerted on a submerged object by the fluid in which it is immersed.
■ **Total pressure**—the combination of atmospheric and hydrostatic pressure.
■ **Gas pressure**—the pressure created by a gas inside a closed container.

Atmospheric Pressure

PRESSURE

1 atm ~ 14.7 psi ~ 101 kPa

Atmospheric pressure results from the weight of the air above us, which varies with both altitude and weather patterns. Standard atmospheric pressure is an average air pressure at sea level, defined as one atmosphere [atm], and is approximately equal to 14.7 pound-force per square inch [psi].

Pressure Measurement

When referring to the measurement of pressure, two types of reference points are commonly used.

Absolute pressure uses a perfect vacuum as a reference point. Most meteorological readings are given as absolute pressure, using units of atmospheres or bars.

Gauge pressure uses the local atmospheric pressure as a reference point. Note that local atmospheric pressure is generally *not* standard atmospheric pressure at sea level. Measurements such as tire pressure and blood pressure are given as gauge pressure.

Absolute pressures are distinguished by an "a" after the pressure unit, such as "psia" to signify "pound-force per square inch absolute." Gauge pressure readings are distinguished by a "g" after the pressure unit, such as "psig" to signify "pound-force per square inch gauge." When using instrumentation to determine the pressure, be sure to note whether the device reads absolute or gauge pressure.

Gauge pressure, absolute pressure, and atmospheric pressure are related by

$$P_{absolute} = P_{gauge} + P_{atmospheric}$$

A few notes on absolute and gauge pressure. Except as otherwise noted, assume that local atmospheric pressure is 14.7 psi.

- 35 psig = 49.7 psia (35 psig + 14.7 psi)
- Using gauge pressure, local atmospheric pressure would be 0 psig, although this would seldom be used.
- If a gauge pressure being measured is less than the local atmospheric pressure, this is usually referred to as **vacuum pressure**, and the negative sign is dropped. Thus, a perfect vacuum created at sea level on the Earth would read about 14.7 psig vacuum pressure. (A perfect vacuum is 0 psia, and thus is about 14.7 psi less than atmospheric pressure.)
- A vacuum pressure of 10 psig is an absolute pressure of 4.7 psia (14.7 psi − 10 psi).
- To illustrate the effect of local atmospheric pressure, consider the following scenario. You fill your automobile's tires to 35 psig on the shore of the Pacific Ocean in Peru, and then drive to Lake Titicaca on the Bolivian border at about 12,500 feet above sea level. Your tire pressure now reads about 40 psig due to the decreased atmospheric pressure (9.5 psia at 12,500 feet altitude versus 14.7 psia at sea level).

Occasionally in industry, it may be helpful to use a point of reference other than atmospheric pressure. For these specific applications, pressure may be discussed in terms of **differential pressure**, distinguished by a "d" after the pressure unit, such as "psid."

Hydrostatic Pressure

Hydrostatic pressure (P_{hydro}) results from the weight of a liquid or gas pushing on an object. *Remember, weight is a force!* A simple way to determine this is to consider a cylinder with a cross-sectional area (A) filled with a liquid of density ρ.

The pressure (P) at the bottom of the container can be found by **Pascal's law**, named after (once again) Blaise Pascal. Pascal's law states the hydrostatic pressure of a fluid is equal to the force of the fluid acting over an area.

IMPORTANT CONCEPT

How does the term $\rho g H$ equal a pressure?

$$P_{hydro} = \frac{F}{A}$$

Weight is a force

$$= \frac{w}{A}$$

$$w = mg \qquad = \frac{mg}{A}$$

$$\rho = m/V \qquad = \frac{\rho V g}{A}$$

$$V = AH \qquad = \frac{\rho(AH)g}{A}$$

$$P_{hydro} = \rho g H$$

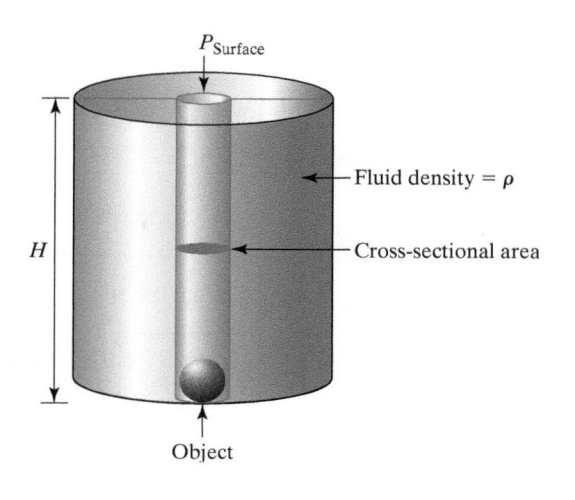

$P_{Surface}$

Fluid density $= \rho$

Cross-sectional area

H

Object

Recreational scuba diving takes place at depths between 0 and 20 meters. At deeper depths, additional training is usually required because of the increased risk of narcosis, a state similar to alcohol intoxication. The relationship between the depth and the level of narcosis is called the "Martini Effect," as it is said divers feel like they have drunk one martini for every 20 meters they descend.

Photo courtesy of E. Stephan

● **EXAMPLE 8-14**

We want to know the hydrostatic pressure in a lake at a depth of 20 feet in units of pascals.

For hydrostatic pressure, we need to know the density of the fluid in the lake. Since a density is not specified, we assume the density to be the standard density of water. We want all quantities in units of kilograms, meters, and seconds, so we use a density of 1,000 kilograms per cubic meter for water.

Step One: Convert to Base SI Units	
Method	**Steps**
(1) Term to be converted	20 ft
(2) Conversion formula	
(3) Make a fraction	$\dfrac{20\ ft}{} \bigg\vert \dfrac{1\ m}{3.28\ ft}$
(4) Multiply	
(5) Cancel, calculate, be reasonable	6.1 m

Step Two: Calculate	
Method	**Steps**
(1) Determine appropriate equation	$P_{hydro} = \rho g H$
(2) Insert known quantities	$P_{hydro} = \dfrac{1{,}000 \text{ kg}}{m^3} \left\| \dfrac{9.8 \text{ m}}{s^2} \right\| 6.1 \text{ m}$
(3) Calculate, be reasonable	$P_{hydro} = 59{,}760 \, \dfrac{kg}{m \, s^2}$

This is apparently our final answer, but the units are puzzling. If the units of pressure are pascals and if this is a valid equation, then our final result for pressure should be pascals. If we consider the dimensions of pressure:

		Exponents			
Quantity	**Common Units**	**M**	**L**	**T**	**Θ**
Pressure	Pa	1	−1	−2	0

A unit of pressure has dimensions, $P\{=\}M/(LT^2)$, which in terms of base SI units would be $P\left[=\right] kg/m \, s^2$. As this term occurs so frequently it is given the special name "Pascal." When we see this term, we know we are dealing with a pressure equal to a pascal.

(3) Calculate, be reasonable	$P_{hydro} = 59{,}760 \, \dfrac{kg}{m \, s^2} \left\| \dfrac{1 \text{ Pa}}{1 \, \frac{kg}{m \, s^2}} \right. = 59{,}760 \text{ Pa}$

Step Three: Convert from Base SI Units to Desired Units
No conversion needed

Total Pressure

We need to realize that Pascal's law is only a part of the story. Suppose we dive to a depth of 5 feet in a swimming pool and measure the pressure. Now we construct an enclosure over the pool and pressurize the air above the water surface to 3 atmospheres. When we dive back to the 5-foot depth, the pressure will have increased by 2 atmospheres.

Consequently, we conclude that total pressure at any depth in a fluid is the sum of hydrostatic pressure and pressure in the air above the fluid.

IMPORTANT CONCEPT

$P_{total} = P_{surface} + P_{hydro}$

$P_{total} = P_{surface} + \rho g H$

● **EXAMPLE 8-15**

When you dive to the bottom of a pool, at 12 feet under water, how much total pressure do you feel in units of atmospheres?

NOTE

A diver at 15 feet will feel a ½ atmosphere pressure increase.

A diver at 10 meters will feel a 1 atmosphere pressure increase.

Step One: Convert to Base SI Units	
Method	**Steps**
(1) Term to be converted	12 ft
(2) Conversion formula	
(3) Make a fraction	$\dfrac{12 \text{ ft}}{} \left\| \dfrac{1 \text{ m}}{3.28 \text{ ft}} \right.$
(4) Multiply	
(5) Cancel, calculate, be reasonable	3.66 m

For hydrostatic pressure, we need to know the density of the fluid in the pool. Since a density is not specified, we assume the density to be the standard density of water. We want all quantities in units of kilograms, meters, and seconds, so we use a density of 1,000 kilograms per cubic meter for water.

For total pressure, we need to know the surface pressure on top of the pool. Since a surface pressure is not specified, we assume the pressure to be 1 atmosphere. We want all quantities in units of kilograms, meters, and seconds, so we use a pressure of 101,325 pascals, or 101,325 kilograms per meter second squared.

Step Two: Calculate	
Method	**Steps**
(1) Determine appropriate equation	$P_{total} = P_{surface} + \rho g H$
(2) Insert known quantities	$P_{total} = \dfrac{101{,}325 \text{ kg}}{\text{m s}^2} + \dfrac{1{,}000 \text{ kg}}{\text{m}^3}\left\lvert\dfrac{9.8 \text{ m}}{\text{s}^2}\right\rvert 3.66 \text{ m}$
(3) Calculate, be reasonable	$P_{total} = 137{,}193\dfrac{\text{kg}}{\text{m s}^2}\left\lvert\dfrac{\text{Pa}}{\frac{\text{kg}}{\text{m s}^2}}\right. = 137{,}193 \text{ Pa}$

Step Three: Convert from Base SI Units to Desired Units	
Method	**Steps**
(1) Term to be converted	137,193 Pa
(2) Conversion formula	
(3) Make a fraction	$\dfrac{137{,}193 \text{ Pa}}{}\left\lvert\dfrac{1 \text{ atm}}{101{,}325 \text{ Pa}}\right.$
(4) Multiply	
(5) Cancel, calculate, be reasonable	1.35 atm

COMPREHENSION CHECK 8-9

An object is completely submerged in a liquid of density 0.75 grams per cubic centimeter at a depth of 3 meters. What is the total pressure on the object? State your answer in atmospheres.

NOTE

At an elevation of 3 miles, the pressure will be about half that at sea level. At an elevation of 10 miles, the pressure is about $\frac{1}{10}$ that at sea level.

Cakes and meats may require as much as ¼ more cooking time at elevations of 5,000 feet because of reduced pressure and lower boiling points.

8.7   GAS PRESSURE

IMPORTANT CONCEPT

Ideal Gas Law

$$PV = nRT$$

Only absolute temperature units (K or °R) can be used in the ideal gas equation.

NOTE

$$R = 8,314 \frac{Pa\,L}{mol\,K}$$
$$= 0.08206 \frac{atm\,L}{mol\,K}$$

Gas pressure results when gas molecules impact the inner walls of a sealed container. The **ideal gas law** relates the quantities of pressure (P), volume (V), temperature (T), and amount (n) of gas in a closed container:

$$PV = nRT$$

In this equation, R is a fundamental constant called the **gas constant**. It can have many different numerical values, depending on the units chosen for pressure, volume, temperature, and amount, just as a length has different numerical values, depending on whether feet or meters or miles is the unit being used. Scientists have defined an "ideal" gas as one where one mole [mol] of gas at a temperature of 273 kelvin [K] and a pressure of one atmosphere [atm] will occupy a volume of 22.4 liters [L]. Using these values to solve for the constant R yields

$$R = \frac{PV}{nT} = \frac{1\,[atm]\,22.4\,[L]}{1\,[mol]\,273\,[K]} = 0.08206 \frac{atm\,L}{mol\,K}$$

Note that we must *use absolute temperature units in the ideal gas equation.* We cannot begin with relative temperature units and then convert the final answer. Also, all pressure readings must be in absolute, not gauge, units.

In previous chapters, we have suggested a procedure for solving problems involving equations and unit conversions. For ideal gas law problems, we suggest a slightly different procedure.

Ideal Gas Law Procedure

1. Examine the units given in the problem statement. Choose a gas constant (R) that contains as many of the units given in the problem as possible.
2. If necessary, convert all parameters into units found in the gas constant (R) that you choose.
3. Solve the ideal gas law for the variable of interest.
4. Substitute values and perform all necessary calculations.
5. If necessary, convert your final answer to the required units and apply reasonableness.

● **EXAMPLE 8-16**

A container holds 1.43 moles of nitrogen (formula: N_2) at a pressure of 3.4 atmospheres and a temperature of 500 degrees Fahrenheit. What is the volume of the container in liters?

Method	Steps
(1) Choose ideal gas constant	Given units: mol, atm, °F, L Select R: $0.08206 \dfrac{atm\,L}{mol\,K}$
(2) Convert to units of chosen R	500°F = 533 K
(3) Solve for variable of interest	$V = \dfrac{nRT}{P}$
(4) Calculate	$V = \dfrac{1.43\,mol}{} \left\| \dfrac{0.08206\,atm\,L}{mol\,K} \right\| \dfrac{533\,K}{} \left\| \dfrac{}{3.4\,atm} \right.$
(5) Convert, be reasonable	$V = 18.4\,L$

● EXAMPLE 8-17

A container holds 1.25 moles of nitrogen (formula: N_2) at a pressure of 350 kilopascals and a temperature of 160 degrees Celsius. What is the volume of the container in liters?

Method	Steps
(1) Choose ideal gas constant	Given units: mol, Pa, °C, L Select R: $8{,}314 \dfrac{\text{Pa L}}{\text{mol K}}$
(2) Convert to units of chosen R	$160°\text{C} = 433 \text{ K}$
(3) Solve for variable of interest	$V = \dfrac{nRT}{P}$
(4) Calculate	$V = \dfrac{1.25 \text{ mol} \left| 8{,}314 \text{ Pa L} \right| 433 \text{ K} \left|\right.}{\left| \text{mol K} \right| \left| 350{,}000 \text{ Pa} \right.}$
(5) Convert, be reasonable	$V = 13 \text{ L}$

● EXAMPLE 8-18

A gas originally at a temperature of 300 kelvin and 3 atmospheres pressure in a 3.9-liter flask is cooled until the temperature reaches 284 kelvin. What is the new pressure of gas in atmospheres?

Since the volume and the mass of the gas remain constant, we can examine the ratio between the initial condition (1) and the final condition (2) for pressure and temperature. The volume of the container (V) and the amount of gas (n) are constant, so $V_1 = V_2$ and $n_1 = n_2$.

Method	Steps
(1) Choose ideal gas constant	Given units: mol, K, L Select R: $0.08206 \dfrac{\text{atm L}}{\text{mol K}}$
(2) Convert to units of chosen R	None needed
(3) Solve for variable of interest, eliminating any variables that remain constant between the initial and final state	$\dfrac{P_1 V_1}{P_2 V_2} = \dfrac{n_1 R T_1}{n_2 R T_2}$ $\dfrac{P_1}{P_2} = \dfrac{T_1}{T_2}$
(4) Calculate	$\dfrac{3 \text{ atm}}{P_2} = \dfrac{300 \text{ K}}{284 \text{ K}}$
(5) Convert, be reasonable	$P = 2.8 \text{ atm}$

COMPREHENSION CHECK 8-10

A 5-gallon container holds 35 grams of nitrogen (formula: N_2, molecular weight = 28 grams per mole) at a temperature of 400 kelvin. What is the container pressure in units of kilopascals?

COMPREHENSION CHECK 8-11	An 8-liter container holds nitrogen (formula: N_2, molecular weight = 28 grams per mole) at a pressure of 1.5 atmospheres and a temperature of 310 kelvin. If the gas is compressed by reduction of the volume of the container until the gas pressure increases to 5 atmospheres while the temperature is held constant, what is the new volume of the container in units of liters?

8.8   ENERGY

Energy is an abstract quantity with several definitions, depending on the form of energy being discussed. You may be familiar with some of the following types of energy.

Types of Energy

- **Work** (W) is energy expended by exertion of a force (F) over a distance (d). As an example, if you exert a force on (push) a heavy desk so that it slides across the floor, which will make you more tired: pushing it 5 feet or pushing it 50 feet? The farther you push it, the more work you do.
- **Potential energy** (PE) is a form of work done by moving a weight (w)—which is a force—a vertical distance (H). Recall that weight is mass (m) times gravity (g). Note that this is a special case of the work equation, where force is weight and distance is height.
- **Kinetic energy** (KE) is a form of energy possessed by an object in motion. If a constant force is exerted on a body, then by $F = ma$, we see that the body experiences a constant acceleration, meaning the velocity increases linearly with time. Since the velocity increases as long as the force is maintained, work is being done on the object. Another way of saying this is that the object upon which the force is applied acquires kinetic energy, also called **energy of translational motion**. For a nonrotating body moving with some velocity (v) the kinetic energy can be calculated by $KE_T = (\frac{1}{2})mv^2$.

  This, however, is not the entire story. A rotating object has energy whether it is translating (moving along a path) or not. If you have ever turned a bicycle upside down, spun one of the wheels fairly fast, then tried to stop it with your hand, you understand that it has energy. This is **rotational kinetic energy**, and for an object spinning in place (but not going anywhere), it is calculated by $KE_R = (\frac{1}{2})I\omega^2$. The Greek letter omega (ω) symbolizes angular velocity or the object's rotational speed, typically given in units of radians per second. The moment of inertia (I) depends on the mass and the geometry of the spinning object. The table shown lists the moments of inertia for a few common objects.

  For an object that is rotating and translating, such as a bowling ball rolling down the lane toward the pins, the total kinetic energy is simply the sum of the two:

$$KE = KE_T + KE_R = (\tfrac{1}{2})mv^2 + (\tfrac{1}{2})I\omega^2 = (\tfrac{1}{2})(mv^2 + I\omega^2)$$

- **Thermal Energy** or heat (Q) is energy associated with a change in temperature (ΔT). It is a function of the mass of the object (m) and the specific heat (C_p), which is a property of the material being heated:

$$Q = mC_p\Delta T$$

IMPORTANT CONCEPT

Work
$$W = F\Delta x$$

Potential Energy
$$PE = mg\Delta H$$

Kinetic Energy, translational
$$KE_T = \tfrac{1}{2}m(v_f^2 - v_i^2)$$

Kinetic Energy, rotational
$$KE_R = \tfrac{1}{2}I(\omega_f^2 - \omega_i^2)$$

Kinetic Energy, total
$$KE = KE_T + KE_R$$

Thermal Energy
$$Q = mC_p\Delta T$$

MOMENT OF INERTIA (I)

m = mass, r = radius

Object	I for KE_R
Cylinder: thin shell	mr^2
Cylinder: solid	$\frac{1}{2}mr^2$
Sphere: thin shell	$\frac{2}{3}mr^2$
Sphere: solid	$\frac{2}{5}mr^2$

Where Does KE = ½*mv*² Come From?

If a constant force is applied to a body,

- That body will have a constant acceleration (remember $F = ma$).
- Its velocity will increase linearly with time.
- Its average velocity is the average of its initial and final values.

This is	$v = (v_f + v_i)/2$
Distance traveled is	$d = vt$
The work done is	$W = Fd$
	$= (ma)d$
	$= mavt$

Acceleration is the change in velocity over time, or $a = (v_f - v_i)/t$
Substituting for a and v in the work equation

$$W = mavt = m[(v_f - v_i)/t][(v_f + v_i)/2][t]$$
$$W = (1/2)m(v_f^2 - v_i^2)$$

This is given the name *kinetic energy*, or the energy of motion. Remember, work and energy are equivalent. This expression is for the *translation* of a body only.

Calories and BTUs and Joules—Oh My!

The SI unit of work is **joule**, defined as one newton of force acting over a distance of one meter (Table 8-10). The unit is named after James Joule (1818–1889), an English physicist responsible for several theories involving energy, including the definition of the mechanical equivalent of heat and Joule's law, which describes the amount of electrical energy converted to heat by a resistor (an electrical component) when an electric current flows through it. In some mechanical systems, work is described in units of foot pound-force [ft lb_f].

For energy in the form of heat, units are typically reported as British thermal units and calories instead of joules. A **British thermal unit** [BTU] is the amount of heat required to raise the temperature of one pound-mass of water by one degree Fahrenheit. A **calorie** [cal] is amount of heat required to raise the temperature of one gram of water by one degree Celsius.

Table 8-10 Dimensions of energy

| Quantity | Common Units | Exponents | | | |
		M	L	T	Θ
Work	J	1	2	−2	0
Thermal energy	BTU	1	2	−2	0
	cal	1	2	−2	0

● EXAMPLE 8-19

A 50-kilogram load is raised vertically a distance of 5 meters by an electric motor. How much work in units of joules was done on the load?

First, we must determine the type of energy. The parameters we are discussing include mass (kilograms) and height (meters). Examining the energy formulas given above, the equation for potential energy fits. Also, the words "load is raised vertically a distance" fits with our understanding of potential energy.

Step One: Convert to Base SI Units	
No conversion needed	
Step Two: Calculate	
Method	**Steps**
(1) Determine appropriate equation	$PE = mg\Delta H$
(2) Insert known quantities	$PE = \dfrac{50 \text{ kg}}{} \left\| \dfrac{9.8 \text{ m}}{s^2} \right\| \dfrac{5 \text{ m}}{}$
(3) Calculate, be reasonable	$PE = 2{,}450 \dfrac{\text{kg m}^2}{s^2}$

This is apparently our final answer, but the units are puzzling. If the units of energy are joules and if this is a valid equation, then our final result for energy should be joules. If we consider the dimensions of energy:

	Common	Exponents			
Quantity	**Units**	**M**	**L**	**T**	**Θ**
Energy	J	1	2	−2	0

A unit of energy has dimensions $E\{=\} M\, L^2/T^2$, which in terms of base SI units would be $E\,[=]\,\text{kg m}^2/s^2$. As this term occurs so frequently it is given the special name "joule." Anytime we see this term $(\text{kg m}^2/s^2)$, we know we are dealing with an energy, equal to a joule.

(3) Calculate, be reasonable	$PE = 2{,}450 \dfrac{\text{kg m}^2}{s^2} \left\| \dfrac{1 \text{ J}}{1 \dfrac{\text{kg m}^2}{s^2}} \right. = 2{,}450 \text{ J}$
Step Three: Convert from Base SI Units to Desired Units	
No conversion needed	

● EXAMPLE 8-20

In the morning, you like to drink your coffee at a temperature of exactly 70 degrees Celsius [°C]. The mass of the coffee in your mug is 470 grams. To make your coffee, you had to raise the temperature of the water by 30 degrees Celsius. How much energy in units of British thermal units [BTU] did it take to heat your coffee? The specific heat of water is 4.18 joules per gram degree Celsius [J/(g °C)].

First, you must determine the type of energy we are using. The parameters discussed include mass, temperature, and specific heat. Examining the energy formulas given above, the equation for thermal energy fits. Also, the words "How much energy . . . did it take to heat your coffee" fits with an understanding of thermal energy.

Step One: Convert to Base SI Units	
No conversion needed	
Step Two: Calculate	
Method	**Steps**
(1) Determine appropriate equation	$Q = mC_p\Delta T$
(2) Insert known quantities	$Q = \dfrac{470\text{ g}}{}\left\|\dfrac{4.18\text{ J}}{\text{g}°\text{C}}\right\|\dfrac{30°\text{C}}{}$
(3) Calculate, be reasonable	$Q = 59{,}370\text{ J}$
Step Three: Convert from Base SI Units to Desired Units	
Method	**Steps**
(1) Term to be converted	59,370 J
(2) Conversion formula	
(3) Make a fraction	$\dfrac{59{,}370\text{ J}}{}\left\|\dfrac{9.48 \times 10^{-4}\text{ BTU}}{1\text{ J}}\right.$
(4) Multiply	
(5) Cancel, calculate, be reasonable	56 BTU

COMPREHENSION CHECK 8-12

You push an automobile with a constant force of 20 pounds-force until 1,500 joules of energy has been added to the car. How far did the car travel in units of meters during this time? You may assume that frictional losses are negligible.

COMPREHENSION CHECK 8-13

One gram of material A is heated until the temperature rises by 10 kelvin. If the same amount of heat is applied to one gram of material B, what is the temperature rise of material B in units of kelvin?

The specific heat (C_p) of material A = 4 joules per gram kelvin [J/(g K)]
The specific heat (C_p) of material B = 2 joules per gram kelvin [J/(g K)]

8.9 POWER

IMPORTANT CONCEPT

Power = energy / time

W = J/s

SI unit of power = watt

Power is defined as energy per time (Table 8-11). The SI unit of power is **watt**, named after James Watt (1736–1819), a Scottish mathematician and engineer whose improvements to the steam engine were important to the Industrial Revolution. He is responsible for the definition of **horsepower** [hp], a unit of power originally used to quantify how the steam engine could replace the work done by a horse.

Table 8-11 **Dimensions of power**

	Common	Exponents			
Quantity	**Units**	**M**	**L**	**T**	**Θ**
Power	W	1	2	−3	0

NOTE

Power is the RATE at which energy is delivered over time.

To help understand the relationship between energy and power, imagine the following. Your 1,000-kilogram car has run out of gas on a level road. There is a gas station not far ahead, so you decide to push the car to the gas station. Assume that you intend to accelerate the car up to a speed of one meter per second (about 2.2 miles per hour), and then continue pushing at that speed until you reach the station. Ask yourself the following questions:

- Can I accelerate the car to one meter per second in one minute?
- On the other hand, can I accelerate it to one meter per second in one second?

Most of you would probably answer "yes" to the first and "no" to the second, but why? Well, personal experience! But that is not really an explanation. Since the change in kinetic energy is the same in each case, to accelerate the car in one second, your body would have to generate energy at a rate 60 times greater than the rate required if you accelerated it in one minute. The key word is rate, or how much energy your body can produce per second. If you do the calculations, you will find that for the one-minute scenario, your body would have to produce about $\frac{1}{90}$ horsepower, which seems quite reasonable. On the other hand, if you try to accomplish the same acceleration in one second, you would need to generate $\frac{2}{3}$ horsepower. Are you two-thirds as powerful as a horse?

As another example, assume that you attend a class on the third floor of the engineering building. When you are on time, you take 2 minutes to climb to the third floor. On the other hand, when you are late for class, you run up the three flights in 30 seconds.

- In which case do you do the most work (expend the most energy)?
- In which case do you generate the most power?

● **EXAMPLE 8-21**

A 50-kilogram load is raised vertically a distance of 5 meters by an electric motor in 60 seconds. How much power in units of watts does the motor use, assuming no energy is lost in the process?

This problem was started in Example 8-19. The energy used by the system was found to be 2,450 joules, the analysis of which is not repeated here.

Step One: Convert to Base SI Units	
No conversion needed	

Step Two: Calculate	
Method	**Steps**
(1) Determine appropriate equation	$\text{Power} = \dfrac{\text{energy}}{\text{time}}$
(2) Insert known quantities	$\text{Power} = \dfrac{2{,}450 \text{ J}}{60 \text{ s}}$
(3) Calculate, be reasonable	$\text{Power} = 41\dfrac{\text{J}}{\text{s}}\left|\dfrac{1 \text{ W}}{1\frac{\text{J}}{\text{s}}}\right. = 41 \text{ W}$

Step Three: Convert from Base SI Units to Desired Units	
No conversion needed	

Note that since power = energy/time, energy = power * time. We pay the electric company for energy calculated this way as kilowatt-hours. If power is constant, we can obtain the total energy involved simply by multiplying the power by the length of time that power is applied. If power is *not* constant, we would usually use calculus to determine the total energy, but that solution is beyond the scope of this book.

8.10 EFFICIENCY

IMPORTANT CONCEPT

Efficiency is always less than 100%.

Efficiency (η, Greek letter eta) is a measure of how much of a quantity, typically energy or power, is lost in a process. In a perfect world, efficiency would always be 100%. All energy put into a process would be recovered and used to accomplish the desired task. We know that this can never happen, so *efficiency is always less than 100%*. If a machine operates at 75% efficiency, 25% of the energy is lost. This means you have to put in "extra" energy to complete the work.

The use of the terms "input" and "output" require some explanation. The **input** is the quantity of energy or power or whatever required by the mechanism from some source to operate and accomplish its task. The **output** is the amount of energy or power or whatever is actually applied to the task itself by the mechanism. Note that the rated power of a device, whether a light bulb, a motor, or an electric heater, refers to the input power—the power needed to operate the device—not the output power. In an ideal, 100% efficient system, the input and output would be equivalent. In an inefficient system (the real world), the input is equivalent to the sum of the output and the power or energy lost. This is perhaps best explained by way of examples.

IMPORTANT CONCEPT

Efficiency (η) = output/input
Efficiency (η) = output/(output + loss)
Input = quantity required by mechanism to operate
Output = quantity actually applied to task
Loss = quantity wasted during the application

Orders of Magnitude

The table below gives you an idea of orders of magnitude of power and energy as related to real-world objects and phenomena. All values are approximate and, in most cases, have been rounded to only one significant figure. Thus, if you actually do the calculations from power to energy, you will find discrepancies.

Unless you are already familiar with the standard metric prefixes, refer to the list on the inside back cover of the book.

A few things of possible interest:

- U.S. power consumption (all types) is one-fifth of the total world power consumption.
- The Tsar Bomba generated 1.5% of the power of the sun, but only lasted 40 nanoseconds.
- Total human power consumption on the planet is about 0.01% (1/10,000) of the total power received from the sun.

Power	"Device"	Energy per Hour	Energy per Year
10 fW	Minimum reception power for cell phone	40 pJ	300 nJ
	Single human cell	4 nJ	30 mJ
10 mW	DVD laser	40 J	300 kJ
500 mW	Cell phone microprocessor	2 kJ	15 MJ
50 W	Modern 2GHz microprocessor	200 kJ	1.5 GJ
100 W	Human at rest	400 kJ	3 GJ
500 W	Human doing strenuous work	2 MJ	15 GJ
750 W	Power per meter bright sunshine	3 MJ	25 GJ
2 kW	Maximum human power for short period	(NA)	
20 kW	Average U.S. home	80 MJ	600 GJ
100 kW	Typical automobile	400 MJ	3 TJ
150 MW	Boeing 747 jet	500 GJ	5 PJ
1 GW	Large commercial nuclear reactor	4 TJ	30 PJ
20 GW	Three Gorges Hydroelectric Dam (China)	80 TJ	600 PJ
4 TW	U.S. total power consumption	15 PJ	100 EJ
20 TW	Total human power consumption	80 PJ	600 EJ
100 TW	Average hurricane	400 PJ	(NA)
200 PW	Total power received on the Earth from the sun	1 ZJ	6 YJ
5 YW	Largest fusion bomb ever built (Russian Tsar Bomba)	(NA) Total yield 200 PJ	
400 YW	Total power of the sun	10^6 YJ	10^9 YJ

● EXAMPLE 8-22   A standard incandescent light bulb has an efficiency of about 5%; thus, $\eta = 0.05$. An incandescent bulb works by heating a wire (the filament) inside the bulb to such a high temperature that it glows white. About 95% of the power delivered to an incandescent bulb is discarded as heat. Only 5% results in "light" energy.

Light energy output (5%)

Energy input (100%)

Heat energy lost (95%)

If a 100-watt bulb is turned on for 15 minutes, how much energy is "lost" as heat during the 15-minute period?

Step One: Convert to Base SI Units	
No conversion needed	

Step Two: Calculate	
Method	**Steps**
(1) Determine appropriate equation	Power = energy/time
(2) Insert known quantities	Power = energy/15 min

For Unknown Quantities, Repeat the Process	
Method	**Steps**
(1) Determine appropriate equation	Input power = output power/efficiency "Lost" power = input power − output power
(2) Insert known quantities	100 W = output power/(0.05)
(3) Calculate, be reasonable	Output power = 5 W "Lost" power = 100 W − 5 W = 95 W

(2) Insert known quantities	95 W = energy/15 min
(3) Calculate, be reasonable	$E = 95 \dfrac{J}{s}\left|\dfrac{15 \text{ min}}{}\right|\dfrac{60 \text{ s}}{1 \text{ min}}$ Energy lost = 85,500 J

Step Three: Convert from Base SI Units to Desired Units	
No conversion needed	

● **EXAMPLE 8-23**

Over the past few decades, the efficiency of solar cells has risen from about 10% to the most recent technologies achieving about 40% conversion of solar energy to electricity. The losses are due to several factors, including reflectance and resistive losses, among others.

Assume you have an array of solar cells mounted on your roof with an efficiency of 28%. If the array is delivering 750 watts of electricity to your home, how much solar power is falling on the photoelectric cells?

NOTE

How much power is wasted by the array of solar cells? If the array received 2,680 watts and delivered 750 watts, then the difference is 2,680 − 750 = 1,930 watts; thus, 1,930 watts are wasted.

Step One: Convert to Base SI Units	
No conversion needed	
Step Two: Calculate	
Method	**Steps**
(1) Determine appropriate equation	Input power = output power/efficiency
(2) Insert known quantities	Input power = 750 W/0.28
(3) Calculate, be reasonable	Input power = 2,680 W
Step Three: Convert from Base SI Units to Desired Units	
No conversion needed	

● EXAMPLE 8-24

If your microwave takes 2 minutes to heat your coffee in Example 8-20, how many watts of power does your microwave require, assuming that it is 80% efficient? Remember that our answer was 59,370 joules, before we converted the final answer to units of BTU.

Step One: Convert to Base SI Units	
No conversion needed	
Step Two: Calculate	
Method	**Steps**
(1) Determine appropriate equation	Input power = output power/efficiency
(2) Insert known quantities	Input power = output power/0.8
For Unknown Quantities, Repeat the Process	
Method	**Steps**
(1) Determine appropriate equation	Output power = energy/time
(2) Insert known quantities	Output power = $\dfrac{59,370 \text{ J}}{}\left|\dfrac{1 \text{ min}}{2 \text{ min}}\right|\dfrac{1 \text{ min}}{60 \text{ s}}\left|\dfrac{1 \text{ W s}}{1 \text{ J}}\right.$
(3) Calculate, be reasonable	Output power = 493 W
(2) Insert known quantities	Input power = 493 W/0.8
(3) Calculate, be reasonable	Input power = 615 W
Step Three: Convert from Base SI Units to Desired Units	
No conversion needed	

COMPREHENSION CHECK 8-14

A motor with an output power of 100 watts is connected to a flywheel. How long, in units of hours, must the motor operate to transfer 300,000 joules to the flywheel, assuming the process is 100% efficient?

COMPREHENSION CHECK 8-15

If a 50-kilogram load was raised 5 meters in 50 seconds, determine the minimum rated wattage of the motor needed to accomplish this, assuming the motor is 80% efficient.

● **EXAMPLE 8-25**

A simple two-stage machine is shown in the diagram below. Initially, an electric motor receives power from the power grid, accessed by being plugged into a standard electrical wall socket. The power received by the motor from the wall socket is the "input" power or the power the motor uses or requires (Point A).

The spinning drive shaft on the motor can then be used to power other devices, such as a hoist or a vacuum cleaner or a DVD drive; the power available from the spinning shaft is the "output" power of the motor (Point B). In the process of making the drive shaft spin, however, some of the input power is lost (Point C) because of both frictional and ohmic heating as well as other wasted forms such as sound.

Since some energy is being lost as heat or other unusable forms every second of operation (remember, power is energy per time!) the output power *must* be less than the input power—the efficiency of the motor is less than 100%. The power available from the spinning shaft of the motor (Point B) is then used to operate some device: the hoist or vacuum cleaner or DVD drive (Point E). In other words, the output power of the motor is the input power to the device it drives. This device will have its own efficiency, thus wasting some of the power supplied to it by the motor (Point D).

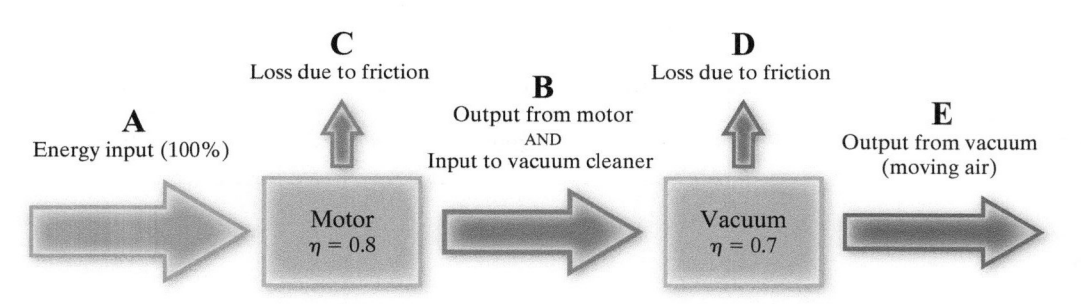

NOTE

The overall efficiency of two linked devices is the product of the two efficiencies.

Assume that a motor with an efficiency of 80% is used to power a vacuum cleaner that has an efficiency of 70%. If the input power to the motor (Point A) is one-half horsepower, what is the output power of the vacuum (Point E)? The output from the motor (Point B) is $P_B = \eta P_A = 0.8\,(0.5\text{ horsepower}) = 0.4\text{ horsepower}.$
This is the input to the vacuum, so the output from the vacuum (Point E) is

$$P_E = \eta P_B = 0.7\,(0.4\text{ hp}) = 0.28\text{ hp}$$

What is the overall efficiency of this machine? The input power (Point A) is 0.5 horsepower, and the output power (Point E) is 0.28 horsepower; thus, the efficiency of this linked system is:

$$\eta = P_A/P_E = 0.28\text{ hp}/0.5\text{ hp} = 0.56,\text{ or an efficiency of }56\%.$$

SO WHAT WAS THE ANSWER TO THE BOAT AND THE STONE QUESTION FROM THE INTRODUCTION?

This is a problem that can be analyzed without the need for any equations or formal mathematics. We will start with Archimedes' principle that states simply: "When a body is submerged in a fluid, the buoyancy force (which pushes the body upward) is equal to the weight of the fluid which the body displaces."

If an object is floating at equilibrium in a fluid, the buoyancy force is equal to the weight of the object. The upward buoyancy force and downward weight of the object (remember, weight is a force!) are the same, so the net force on the object is zero. For example, when a 500 pound-mass boat is placed in a pool, its weight acts downward (with a value of 500 pounds-force if at sea level on the Earth), and it sinks deeper and deeper, displacing more and more fluid, until it has displaced 500 pounds-mass of fluid. At that point, the buoyancy force is 500 pounds-force and this opposes the weight of the boat so that it rests at equilibrium.

If the body we place in a fluid weighs more than the fluid it displaces when completely submerged, then the body sinks, but it still experiences a buoyancy force equal to the weight of the fluid displaced. This is one reason astronauts train under water—the net downward force of themselves and of objects they are manipulating is greatly reduced although their mass is the same.

If we place the same 500 pound-mass boat in a pool, and put a 200 pound-mass person in it, the boat will sink in the fluid more deeply than before, until it displaces 700 pound-mass of fluid. At this new level of submergence, the upward and downward forces are equal and the new "system" of boat and person will rest at equilibrium. If we add a stone in the boat, the new system of the boat, the person, and the stone will sink even deeper until it displaces a mass of fluid equal to the combined masses of the boat, the person, and the stone. In each of these situations the displaced fluid has to go some-where, so the level of the liquid in the pool rises.

If we assume that the stone will sink when tossed overboard, it will displace a volume of liquid equal to the volume of the stone. Since the stone is denser than the liquid (has more mass per volume), it now displaces less liquid than it did when it was in the boat. Thus, when the stone is placed in the pool, the water level will drop.

In-Class Activities

ICA 8-1

Complete the following table, using the equation weight = (mass) (gravity) as needed:

	Pound-mass	Kilogram	Newton	Pound-force
Abbreviation		[kg]		
Example	0.33	0.15	1.47	0.33
(a)	10			
(b)			700	
(c)				25

ICA 8-2

Complete the following table, using the equation weight = (mass) (gravity) as needed:

	Slug	Grams	Newton	Pound-force
Abbreviation		[g]		
(a)		130		
(b)	50			
(c)			50	
(d)				30

ICA 8-3

Complete the following table:

	Compound	SG	Density [lb$_m$/ft^3]	Density [g/cm^3]	Density [kg/m^3]
Example	Ethyl alcohol	1.025	64.0	1.025	1,025
(a)	Acetic acid			1.049	
(b)	Octane				703
(c)	Tetrachloroethane		100		
(d)	Chloroform	1.489			

ICA 8-4

Complete the following table:

	Compound	SG	[lb$_m$/ft^3]	[g/cm^3]	[kg/m^3]
				Density	
(a)	Gallium	5.91			
(b)	Aluminum		168.5		
(c)	Zinc oxide				5,600
(d)	Sugar, powdered			0.801	
(e)	Lead	11.4			

ICA 8-5

Complete the following table. Assume you have a cube composed of each material, with "length" indicating the length of one side of the cube.

	Material	Mass [g]	Length [cm]	Volume [cm^3]	Density [g/cm^3]
Example	Tungsten	302	2.5	15.6	19.3
(a)	Zinc			25	7.14
(b)	Copper	107			8.92
(c)	Lead	1,413			11.35

ICA 8-6

Complete the following table. Assume you have a cylinder, composed of each material, with "radius" and "height" indicating the dimensions of the cylinder.

	Material	Mass [kg]	Radius [m]	Height [m]	Density [kg/m^3]
(a)	Silicon	2,750	0.50	1.5	
(b)	Aluminum		1.25	0.75	2,700
(c)	Tin	10,000	0.25		7,290
(d)	Titanium	8,000		1.0	4,540

ICA 8-7

Complete the following table:

	Compound	[°F]	[°C]	[K]	[°R]
			Boiling Temperature		
(a)	Acetic acid	180			
(b)	Ethyl alcohol				815
(c)	Octane		126		
(d)	Tetrachloroethane			419	

ICA 8-8

A **eutectic alloy** of two metals contains the specific percentage of each metal that gives the lowest possible melting temperature for any combination of those two metals. Eutectic alloys are often used for soldering electronic components to minimize the possibility of thermal damage. In the past, the most common eutectic alloy used in this application has been 63% Sn, 37% Pb, with a melting temperature of about 361 degrees Fahrenheit. To reduce lead pollution in the environment, many other alloys have been tried, including those in the table below. Complete the following table:

	Compound	Eutectic Temperature			
		[°F]	[°C]	[K]	[°R]
(a)	48% Sn, 52% In	244			
(b)	42% Sn, 58% Bi		138		
(c)	91% Sn, 9% Zn			472	
(d)	96.5% Sn, 3.5% Ag				890

ICA 8-9

In the Spring of 2004, NASA discovered a new planet beyond Pluto named Sedna. In the news report about the discovery, the temperature of Sedna was reported as "never rising above −400 degrees." What are the units of the reported temperature?

ICA 8-10

Is there a physical condition at which a Fahrenheit thermometer and Celsius thermometer will read the same numerical value? If so, what is this value?

ICA 8-11

Is there a physical condition at which a Fahrenheit thermometer and a Kelvin thermometer will read the same numerical value? If so, what is this value?

ICA 8-12

Determine the mass in units of grams of 0.025 moles of caffeine (formula: $C_8H_{10}N_4O_3$). The components are hydrogen (formula: H, amu = 1); carbon (formula: C, amu = 12); nitrogen (formula: N, amu = 14); and oxygen (formula: O, amu = 16).

ICA 8-13

Determine the mass in units of grams of 0.15 moles of the common analgesic naproxen sodium (formula: $C_{14}H_{13}NaO_3$). The components are hydrogen (formula: H, amu = 1); carbon (formula: C, amu = 12); sodium (formula: Na, amu = 23); and oxygen (formula: O, amu = 16).

ICA 8-14

Determine the amount in units of moles of 5 grams of another common analgesic acetaminophen (formula: $C_8H_9NO_2$). The components are hydrogen (formula: H, amu = 1); carbon (formula: C, amu = 12); nitrogen (formula: N, amu = 14); and oxygen (formula: O, amu = 16).

ICA 8-15

Complete the table:

	Atmosphere	Pascal	Inches of Mercury	Pound-force per Square Inch
Abbreviation	[atm]			
Example	0.030	3,000	0.886	0.435
(a)			30	
(b)				50
(c)	2.5			

ICA 8-16

Complete the table:

	Atmosphere	Pascal	Inches of Mercury	Pound-force per Square Inch
Abbreviation	[atm]			
(a)		500,000		
(b)				5
(c)	10			
(d)			25	

ICA 8-17

Complete the table, using the equation for total pressure:

	Fluid Density [kg/m^3]	Height of Fluid [ft]	Surface Pressure [atm]	Total Pressure [atm]
(a)	787	10	1	
(b)		50	1	2
(c)	1,263		3	5.4
(d)	1,665	35		3.25

ICA 8-18

Complete the table, using the equation for total pressure:

	Fluid Specific Gravity	Height of Fluid [m]	Surface Pressure [atm]	Total Pressure [psi]
(a)	0.787	15	1	
(b)		75	1	30
(c)	1.263		3	80
(d)	1.665	20		48

ICA 8-19

Complete the table, using the ideal gas law:

	Compound	Mass [g]	MW [g/mol]	Amount [mol]	Pressure [atm]	Volume [L]	Temperature [K]
(a)	Oxygen (O$_2$)	8	32		2.0		400
(b)	Nitrogen (N$_2$)	5.6	28			5	373
(c)	Chlorine (Cl$_2$)		71	0.5	2.5	5	
(d)	Xylene	265		2.5	2.5		273

ICA 8-20

Complete the table, using the ideal gas law:

	Compound	Mass [lb$_m$]	MW [g/mol]	Amount [mol]	Pressure [Pa]	Volume [gal]	Temperature [°C]
(a)	Acetylene (C$_2$H$_2$)	0.1	26		303,975		−23
(b)	Benzene (C$_6$H$_6$)	0.04	78			1.32	100
(c)	Naphthalene	0.07		0.25	131,723	1.32	
(d)	Toluene	0.425		2.1	354,638		27

ICA 8-21

Complete the table for specific heat conversions:

	Compound	[cal/(g °C)]	[BTU/(lb$_m$ °F)]	[J/(kg K)]
(a)	Neon			1,030
(b)	Benzene		0.0406	
(c)	Mercury	0.03325		
(d)	Aluminum			0.897
(e)	Ethanol			2,440
(f)	Copper		0.0912	

ICA 8-22

Complete the table for thermal conductivity conversions:

	Compound	[W/(m °C)]	[BTU/(ft h °F)]	[cal/(cm min K)]
(a)	Zinc		122	
(b)	Silver	420		
(c)	Lead	35		
(d)	Sandstone		1.387	
(e)	Copper		232	
(f)	Glass	1.1		

ICA 8-23

Complete the table. This problem involves the power required to raise a mass a given distance in a given amount of time.

	Mass [kg]	Distance [m]	Energy [J]	Time [s]	Power [W]
(a)	250	11		200	
(b)	440	52			100
(c)	60		2,940	60	
(d)		10		50	100

ICA 8-24

Complete the table. This problem involves the power required to raise a mass a given distance in a given amount of time.

	Mass [lb$_m$]	Distance [ft]	Energy [J]	Time [min]	Power [hp]
(a)	220	15		0.5	
(b)	1,875	145			0.268
(c)	200		4,000	1	
(d)		35		2	0.134

ICA 8-25

The specific heat of copper is 0.09 British thermal units per pound-mass degree Fahrenheit. Convert this value into units of joules per gram kelvin.

ICA 8-26

The specific heat of helium is 5.24 joules per gram kelvin. Convert this value into units of British thermal units per pound-mass degree Fahrenheit.

ICA 8-27

The thermal conductivity of a plastic is 0.325 British thermal units per foot hour degree Fahrenheit. Convert this value in units of watts per meter kelvin.

ICA 8-28

The heat transfer coefficient of steel is 25 watts per square meter degree Celsius. Convert this value into units of calories per square centimeter second kelvin.

ICA 8-29

One problem with solar energy is that any given point on the planet is illuminated by the sun for only half of the time at best. It would be helpful, therefore, if there were a simple, affordable, and efficient means for storing any excess energy generated on sunny days for use during the night or on cloudy days.

You are investigating the electrodes used in electrolysis cells as part of a three-stage process for solar energy collection and storage.

1. Convert sunlight to electricity with photovoltaic cells.
2. Use the electricity generated in an electrolysis cell to split water into its component elements, hydrogen and oxygen. The hydrogen can be stored indefinitely. The oxygen can simply be released into the atmosphere.
3. Use a fuel cell to recombine the stored hydrogen with oxygen from the atmosphere to generate electricity.

You have obtained an array of new high-efficiency, thin-film photovoltaic cells with an efficiency of 41%. The efficiency of fuel cells varies with the current demands placed on them, but the cells you have obtained yield an overall efficiency of 37% at the anticipated load.

Assume the total solar power on the solar cells is 2,000 watts. You conduct four experiments, each with a different alloy of palladium, platinum, gold, copper, and/or silver for the electrodes in the electrolysis cell. The final output power from the fuel cell is measured for each case, and the results are tabulated below. Determine the efficiency of each electrolysis cell and complete the table.

Alloy	Output Power (P_0) [W]	Electrolysis Cell Efficiency (η)
Alloy A	137	
Alloy B	201	
Alloy C	67	
Alloy D	177	

ICA 8-30

Materials

Bag of cylinders	Scale	Calipers	Ruler

Procedure

For each cylinder, record the mass, length, and diameter in the table provided.

Analysis

- Calculate the volume and density for each cylinder, recording the results in the table provided.
- Rank the rods in order of increasing density, with the least dense rod first on the list.
- Using the density, determine the material of each rod.

Data Worksheet

Description	Measured Values			Calculated Values	
	Mass	Length	Diameter	Volume	Density
Units					
Rod 1					
Rod 2					
Rod 3					
Rod 4					
Rod 5					
Rod 6					
Rod 7					
Rod 8					
Rod 9					
Rod 10					

Rank Rods Increasing Density	Density	Material

ICA 8-31

Materials

25 mL graduated cylinder   Scale   Paper towels

Unknown liquids   Basket labeled "Wash"   Water bottle

Wastewater bucket

Procedure

Record the following data in the table provided:

1. Weigh the empty graduated cylinder and record the value.
2. Pour 15 milliliters [mL] of water into the cylinder.
3. Weigh the cylinder with water and record the value.

4. Pour the water into the wastewater bucket.
5. Pour 15 milliliters [mL] of unknown liquid (UL) 1 into a cylinder.
6. Weigh the cylinder with UL 1 and record the value.
7. Pour the UL back into the original container.
8. Place the graduated cylinder in the "Wash" basket if more than one cylinder is available. If only one cylinder is being used, wash the cylinder with water so no trace of the UL is left in the cylinder.
9. Repeat Steps 5–9 with each unknown liquid provided.

Analysis

- Calculate the density and specific gravity for each fluid, recording the results in the table provided.
- Rank the fluids in order of increasing density, with the least dense fluid first on the list.
- Using the specific gravity, determine the type of liquid in each container.

Data Worksheet

	Measured			Calculated	
Description	Total Mass	Volume	Liquid Mass	Density	Specific Gravity
Units					
Empty cylinder					
Water					
UL 1					
UL 2					
UL 3					
UL 4					
UL 5					

Rank Liquids Increasing Density	Density	Liquid

1. If a person weighs 700 newtons, what is the mass of the person in units of kilograms?
2. If a person weighs 700 newtons, what is the mass of the person in units of pounds-mass?
3. If a person weighs 700 newtons, what is the mass of the person in units of slugs?
4. A football lineman weighs 300 pounds-force. What is his mass in units of kilograms?
5. A football lineman weighs 300 pounds-force. What is his mass in units of pounds-mass?
6. A football lineman weighs 300 pounds-force. What is his mass in units of slugs?
7. The weight of a can of soda on the moon (where the acceleration of gravity is 1.6 meters per second squared) is 0.6 newtons. What is the mass of the can of soda on the Earth in units of kilograms?
8. The weight of a can of soda on the moon (where the acceleration of gravity is 1.6 meters per second squared) is 0.6 newtons. What is the mass of the can of soda on the Earth in units of pounds-mass?
9. If the density of silicon is 10.5 grams per cubic centimeter, what is this in units of pounds-mass per cubic foot?
10. If the density of sulfur is 131 pounds-mass per cubic foot, what is this in units of grams per cubic centimeter?
11. If the density of sodium is 98 kilograms per cubic meter, what is this in units of slugs per gallon?
12. A basketball has a mass of approximately 624 grams and a volume of 0.25 cubic feet. Determine the density of the basketball in units of pounds-mass per cubic foot.
13. Consider the following strange, but true, units:

    1 arroba = 11.5 kilograms
    1 peck = 9 liters

    A basketball has a mass of approximately 624 grams and a volume of 0.25 cubic feet. Determine the density of the basketball in units of arroba per peck.
14. Consider the following strange, but true, units:

    1 batman = 3 kilograms
    1 hogshead = 63 gallons

    A basketball has a mass of approximately 624 grams and a volume of 0.25 cubic feet. Determine the density of the basketball in units of batman per hogshead.
15. The specific gravity of acetic acid (vinegar) is 1.049. State the density in units of pounds-mass per cubic foot.
16. The specific gravity of ethyl alcohol is 0.785. State the density in units of grams per cubic centimeter.
17. The specific gravity of chloroform is 1.489. State the density in units of kilograms per cubic meter.
18. The specific gravity of iodine is 4.927. State the density in units of slugs per liter.
19. A cube of material X, 1 inch on all sides, has a mass of 0.05 kilograms. Determine the specific gravity of material X.
20. The specific gravity of gold is 19.3. What is the length of one side of a 0.4 kilogram cube of solid gold, in units of inches?
21. The density of gasoline is 0.72 grams per cubic centimeter. What is the mass in units of kilograms of a 5-gallon container filled completely with gasoline? Ignore the mass of the container.
22. A lab reports that the density of a new element is X kilograms per cubic foot and Y grams per cubic meter. Which of the following statements is true?
    (A) $X > Y$.
    (B) $X < Y$.
    (C) $X = Y$.
    (D) Cannot be determined.

23. The Eco-Marathon is an annual competition sponsored by Shell Oil, in which participants build special vehicles to achieve the highest possible fuel efficiency. The Eco-Marathon is held around the world with events in the United Kingdom, Finland, France, Holland, Japan, and the United States.

   A world record was set in Eco-marathon by a French team in 2003 called Microjoule with a performance of 10,705 miles per gallon. The Microjoule runs on ethanol. If the cars are given 100 grams of ethanol (specific gravity = 0.789) and drive until the fuel runs out, how far did the Microjoule drive in kilometers?

24. A golden bar of metal (5 centimeters by 18 centimeters by 4 centimeters) being transported by armored car is suspected of being fake, made from a less valuable metal with a thin coating of pure gold. The bar is found to have a mass of 2.7 kilograms. If the specific gravity of gold is 19.3, is the bar fake? Justify your answer.

25. A rod on the surface of Jupiter's moon Callisto has a volume of 0.3 cubic meters. Determine the weight of the rod in units of pounds-force. The density is 4,700 kilograms per cubic meter. Gravitational acceleration on Callisto is 1.25 meters per second squared.

26. A substance used to remove the few remaining molecules from a near vacuum by reacting with them or adsorbing them is called a getter. There are numerous materials used and several ways of deploying them within a system enclosing a vacuum, but here we will look at a common method used in vacuum tubes, once the workhorse of electronics but now relegated to high-end audio systems and other niche markets. In vacuum tubes, after the air is evacuated with a vacuum pump, getters are usually deposited inside the hemispherical top by flash deposition. Assume that it is desired to flash deposit 1.5×10^{-3} moles of a getter onto the hemispherical top of a vacuum tube with an inside diameter of three-quarters of an inch. For each of the following getter materials, how thick will the coating be? Report your answers using meters with an appropriately chosen prefix.

   The 12AX7 is a very common dual triode vacuum tube first developed for audio applications in the mid-1940s and still in common use in guitar amplifiers.

Getter Material	Specific Gravity	Atomic Weight [g/mol]
Aluminum	2.7	26.981
Barium	3.51	137.33
Calcium	1.55	40.078
Magnesium	1.738	24.305
Sodium	0.968	22.99
Strontium	2.64	87.62

27. The largest temperature decline during a 24-hour period was 56 degrees Celsius in Browning, Montana. Express this as degrees Fahrenheit per minute.

28. The largest temperature decline during a 24-hour period was 56 degrees Celsius in Browning, Montana. Express this as degrees Rankine per second.

29. The world's lowest recorded temperature was −129 degrees Fahrenheit in Vostok, Antarctica. State this temperature in units of degrees Celsius.

30. The world's lowest recorded temperature was −129 degrees Fahrenheit in Vostok, Antarctica. State this temperature in units of kelvin.

31. If we increase the temperature in a reactor by 90 degrees Fahrenheit, how many degrees Celsius will the temperature increase?

32. We are making a cup of coffee and want the temperature to be just right, so we measure the temperature with both Fahrenheit and Celsius thermometers. The Fahrenheit meter registers 110 degrees Fahrenheit, but you prefer to it to be slightly hotter at 119 degrees Fahrenheit, so we heat it up a little. How much will the Celsius thermometer increase when we make this change?

33. Which of the following plastics has the highest melting temperature? You must prove your answer for credit!
    (A) Acrylic at 150 degrees Fahrenheit.
    (B) Polyethylene terephthalate (PET) at 423 kelvin.
    (C) High-density polyethylene (HDPE) at 710 degrees Rankine.

34. The tiles on the space shuttle are constructed to withstand a temperature of 1,950 kelvin. What is the temperature in units of degrees Rankine?

35. The tiles on the space shuttle are constructed to withstand a temperature of 1,950 kelvin. What is the temperature in units of degrees Fahrenheit?

36. The boiling point of propane is −43 degrees Celsius. What is the temperature in units of degrees Fahrenheit?

37. The boiling point of propane is −43 degrees Celsius. What is the temperature in units of kelvin?

38. We want to construct a thermometer using mercury (Hg). As the mercury in the bulb is heated, it expands and moves up the thin capillary tube connected to the bulb. The symbol used for the coefficient of volume expansion of a substance due to a temperature increase is β. It is used in the following equation:

$$\Delta V = \beta V (\Delta T)$$

Here, ΔV is the increase in volume, V is the original volume, and ΔT is the temperature increase. The value of β for mercury is 1.8×10^{-4} [1/degree Celsius]. If the bulb contains 0.2 milliliters and the tube has a diameter of 0.2 millimeters, how much will the mercury rise in the tube in units of centimeters if we increase the temperature from 30 degrees Fahrenheit to 70 degrees Fahrenheit?

39. You are designing a new thermometer using Galinstan®, an alloy of gallium, indium, and tin that is liquid at normal living temperatures. The specific alloy used has a coefficient of thermal expansion $\beta = 190 \times 10^{-6}$ [1/kelvin].

    The change in volume (ΔV) for a given change in temperature (ΔT) can be determined by

$$\Delta V = \beta V (\Delta T)$$

Here, ΔV is the increase in volume, V is the original volume, and ΔT is the temperature increase. The thermometer will contain two cubic centimeters of Galinstan®, most of which is in the "bulb" or reservoir that is connected to a capillary tube up which the liquid moves as it expands. If your design specifications are to have a 2-millimeter change in the position of the liquid in the capillary tube for each degree Fahrenheit change in temperature, what is the diameter of the capillary tube, assuming it has a circular cross section?

40. If the pressure is 250 feet of water, what is the pressure in units of inches of mercury?

41. If the pressure is 250 feet of water, what is the pressure in units of millimeters of mercury?

42. If the pressure is 250 feet of water, what is the pressure in units of pounds-force per square inch?

43. If the pressure is 100 millimeters of mercury, what is the pressure in units of feet of water?

44. If the pressure is 100 millimeters of mercury, what is the pressure in units of pascals?

45. If the pressure is 100 millimeters of mercury, what is the pressure in units of atmospheres?

46. A "normal" blood pressure is 120 millimeters of mercury (systolic reading) over 80 millimeters of mercury (diastolic reading). Convert 120 millimeters of mercury into units of pounds-force per square inch.

47. A "normal" blood pressure is 120 millimeters of mercury (systolic reading) over 80 millimeters of mercury (diastolic reading). Convert 80 millimeters of mercury into units of pascals.

48. A car tire is inflated to 30 pounds-force per square inch. If the tire has an area of 0.25 square feet in contact with the road, how much force is exerted by all four tires?

49. The force on the inside of a cork in a champagne bottle is 10 pound-force. If the cork has a diameter of 0.5 inches, what is the pressure inside the bottle in units of feet of water?

50. If a force of 15 newtons is applied to a surface and the pressure is measured as 4,000 pascals, what is the area of the surface in units of square meters?

51. A sensor is submerged in a silo to detect any bacterial growth in the stored fluid. The stored fluid has a density of 2.2 grams per cubic centimeters. What is the hydrostatic pressure felt by the sensor at a depth of 30 meters in units of atmospheres?

52. One of the National Academy of Engineering Grand Challenges for Engineering is **Develop Carbon Sequestration Methods.** The NAE defines carbon sequestration as "capturing the carbon dioxide produced by burning fossil fuels and storing it safely away from the atmosphere." The most promising storage location is underground, possibly in sedimentary brine formations. You are assigned to develop instrumentation to measure the properties of a brine formation, located 800 meters deep. Assume the instruments will feel an equivalent amount of pressure to the amount of hydrostatic pressure felt at the bottom of an 800-meter high column of brine, with a specific gravity of 1.35. To what hydrostatic pressure, in units of atmospheres, must the instrumentation be built to withstand?

53. A cylindrical tank filled to a height of 25 feet with tribromoethylene has been pressurized to 2 atmospheres ($P_{surface} = 2$ atmospheres). The total pressure at the bottom of the tank is 4 atmospheres. Determine the density of tribromoethylene in units of kilograms per cubic meter.

54. A submersible vehicle is being designed to operate in the Atlantic Ocean. Density of ocean water is 1.025 grams per cubic centimeter. For a maximum depth of 300 feet, what is the total pressure the hull of the submersible must be designed to withstand? Give your answer in units of pounds per square inch.

55. If the total pressure on the bottom of an open container is 2.5 atmospheres, what would the atmospheric pressure have to be to double the total pressure on the bottom?

56. NASA is designing a mission to explore Titan, the largest moon of Saturn. Titan has numerous hydrocarbon lakes containing a mix of methane and ethane in unknown proportions. As part of the mission, a small submersible vehicle will explore Kraken Mare, the largest of these lakes, to determine, among other things, how deep it is. Assuming that the maximum depth of Kraken Mare is less than 400 meters, how much pressure in atmospheres must the submersible be designed to withstand? Assume the surface pressure on Titan is 147 kilopascals, the surface temperature is 94 kelvin, and the gravity is 1.35 meters per second squared. The specific gravity of liquid methane is 0.415 and the specific gravity of liquid ethane is 0.546.

57. Airspeed (v), is determined from dynamic pressure using the following formula: $P_{dynamic} = \frac{1}{2} \rho v^2$. Determine the dynamic pressure, in units of pascals, for an aircraft moving at an airspeed of 600 miles per hour. Air density is 1.20 kilograms per cubic meter.

58. A 10-liter flask contains 1.3 moles of an ideal gas at a temperature of 20 degrees Celsius. What is the pressure in the flask in units of atmospheres?

59. An ideal gas, kept in a 5-liter container at 300 kelvin, exhibits a pressure of 2 atmospheres. If the volume of the container is decreased to 2.9 liters, but the temperature remains the same, what is pressure in the new container in units of atmospheres?

60. An ideal gas is kept in a 10-liter container at a pressure of 1.5 atmospheres and a temperature of 310 kelvins. If the gas is compressed until its pressure is raised to 3 atmospheres while holding the temperature constant, what is the new volume in units of liters?

61. A 5-liter container holds nitrogen (formula: N_2, molecular weight = 28 grams per mole) at a pressure of 1.1 atmospheres and a temperature of 400 kelvins. What is the amount of nitrogen in the container, in units of grams?

62. An ideal gas in a 1.25-gallon container is at a temperature of 125 degrees Celsius and pressure of 2.5 atmospheres. If the gas is oxygen (formula: O_2, molecular weight = 32 grams per mole), what is the amount of gas in the container in units of grams?

63. A 10-liter flask contains 5 moles of gas at a pressure of 15 atmospheres. What is the temperature in the flask in units of kelvin?

64. A container holding 1.5 moles of oxygen (formula: O_2, molecular weight = 32 grams per mole) at a pressure of 1.5 atmospheres and a temperature of 310 kelvins is heated to 420 kelvins, while maintaining constant volume. What is the new pressure inside the container in units of pascals?

65. The specific heat of neon is 1.03 joules per gram kelvin. Convert this value into units of calorie per kilogram degree Celsius.

66. The specific heat of copper is 0.386 joules per gram kelvin. Convert this value into units of British thermal units per pound-mass degree Fahrenheit.

67. The specific heat of octane is 0.51 calorie per gram degree Celsius. Convert this value into units of joules per gram kelvin.

68. The specific heat of tungsten is 0.134 calorie per gram degree Celsius. Convert this value into units of British thermal units per pound-mass degree Fahrenheit.

69. Which of the following requires the expenditure of more work? You must show your work to receive credit.
    (A) Lifting a 100-newton weight a height of 4 meters.
    (B) Sliding a sofa, weighing 200 pounds-force, 30 feet across a room. Assume an additional 50 pounds-force is required to overcome the resisting friction.
70. Which object—A, B, or C—has the most potential energy when held a distance H above the surface of the ground? You must show your work to receive credit.

    | Object A: | mass = 1 kilogram | height = 3 meters |
    | Object B: | mass = 1 slug | height = 3 feet |
    | Object C: | mass = 1 gram | height = 1 centimeter |

71. A 10-gram rubber ball is released from a height of 6 meters above a flat surface on the moon. Gravitational acceleration on the moon is 1.62 meters per second squared. Assume that no energy is lost from frictional drag. What is the velocity, in units of meters per second, of the rubber ball the instant before it strikes the flat surface?
72. A robotic rover on Mars finds a spherical rock with a diameter of 10 centimeters. The rover picks up the rock and lifts it 20 centimeters straight up. The resulting potential energy of the rock relative to the surface is 2 joules. Gravitational acceleration on Mars is 3.7 meters per second squared. What is the specific gravity of the rock?
73. If a person weighs 200 pounds-mass, how fast must they run in units of meters per second to have a kinetic energy of 1,000 calories?
74. Measurements indicate that boat A has twice the kinetic energy of boat B of the same mass. How fast is boat A traveling if boat B is moving at 30 knots? 1 knot = 1 nautical mile per hour; 1 nautical mile = 6,076 feet.
75. If a 10-kilogram rotating solid cylinder moves at a velocity (v), it has a kinetic energy of 36 joules. Determine the velocity the object is moving in units of meters per second if the kinetic energy is given by $KE = \frac{1}{2}\,mv^2 + \frac{1}{4}\,mv^2$.
76. If a ball is dropped from a height (H) its velocity will increase until it hits the ground (assuming that aerodynamic drag due to the air is negligible). During its fall, its initial potential energy is converted into kinetic energy. If the mass of the ball is doubled, how will the impact velocity change?
77. If a ball is dropped from a height (H) its velocity will increase until it hits the ground (assuming that aerodynamic drag due to the air is negligible). During its fall, its initial potential energy is converted into kinetic energy. If the ball is dropped from a height of 800 centimeters, and the impact velocity is 41 feet per second, determine the value of gravity in units of meters per second.
78. A ball is thrown vertically into the air with an initial kinetic energy of 2,500 joules. As the ball rises, it gradually loses kinetic energy as its potential energy increases. At the top of its flight, when its vertical speed goes to zero, all of the kinetic energy has been converted into potential energy. Assume that no energy is lost to frictional drag, etc. How high does the ball rise in units of meters if it has a mass of 5 kilograms?
79. The specific heats of aluminum and iron are 0.214 and 0.107 calories per gram degree Celsius, respectively. If we add the same amount of energy to a cube of each material of the same mass and find that the temperature of the aluminum increases by 30 degrees Fahrenheit, how much will the iron temperature increase in degrees Fahrenheit?
80. We go out to sunbathe on a warm summer day. If we soak up 100 British thermal units per hour of energy, how much will the temperature of 60,000-gram person increase in 2 hours in units of degrees Celsius? We assume that since our bodies are mostly water they have the same specific heat as water. The specific heat of water is 4.18 joules per gram degree Celsius.
81. A 3-kilogram projectile traveling at 100 meters per second is stopped by being shot into an insulated tank containing 100 kilograms of water. If the kinetic energy of the projectile is completely converted into thermal energy with no energy lost, how much will the water increase in temperature in units of degrees Celsius? The specific heat of water is 1 calorie per gram per degree Celsius.
82. The thermal conductivity of ice is 1.6 watts per meter kelvin. Convert this into units of calories per centimeter second degree Celsius.

83. The thermal conductivity of nickel is 91 watts per meter kelvin. Convert this into units of British thermal units per foot hour degree Fahrenheit.

84. The thermal conductivity of gold is 179 British thermal units per foot hour degree Fahrenheit. Convert this into units of watts per meter kelvin.

85. The thermal conductivity of beryllium is 126 British thermal units per foot hour degree Fahrenheit. Convert this into units of calories per centimeter second degree Celsius.

86. The heat transfer coefficient of water is 300 British thermal units per square foot hour degree Fahrenheit. Convert this into units of watts per square meter kelvin.

87. The heat transfer coefficient of stainless steel is 21 watts per square meter kelvin. Convert this into units of calories per square centimeter second degree Celsius.

88. The heat transfer coefficient of material A is 85 calories per square centimeter second degree Celsius. Convert this into units of watts per square meter kelvin.

89. The heat transfer coefficient of material X is 130 British thermal units per square foot hour degree Fahrenheit. Convert this into units of calories per square centimeter second degree Celsius.

90. When we drive our car at 100 feet per second, we measure an aerodynamic force (called drag) of 66 pounds-force that opposes the motion of the car. How much horsepower is required to overcome this drag?

91. The power required by an airplane is given by $P = Fv$, where P is the engine power, F is the thrust, and v is the plane speed. At what speed will a 500-horsepower engine with 1,000 pounds-force of thrust propel the plane?

92. The power required by an airplane is given by $P = Fv$, where P is the engine power, F is the thrust, and v is the plane speed. What horsepower is required for 1,000 pounds-force of thrust to propel a plane 400 miles per hour?

93. The power required by an airplane is given by $P = Fv$, where P is the engine power, F is the thrust, and v is the plane speed. Which of the following planes has the most power? You must show your work to receive credit.

Plane A:	Thrust = 2,000 pounds-force	Speed = 200 meters per second
Plane B:	Thrust = 13,000 newtons	Speed = 500 feet per second

94. When gasoline is burned in the cylinder of an engine, it creates a high pressure that pushes on the piston. If the pressure is 100 pound-force per square inch, and it moves the 3-inch diameter piston a distance of 5 centimeters in 0.1 seconds, how much horsepower does this action produce?

95. A 100-watt motor (60% efficient) is used to raise a 100-kilogram load 5 meters into the air. How long, in units of seconds, will it take the motor to accomplish this task?

96. A 100-watt motor (60% efficient) is available to raise a load 5 meters into the air. If the task takes 65 seconds to complete, how heavy was the load in units of kilograms?

97. You need to purchase a motor to supply 400 joules in 10 seconds. All of the motors you can choose from are 80% efficient. What is the minimum wattage on the motor you need to choose?

98. A robotic rover on Mars finds a spherical rock with a diameter of 10 centimeters. The rover picks up the rock and lifts it 20 centimeters straight up. The rock has a specific gravity of 4.75. The gravitational acceleration on Mars is 3.7 meters per second squared. If the robot's lifting arm has an efficiency of 40% and required 10 seconds to raise the rock 20 centimeters, how much power (in watts) did the arm use?

99. Consider the following strange, but true, unit:

    1 donkeypower = 0.33 horsepower

    A certain motor is rated to supply an input power of 2,500 calories per minute at an efficiency of 90%. Determine the amount of output power available in units of donkeypower.

100. When boiling water, a hot plate takes an average of 8 minutes and 55 seconds to boil 100 milliliters of water. Assume the temperature in the lab is 75 degrees Fahrenheit. The hot plate is rated to provide 283 watts. How efficient is the hot plate?

101. When boiling water, a hot plate takes an average of 8 minutes and 55 seconds to boil 100 milliliters of water. Assume the temperature in the lab is 75 degrees Fahrenheit. The hot plate is rated to provide 283 watts. If we wish to boil 100 milliliters of acetone using this same hot plate, how long do we expect the process to take? Acetone has a boiling point of 56 degrees Celsius. [*Hint:* You must determine the efficiency of the hotplate.]

102. You are part of an engineering firm on contract by the U.S. Department of Energy's Energy Efficiency and Renewable Energy task force to measure the power efficiency of home appliances. Your job is to measure the efficiency of stove-top burners. In order to report the efficiency, you will place a pan containing one gallon of room temperature water on their stove, record the initial room temperature, turn on the burner, and wait for it to boil. When the water begins to boil, you will record the time it takes the water to boil and look up the power for the burner provided by the manufacturer. After measuring the following stove-top burners, what is the efficiency of each burner?

Room Temp [°F]	Time to Boil [min]	Rated Burner Power [W]
(a) 70	20	1400
(b) 71	25	1300
(c) 72	21	1500
(d) 68	26	1400
(e) 69	18	1350

103. The power available from a wind turbine is calculated by the following equation:

$$P = \frac{1}{2}A\rho v^2$$

where P = power [watts], A = sweep area (circular) of the blades [square meters], ρ = air density [kilograms per cubic meter], and v = velocity [meters per second]. The world's largest sweep area wind turbine generator in Spain has a blade diameter of 420 feet. The specific gravity of air is 0.00123. Assuming a velocity of 30 miles per hour and an actual power of 5 megawatts, determine the efficiency of this turbine.

104. The maximum radius a falling liquid drop can have without breaking apart is given by the equation $R = \sqrt{\sigma/(g\rho)}$, where σ is the liquid surface tension, g is the acceleration due to gravity, and ρ is the density of the liquid. For bromine at 20 degrees Celsius, determine the surface tension (σ) in units of joules per meter squared if the maximum radius of a drop is 0.8 centimeter and the specific gravity of the liquid is 2.9.

105. The maximum radius a falling liquid drop can have without breaking apart is given by the equation $R = \sqrt{\sigma/g\rho}$, where σ is the liquid surface tension, g is the acceleration due to gravity, and ρ is the density of the liquid. For acetone at 20 degrees Celsius, determine the surface tension (σ) in units of joules per meter squared if the maximum radius of a drop is 1 centimeter and the specific gravity of the liquid is 0.79.

106. When a flowing fluid is stopped, its pressure increases. This is called stagnation pressure. The stagnation pressure is determined by: $P_{stagnation} = \frac{1}{2}\rho v^2 + P_{surface}$, where ρ is the fluid density, v the fluid speed, and $P_{surface}$ the atmospheric pressure. Calculate the stagnation pressure in units of atmospheres for acetone flowing at 15 feet per second. Assume the density of acetone to be 790 kilograms per cubic meter.

107. When a flowing fluid is stopped, its pressure increases. This is called stagnation pressure. The stagnation pressure is determined by $P_{stagnation} = \frac{1}{2}\rho v^2 + P_{surface}$, where ρ is the fluid density, v is the fluid speed, and $P_{surface}$ is the atmospheric pressure. If the stagnation pressure is 18 pounds-force per square inch, what is the fluid speed in units of feet per minute? Assume the fluid is methyl ethyl ketone (MEK) and the density of is 805 kilograms per cubic meter.

Chapter 9
DIMENSIONLESS NUMBERS

Recall that in Chapter 7, we discussed the concept of dimensions. A **dimension** is a measurable physical idea; it generally consists solely of a word description with no numbers. A **unit** allows us to quantify a dimension, to state a number describing how much of that dimension exists in a specific situation. Units are defined by convention and related to an accepted standard. Table 9-1 (which is the same as Table 7-1) shows the seven base units and their corresponding fundamental dimensions.

Table 9-1 Fundamental dimensions and base units

Dimension	Symbol	Unit	Symbol
Length	L	meter	m
Mass	M	kilogram	kg
Time	T	second	s
Temperature	Θ	kelvin	K
Amount of substance	N	mole	mol
Light intensity	J	candela	cd
Electric current	I	ampere	A

9.1 COMMON DIMENSIONLESS NUMBERS

Sometimes, we form the ratio of two parameters, where each parameter has the same dimensions. Sometimes, we form a ratio with two groups of parameters, where each group has the same dimensions. The final result in both cases is dimensionless.

Pi (π): One example is the parameter π, used in the calculation of a circumference or area of a circle. The reason π is dimensionless is that it is actually defined as the ratio of the circumference of a circle to its diameter:

$$\pi = \frac{C}{D} = \frac{\text{circumference}}{\text{diameter}} \; \{=\} \; \frac{\text{length}}{\text{length}} = \frac{L^1}{L^1} = L^0$$

The ratio of one length to another length yields a dimensionless ratio. We can see this in another way through reversing the process. For the circumference of a circle:

$$C = \pi D$$

231

and if dimensions are inserted,

$$\{L^1\} = \pi\{L^1\}$$

This equation is dimensionally correct only if π has no dimensions. The same result is obtained for the equation of the area of a circle.

$$A = \pi r^2$$

Inserting dimensions:

$$\{L^2\} = \pi\{L^1\}\ \{L^1\} = \pi\{L^2\}$$

Again, this equation is dimensionally correct only if π is dimensionless.

Specific Gravity (SG): The specific gravity is the ratio of the density of an object to the density of water.

$$\text{Specific gravity} = \frac{\text{density of the object}}{\text{density of water}} = \frac{\text{mass/volume}}{\text{mass/volume}}\ \{=\}\frac{\{M/L^3\}}{\{M/L^3\}} = \{M^0 L^0\}$$

Mach Number (Ma): We often describe the speed at which an airplane or rocket travels in terms of the Mach number, named after Ernst Mach, an Austrian physicist. This number is the ratio of the speed of the plane compared with the speed of sound in air.

$$\text{Mach number} = \frac{\text{speed of the object}}{\text{speed of sound in air}}\ \{=\}\frac{\{L/T\}}{\{L/T\}} = \{L^0 T^0\}$$

Radian [rad]: The derived unit of a radian is defined as the angle at the center of a circle formed by an arc (S) equal in length to the radius (r) of that circle. In a complete circle, there are two π radians. Since by definition a radian is a length (S) divided by a length (r), it is a dimensionless ratio. Note, however, that angles are often measured using the radian as a unit, even though it is dimensionless.

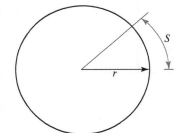

$$1\ \text{radian [rad]} = \frac{S}{r}\{=\}\frac{L}{L} = L^0$$

Table 9-2 Some common dimensionless parameters

Name	Phenomena Ratio	Symbol	Expression
Coefficient of friction	Sideways force (F)/weight of object (w) [object static or kinetic (object sliding)]	μ_{st} and μ_k	F/w
Drag coefficient	Drag force (F_d)/inertia force (ρ, density; v, speed; A body area)	C_d	$F_d/(\tfrac{1}{2}\rho v^2 A)$
Mach number	Object speed (v)/speed of sound (v_{sound})	Ma	v/v_{sound}
Pi	Circle circumference (C)/circle diameter (D)	π	C/D
Poisson's ratio	Transverse contraction (ε_{trans})/longitudinal extension (ε_{long})	ν	$\varepsilon_{trans}/\varepsilon_{long}$
Radian	Arc length (S)/circle radius (r)	rad	S/r
Specific gravity	Object density/density of water	SG	ρ/ρ_{H_2O}

We must remind ourselves that it is always essential to use the appropriate dimensions and units for every parameter. Suppose that we are interested in computing the sine of an angle. This can be expressed as a dimensionless number by forming the ratio of the length of the opposite side divided by the length of the hypotenuse of a right triangle.

$$\sin(x) = \frac{\text{length opposite side}}{\text{length hypotenuse}} \{=\} \frac{L}{L} = L^0$$

In addition to the ratio of two lengths, you will know from one of your math classes that the sine can be also be expressed as an infinite series given by:

$$\sin(x) = x - \frac{x^3}{3!} + \frac{x^5}{5!} - \frac{x^7}{7!} + \cdots$$

LAW OF ARGUMENTS

Any function that can be computed using a series must employ a *dimensionless* argument.

This includes all the trigonometric functions, logarithms, and e^x, where e is the base of natural logarithms.

Let us suppose that the argument x had the units of length, say, feet. The units in this series would then read as:

$$\text{ft} - \frac{\text{ft}^3}{3!} + \frac{\text{ft}^5}{5!} - \frac{\text{ft}^7}{7!} + \cdots$$

We already know that we cannot add two terms unless they have the same units; recall the Plus law from Chapter 7. This is clearly not the case in the example above. The only way we can add these terms, all with different exponents, is if each term is dimensionless. Consequently, when we calculate $\sin(x)$, we see that the x must be dimensionless, which is why we use the unit of radians. This conclusion is true for any function that can be computed using a series form, leading to the **Law of Arguments**.

● **EXAMPLE 9-1**

What are the dimensions of k in the following equation, where d is distance and t is time?

$$d = Be^{kt}$$

Since exponents must be dimensionless, the product of k and t must not contain any dimensions. The dimensions of time are {T}

$$kT^1 \{=\} M^0 L^0 T^0 \Theta^0$$

Solving for k yields:

$$k \{=\} T^{-1}$$

k is expressed in dimensions of inverse time or "per time."

9.2 DIMENSIONAL ANALYSIS

Dimensionless quantities are generated as a result of a process called **dimensional analysis**. As an example, suppose we want to study rectangles, assuming that we know nothing about rectangles. We are interested in the relationship between the area of a rectangle, the width of the rectangle, and the perimeter of the rectangle. We cut out a lot of paper rectangles and ask students in the class to measure the area, the perimeter, and the width (Table 9-3).

Table 9-3 **Rectangle measurements**

Perimeter (P) [cm]	Area (A) [cm²]	Width (W) [cm]
4.02	1.0	1.1
8.75	4.7	1.9
6	2.3	1.55
13.1	6.0	1.1
17.75	19	5.25
10.25	1.2	0.25
12.1	3.0	5.5
6	0.3	2.9
16.25	15.4	5.1
17	7.8	1.05

If we graph the area against the perimeter, we obtain the following plot:

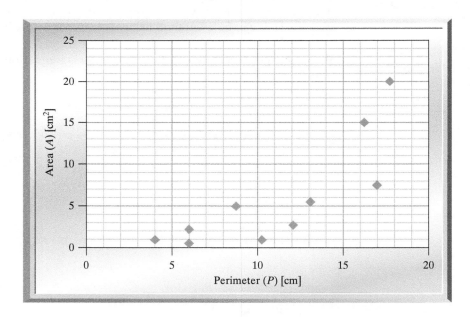

From this, we see that the data are scattered. We would not have a great deal of confidence in drawing conclusions about how the area depended on the perimeter of the rectangle (or in trying to draw a line through the data). The best we could do is to make a statement such as, "It seems that the larger the perimeter, the larger the area." However, close examination of the data table shows that as the perimeter increases from 8.75 to 10.25 centimeters and from 16.25 to 17 centimeters, the area actually decreases in each case. One reason for this problem is that our plot has omitted one important parameter: the width.

Analysis shows that one way in which to generalize plots of this type is to create dimensionless parameters from the problem variables. In this case, we have perimeter with dimension of length, width with the dimension of length, and area with the dimension of length squared. A little thought shows that we could use the ratio of P/W (or W/P) instead of just P on the abscissa. The ratio W/P has the dimensions of length/length, so it is dimensionless. It does not matter whether this is miles/miles, or centimeters/centimeters, but the ratio is dimensionless. Similarly, we could write $A/(W^2)$, and this would also be dimensionless.

These ratios are plotted and shown below. The scatter of the first plot disappears and all the data appear along a single line.

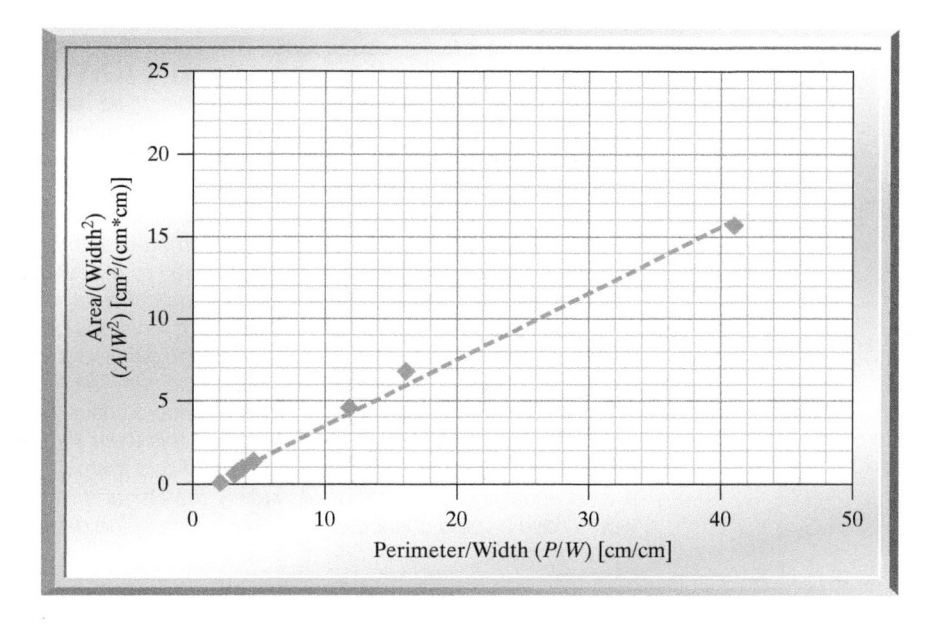

To understand how to read data from this chart, let us examine the following question. If a rectangle has a perimeter of 20 feet and a width of 2 feet, what is the area?

Step A: $P/W = (20\text{ ft})/(2\text{ ft}) = 10$ (with no units).

Step B: From the chart, at a P/W value of 10, we read a value from the line of $A/(W^2) = 3.5$.

Step C: Calculate A from this as $A = 3.5 * (2\text{ ft} * 2\text{ ft}) = 14\text{ ft}^2$.

Some of you may be thinking that we made this problem unnecessarily difficult. After all, anyone who manages to get to college knows that the "sensible" measurements to make are length, width, and area. However, many phenomena are far more complicated than simple rectangles, and it is often not at all obvious what parameters should be measured to characterize the behavior of the system we are studying. In situations of this type, dimensionless analysis can become a powerful tool to help us understand *which* parameters affect the behavior of the system and *how* they affect it. With this in mind, let us look at a slightly more complicated example.

● **EXAMPLE 9-2**

A not-so-famous scientist, Dr. Triticale, decided to apply his scientific skills to cooking. He had always been fascinated with the process of cooking pancakes, so it seemed reasonable that he start there. He wanted to learn how to flip the flapjacks in a graceful arc in the air and then catch them.

He spent long summer days pondering this process until he finally was able to produce a list of the parameters that he felt were important. He kept asking himself, "If I change this parameter, will the trajectory of the pancake change?" If he could answer "Yes!" or even "Probably," he then considered the parameter as important enough to include on his list. As he saw it, these parameters were:

Speed of the frying pan, U	Mass of the flapjack, m
Height of the flip, H	Gravity (it pulls the flapjack back down), g

He then wrote this dependency in equation form as $H = f:(U, m, g)$.

Dr. Triticale realized that while he felt that gravity was important, it would not be easy to change the value of gravity in his tests (he could have gone to a high mountain or the moon, but this was too hard). His plan was to do many tests (and consequently eat many pancakes). He would make many measurements for many different flipping speeds and pancake masses, and try to fit a curve to the data.

Based on his work with conversion factors and his knowledge of the Per law, he reasoned that it is acceptable to multiply parameters with different dimensions. It is also fine to raise a parameter (and its associated units) to a power. Based on his understanding of the Plus law, he knew it is not acceptable to add parameters with different dimensions.

Using this information, he decided that it would be permissible to try to "fit" the dependence of pancake flipping to the important parameters raised to different powers and multiplied together. This would create a single term like $k_1 U^{a_1} m^{b_1} g^{c_1}$.

He also knew that if this term were made to have the same dimensions as H, it just might be a legitimate expression. In fact, if this were the case, he could use many terms, each of which had the dimensions of H and add them all together. While this might not be a valid equation, at least it would satisfy the Per and Plus laws, and with many terms he would have a good chance of his equation fitting the data. So, he boldly decided to try the following series:

$$H = k_1 U^{a_1} m^{b_1} g^{c_1} + k_2 U^{a_2} m^{b_2} g^{c_2} + k_3 U^{a_3} m^{b_3} g^{c_3} + \cdots$$

He needed to determine the values of the dimensionless k constants as well as all of the exponents. He knew that all the terms on the right-hand side must have the same dimensions, or they could not be added together. He also knew that the dimensions on the left and right sides must match.

With this, he then realized that he could examine the dimensions of any term on the right-hand side since each had to be the same dimensionally. He did this by comparing a typical right-hand term with the left-hand side of the equation, or

$$H = k U^a m^b g^c$$

The next step was to select the proper values of a, b, and c, so that the dimensions of the right-hand side would match those on the left-hand side. To do this, he substituted the dimensions of each parameter:

$$L^1 M^0 T^0 = \{LT^{-1}\}^a \{M\}^b \{LT^{-2}\}^c = \{L\}^{a+c} \{M\}^b \{T\}^{-a-2c}$$

For this to be dimensionally correct, the exponents for L, M, and T on the right and left would have to match, or

$$L: 1 = a + c \quad M: 0 = b \quad T: 0 = -a - 2c$$

This yields

$$a = 2 \quad b = 0 \quad c = -1$$

From this, Dr. Triticale settled on a typical term as

$$k\, U^2 m^0 g^{-1}$$

Finally, he wrote the "curve fitting" equation (with a whole series of terms) as

$$H = \sum_{i=1}^{\infty} k_1 U^2 g^{-1} + k_2 U^2 g^{-1} + k_3 U^2 g^{-1} + \cdots = \frac{U^2}{g} \sum_{i=1}^{\infty} k_i = (K)\left(\frac{U^2}{g}\right)$$

Now, armed with this expression, he was sure that he could flip flapjacks with the best, although he knew that he would have to conduct many experiments to make sure the equation was valid (and to determine the value of K). What he did not realize was that he had just performed a procedure called "dimensional analysis."

9.3 RAYLEIGH'S METHOD

In this section we formalize the discussion presented in Example 9-2 by introducing a method of dimensional analysis devised by Lord Rayleigh, John William Strutt, the third Baron Rayleigh (1842–1919). Three detailed examples illustrate his approach to dimensionless analysis:

- Example 9-3, in which we analyze factors affecting the distance traveled by an accelerating object
- Example 9-4, in which we determine the most famous named dimensionless number, Reynolds number
- Example 9-5, in which we simplify one use of Rayleigh's method

No matter the problem, the way we solve it stays the same:

Step 1: Write each variable and raise each to an unknown exponent (use *all* the variables, even the dependent variable). Order and choice of exponent do not matter.

Step 2: Substitute dimensions of the variables into Step 1. Be sure to raise each dimension to the proper exponent groups from Step 1.

Step 3: Group by dimension.

Step 4: Exponents on each dimension must equal zero for dimensionless numbers, so form a set of equations by setting the exponent groups from Step 3 for each dimension equal to zero.

Step 5: Solve the simultaneous equations (as best as you can).

> *Hint:* Number of unknowns – number of equations = number of groups you will have!

Step 6: Substitute results of Step 5 back into Step 1 exponents.

Step 7: Group variables by exponent. These resulting groups are your dimensionless numbers.

Step 8: Be sure to *check* it out!! Are *all* of the ratios really dimensionless?

> *Hint:* If the resulting groups are *not* dimensionless, you most likely goofed in either Step 2 or Step 5!

Rayleigh's analysis is quite similar to the Buckingham Pi method, another method to determine dimensionless groups. Rayleigh's method is, however, a bit more direct and often seems less "mysterious" to those who are new to dimensional analysis. Both methods use a general form with multiplied and exponentiated variables. Any inspection of physics, engineering, and mathematical texts reveal many examples of this form of equation governing a myriad of behaviors.

● **EXAMPLE 9-3**

To develop an understanding of how initial velocity, acceleration, and time all affect the distance traveled by an accelerating object, we conduct some experiments and then analyze the resulting data. We asked a student to conduct a series of tests for us. She observed 25 different moving bodies with a wide range of initial speeds and different accelerations. For each, she measured the distance the bodies traveled for some prescribed time interval. Results are given in Table 9-4.

Table 9-4 Position of a body as a function of initial velocity, acceleration, and time

Test	Initial Velocity (v_0) [m/s]	Acceleration (a) [m/s^2]	Time (t) [s]	Distance (d) [m]
1	3	1	6	36
2	3	2	6	54
3	1.5	5	6	99
4	5	4	6	44
5	5	3	8	136
6	5	5	2	20
7	10	1	9	131
8	14	2	11	275
9	20	3	4	104
10	10	2	4	56
11	10	4	3	48
12	10	6	2	32
13	5	2	2	14
14	8	2	10	180
15	12	2	4	64
16	6	1	4	32
17	2	2	9	99
18	3	3	12	252
19	6	4	6	108
20	15	5	2.4	50
21	4	7	7.2	210
22	2	2	8	80
23	9	8	6.2	210
24	6.7	2	1.7	14
25	3.1	2	10	131

In addition, we would like to use this data set to help make predictions of the distance traveled by other bodies under different conditions. For example, we might want to answer the following question:

■ What is the acceleration needed to travel 4,800 meters in 200 seconds, if the initial velocity is 8 meters per second?

There are several independent variables (initial velocity, acceleration, and time), so it is not obvious what to plot. We can write the dependency as

$$d = f: (v_0, a, t)$$

We anticipate that it is difficult to draw conclusions regarding the interdependence of all of these variables. Realizing this, we plot distance against time without worrying about the initial velocity and the acceleration.

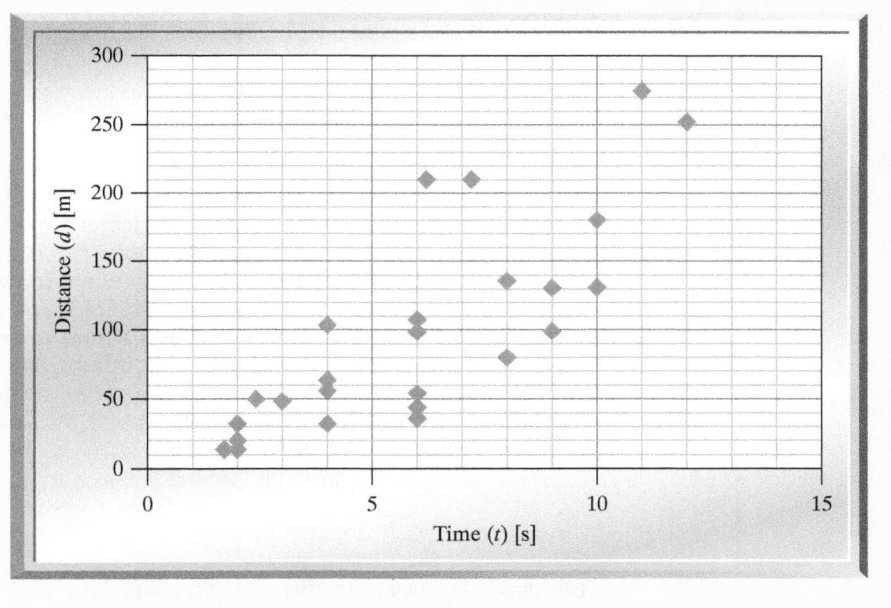

It seems that, in general, the longer one travels, the farther one goes. Upon closer inspection, however, it is obvious that this is not always the case. For example, for a travel time of 6 seconds, the distance traveled varies from about 25 to 210 meters. Since enough tests were not conducted with systematic variation of the initial velocity or acceleration, it is not possible to do much better than this. We certainly have no hope of answering the questions above with any confidence. In addition, since the values are so scattered, we realize that we have no good way to determine if any of our measurements were "bad."

With this disheartening conclusion, we perform a dimensional analysis in an attempt to place the parameters into fewer groups. The immediate problem we face is how to combine the parameters to give dimensionless groups. For rectangles, this was relatively easy to do by inspection. The parameters in this new problem are slightly more complicated, and although we might find suitable groups by inspection, as the problems become a lot harder (and they will), we need some sort of standard method, or algorithm, to define suitable dimensionless groups.

This technique is relatively simple and comprises the following eight steps:

Step 1: Raise each variable to a different unknown power, using symbols for the power variables that do not already appear in the problem, and then multiply all of these individual terms together. For example, since the current problem has both an a and d used as variables, we should not use a and d for the powers; hence we choose the letters p through s for the exponents. The order in which we list the variables and assign exponents is completely random.

This gives us the term: $d^p v_0^q a^r t^s$

Step 2: Substitute the correct dimensions for each variable.

$$\{L\}^p \left\{\frac{L}{T}\right\}^q \left\{\frac{L}{T^2}\right\}^r \{T\}^s$$

Step 3: Expand the expression to have each dimension as a base raised to some power.

$$\{L\}^{p+p+r} \{T\}^{-q-2r+2}$$

Step 4: For the expression in Step 3 to be dimensionless, each exponent must equal zero, or

$$p + q + r = 0 \text{ and } -q - 2r + s = 0$$

Step 5: Solve for the exponents. In this case, we have two equations and four unknowns, so it is not possible to solve for all the unknowns in terms of an actual number. We must be satisfied with finding two of the exponents in terms of the other two. This might seem problematic, but we will find that this not only is not a difficulty, but also is quite common in this type of analysis. **Note that there are many ways to do this and all will lead to two dimensionless ratios. If you do not like the plot you get from doing it one way, try solving for different exponents and see if that provides a better plot. All will be correct, but some are easier to use than others.** Although several procedures will lead to solutions, in general, we will solve for one of the variables, and then substitute into the other equations to reduce the number of variables. If a variable appears in all or most of the equations, that may be a good one to begin with.

In our example, we solve the second equation for q.

$$q = -2r + s$$

Substituting for q into the other equation gives

$$p - 2r + s + r = 0$$

thus,

$$p = r - s$$

At this point, we have defined p and q in terms of the other two variables, r and s.

Step 6: Substitute into the original expression.

$$d^{r-s} v_0^{-2r+s} a^r t^s$$

Note that all of the exponents are now expressed in terms of only two variables, r and s.

Step 7: Simplify by collecting all terms associated with the remaining exponential variables (r and s in this case).

$$\left(\frac{da}{v_0^2}\right)^r \left(\frac{tv_0}{d}\right)^s$$

Step 8: The simplification in Step 7 gives the dimensionless ratios we are looking for. Dropping the exponents assumed in Step 1 gives the following groups:

$$\left(\frac{da}{v_0^2}\right) \text{ and } \left(\frac{tv_0}{d}\right)$$

We need to double-check to make sure that both the groups are dimensionless. Before plotting them, we make two additional observations. (1) The variables of distance and initial velocity appear in both quantities. This may not always be desirable. (2) The initial velocity appears in the denominator of the first ratio. This may cause problems if we are examining data in which the initial velocity is very small, making the ratio very large. While dimensional analysis is much more involved than the examples given here, there are several important facts for you to remember.

First, since the results of the dimensional analysis produces dimensionless ratios, these ratios may be used as they appear above or they may be inverted. In other words, for this example, we can use $\frac{da}{v_0^2}$ or $\frac{v_0^2}{da}$ equally well.

To eliminate the problem of very small initial velocity values, the second form is preferable for our work here. As a side note, if we are interested in the behaviors at very small times, then we would prefer for time to appear in the numerator of the second ratio (and it already does).

Second, it is permissible to alter the form of one of the ratios by multiplying it by the other one or by the inverse of the other one or by the other one squared, etc. This will change the form of the first ratio and may produce results that are easier to interpret. A simple example can be used to show this. For the two ratios here, multiply the first ratio by the second ratio squared. This yields a "new" first ratio as $\left[(at^2)/d\right]$ and this could be used along with the second ratio $[(tv_0)/d]$. This result may have the advantage of initial velocity appearing in only one of the ratios. To continue this example, we create a spreadsheet with the four columns of data and then add two extra columns, one for each of the two dimensionless ratios $\left[v_0^2/(da)\right]$ and $[(v_0t)/d]$. Once this is done, it is a straightforward matter to plot one against the other. This result is shown below:

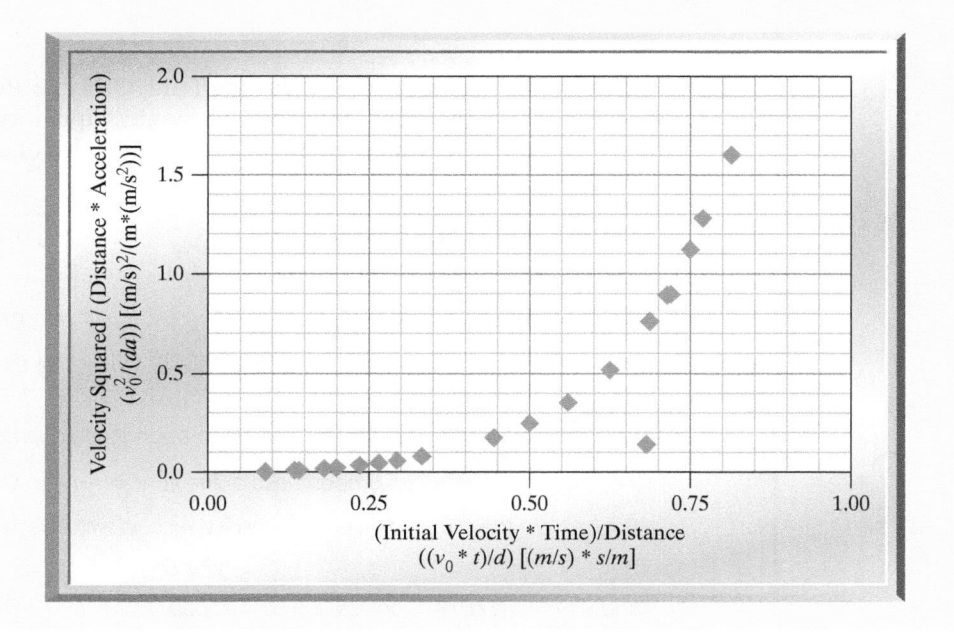

NOTE

There seems to be one "bad" data point. Would you have been able to pick out this point from the original data or from the dimensional plot?

Now the scatter from the original dimensional plot is gone, and all but one data point seems to lie on a smooth curve. We can use this plot to determine the relationship between distance traveled, acceleration, time, and initial velocity. Let us see how to do this for the question we posed earlier.

What acceleration is required to go 4,800 meters in 200 seconds if the initial car velocity is 8 meters per second?

On the x-axis: [(8 m/s) (200 s)]/(4,800 m) = 0.33.
Reading from the graph: $v_0^2/(da) = 0.075$.
Solving for acceleration: $a = (8 \text{ m/s})^2/(0.075) (4,800 \text{ m}) = 0.18 \text{ m/s}^2$.

Several important conclusions can be drawn from this exercise.

- Dimensionless parameters often allow us to present data in an easily interpretable fashion when the "raw" data have no recognizable pattern.
- When we use the exponent approach to find dimensionless parameters, we need to remember that the exponents could be either positive or negative. Thus, in the case of the rectangle, *P/W* is just as good as *W/P*. You can always try both to see which gives the best-looking results. The choice is yours, and sometimes depends on whether one of the variables goes to zero; since you cannot divide by zero, that variable should not be in the denominator, if possible.
- If we "collapse" the data by using dimensionless parameters so that a single curve can fit through the resulting points, *bad data points will usually become obvious.*
- Finally, this approach can reduce literally thousands of different measurements into one simple curve. In the case of the car, the single line we obtained will work for all possible combination of times, initial velocities, accelerations, and distance. If we used dimensional plots, we would need more plots, with many lines on each plot. This would require an entire book of plots rather than the single plot with a single line that we obtained above by dimensionless ratios.

● EXAMPLE 9-4

To classify the smoothness of a flowing fluid, Osborne Reynolds (1842–1912, British, ME) developed the now famous dimensionless quantity of **Reynolds number**. His theory stated that the smoothness or roughness (a lot of eddies or swirling) of a fluid depended upon:

How fast the fluid was moving (velocity)	$v \ [=] \text{ m/s}$
The density of the fluid	$\rho \ [=] \text{ kg/m}^3$
The diameter of the pipe	$D \ [=] \text{ m}$
How hard it was to move the fluid (viscosity)	$\mu \ [=] \text{ g/(cm s)}$

Reynolds knew the smoothness depended upon these quantities:

$$\text{Smoothness of the flow} = f\text{: } (v, \rho, D, \mu)$$

But how did they depend on one another? We could write the four variables above as

$$v^a \rho^b D^c \mu^d$$

and if this was dimensionless, it would appear as $M^0 \ L^0 \ T^0 \ \Theta^0$.

To make this grouping dimensionless, first we substitute in the dimensions of the four variables to obtain:

$$\left\{\frac{L}{T}\right\}^a\left\{\frac{M}{L^3}\right\}^b\{L^c\}\left\{\frac{M}{LT}\right\}^d = M^{b+d}L^{a-3b+c-d}T^{-a-d}$$

Note we generally have dimensions of mass, length, time, and temperature in this problem; there is no temperature dimension. If this is to be dimensionless, then the exponents on all of the dimensions must equal zero, therefore:

M: $b + d = 0$
L: $a - 3b + c - d = 0$
T: $-a - d = 0$

This gives three equations in four unknowns, so we will have to solve for three of the variables in terms of the fourth. In this example, we solve for the three unknowns a, b, c in terms of d:

M: $b = -d$
T: $a = -d$
L: $c = -a + 3b + d = d - 3d + d = -d$

Substituting these back into the original parameters gives:

$$v^{-d}\rho^{-d}D^{-d}\mu^d$$

We see that there is one dimensionless group, since all the parameters have an exponent of d. We can write

$$\frac{\mu}{v\rho D}\{=\}\frac{\dfrac{M}{LT}}{\dfrac{L}{T}\dfrac{M}{L^3}L}$$

Since the variables of diameter and velocity can approach zero, the Reynolds number is commonly written as follows:

$$Re = \frac{\rho D v}{\mu}$$

*If the Reynolds number has a value less than 2,000, the flow is described as **laminar**, meaning it moves slowly and gently with no mixing or churning. If the Reynolds number has a value greater than 10,000, the flow is described as **turbulent**, meaning it moves quickly with much mixing and churning (lots of eddies) occurring. The region in between 2,000 and 10,000 is called the **transition region**.*

NOTE

The Reynolds number is used to describe fluid flow.

$Re < 2,000$ = laminar

$2,000 < Re < 10,000$ = transitional

$Re < 10,000$ = turbulent

● **EXAMPLE 9-5**

Suppose we conduct an experiment with a ball that we throw from the top of a tall tower of height H. We throw it directly downward with some initial velocity v, and then measure the elapsed time t until it hits the ground. We vary the initial height and the initial velocity. The variables of interest in this problem are H, v, and t. A little thought leads us to include g, since it is the force of gravity that causes the ball to fall in the first place.

Using Rayleigh's method, find a set of dimensionless ratios that can be used to correlate our data.

Step 1: *Write each variable and raise each to an unknown exponent (use all the variables, even the dependent variable).*

$$t^a H^b v^c g^d$$

Step 2: *Substitute dimensions of the variables into Step 1. Be sure to raise each dimension to the proper exponent from Step 1.*

$$t^a \{=\} \mathsf{T}^a \quad H^b \{=\} \mathsf{L}^b \quad v^c \{=\} \mathsf{L}^c \mathsf{T}^{-c} \quad g^d \{=\} \mathsf{L}^d \mathsf{T}^{-2d}$$

Step 3: *Group by dimension.*

$$\mathsf{L}^{b+c+d} \mathsf{T}^{a-c-2d}$$

Step 4: *Exponents on each dimension must equal zero for dimensionless numbers! Form a set of equations by setting the exponents for each dimension equal to zero.*

$$b + c + d = 0 \quad a - c - 2d = 0$$

Step 5: *Solve the simultaneous equations (as best as you can).*

$$b = -c - d \quad a = c + 2d$$

Step 6: *Substitute results of Step 5 back into Step 1 exponents.*

$$t^{c+2d} H^{-c-d} v^c g^d$$

Step 7: *Group variables by exponent. These resulting groups are your dimensionless numbers.*

$$\left[\frac{v\, t}{H} \right]^c \quad \left[\frac{g\, t^2}{H} \right]^d$$

Step 8: *Be sure to check it out!! Are all of the ratios really dimensionless?*

NOTE

We are not sure that the results of this technique are *physically correct*, only that they are *dimensionally correct*.

At the beginning of the analysis, when in doubt about the importance of a parameter, put it in the list of important parameters.

Always remember that we initiate this procedure simply by providing a list of parameters we think are important to the situation at hand. If we omit an important parameter, our final result will not be physically correct, even if it is dimensionally correct. Consequently, if we select an improper parameter, then when tests are conducted, we will discover that it was not important to the problem and we can drop it from further consideration. *We cannot decide whether any variable is important until we conduct some experiments.*

Consequently, if we are *sure* that a parameter is important, then we know it should *not* drop from the analysis. The only way it can be retained is if at least one other parameter contains the missing dimension. In this case, we need to ask ourselves what other parameters might be important, add them to our list, and rework the analysis.

Dimensional analysis helps us organize data by allowing us to plot one-dimensionless parameter against another, resulting in one line on a single plot. This is a powerful result, and reduces a problem of multiple initial parameters to one containing only two. This discussion leads to the **Problem Simplification Rule**:

By performing dimensional analysis of the parameters, we can generally find dimensionless groupings to effectively reduce the number of parameters, facilitating the presentation of interdependencies and often simplifying the problem.

In-Class Activities

ICA 9-1

Complete the following table:

	Quantity	SI Units	Dimensions				
			M	L	T	Θ	N
Example	Acoustic impedance	(Pa s)/m	1	–2	–1	0	0
(a)	Fuel consumption	kg/(kW h)					
(b)	Heat transfer coefficient	W/(m^2 K)					
(c)	Ideal gas constant	(Pa L)/(mol K)					
(d)	Latent heat	BTU/lb$_m$					
(e)	Mass density	kg/m^3					
(f)	Molar heat capacity	cal/(mol °C)					
(g)	Rate of drying	lb$_m$/(ft^2 h)					
(h)	Specific heat	J/(g °C)					
(i)	Specific weight	N/m^3					
(j)	Surface tension	J/m^2					
(k)	Thermal conductivity	cal/(cm s °C)					
(l)	Thermal resistance	(K m^2)/W					

ICA 9-2

Calculate the numerical value of each of the dimensionless parameters listed in the table. Be sure to check that the ratio is actually dimensionless after you insert the values.

	Situation	Name	Expression	Value
(a)	Water in a pipe	Reynolds number, Re	$\dfrac{\rho v_w D_{pipe}}{\mu}$	
(b)	Hot water	Prandtl number, Pr	$\dfrac{\mu C_p}{k}$	
(c)	Air over a flat plate	Nusselt number, Nu	$\dfrac{hL}{k}$	
(d)	Sphere in air	Drag coefficient, C_d	$\dfrac{F}{\frac{1}{2}\rho v_a^2 A}$	
(e)	Water: Effect of surface tension	Weber number, We	$\dfrac{\rho v_w^2 d}{\sigma}$	
(f)	Water in a river	Froude number, Fr	$\dfrac{v_w}{\sqrt{gH}}$	
(g)	Wind making a wire "sing"	Strouhal number, St	$\dfrac{\omega D_{wire}}{v_a}$	

Properties and definitions for this problem:

Property	Symbol	Units	Air	Water
Density	ρ	slugs/ft^3	0.002378	1.94
Dynamic viscosity	μ	kg/(m s)	2×10^{-5}	4×10^{-4}
Heat transfer coefficient	h	W/(m^2 °C)	20	—
Thermal conductivity	k	W/(m K)	0.025	0.7
Surface tension	σ	dynes/cm	—	70
Specific heat	C_p	cal/(g °C)	0.24	1

Property	Symbol	Units	Value
Plate length	L	ft	2
Silhouette area of object	A	in^2	120
Water depth	H	m	3
Water speed	v_w	cm/s	210
Air speed	v_a	mph	60
Pipe diameter	D_{pipe}	in	6
Drag force on sphere	F	N	30
Depth of water film	d	cm	3
Oscillation frequency	ω	Hz (or cycles/s)	140
Wire diameter	D_{wire}	mm	20

ICA 9-3

We have encountered some equations in an old set of laboratory notes, each having two terms on the right-hand side of the equation. We realize we cannot read the final variable or variables listed in each equation. Using dimensions and the equation laws, determine the missing variable from the list below, and if that variable is multiplied or divided. In some questions, more than one variable may be required to form the necessary dimensions.

Variable choices:

Area	Acceleration	Density	Height
Mass	Speed	Time	Volume

(a) Distance = (speed) * (time) + (acceleration) ___ (___)
(b) Volume = (dimensionless constant) * (length) * (area) + (speed) ___ (___)
(c) Specific gravity = (density) * (volume)/(mass) + (height) * (length) ___ (___)
(d) Speed = (distance)/(time) + (acceleration) ___ (___)
(e) Energy = (mass) * (speed)^2 + (mass) * (height) ___ (___)
(f) Power = (mass) * (area)/(time)^3 + (mass) * (acceleration) ___ (___)
(g) Pressure = (density) * (area)/(time)^2 + (mass) * (acceleration) ___ (___)

ICA 9-4

A fluid with a specific gravity of 0.91 and a viscosity of 0.38 pascal-seconds is pumped through a 25-millimeter diameter smooth pipe at an average velocity of 2.6 meters per second. Determine the Reynolds number in the pipe for the system and indicate if the flow is laminar, transitional, or turbulent.

ICA 9-5

Brine, with a density of 1.25 grams per cubic centimeter and a viscosity of 0.015 grams per centimeter second is pumped through a 5-centimeter radius steel pipe at an average velocity of 15 centimeters per second. Determine the Reynolds number in the pipe for the system and indicate if the flow is laminar, transitional, or turbulent.

ICA 9-6

The Euler number is a function of the pressure drop, velocity, and density. Determine the form of the Euler number with Rayleigh's method.

Pressure drop	ΔP	pascal
Density	ρ	grams per cubic centimeter
Velocity	v	meters per second

ICA 9-7

When a simple turbine is used for mixing, the following variables are involved:

Power requirement	P	watt
Shaft speed	N	hertz
Blade diameter	D	meters
Blade width	W	meters
Liquid density	ρ	kilograms per meter cubed

Determine a set of dimensionless groups for the turbine, using Rayleigh's method.

ICA 9-8

We assume that the total storm water runoff (R, given in volume units) from a plot of land depends on the length of time that it rains (t), the area of the land (A), and the rainfall rate (r, given in inches per hour).

Rainfall Rate (r) [in/h]	Land Area (A) [acres]	Rainfall Duration (t) [h]	Measured Runoff (R) [ft^3]
0.50	2	3.0	49
0.30	14	2.5	172
0.78	87	4.1	4,563
0.15	100	2.2	541
0.90	265	0.4	1,408
0.83	32	7.6	3,310
1.40	18	1.8	744
0.22	6	4.7	102
0.67	26	3.1	886
0.48	62	4.9	2,392

(a) Using the data, construct a plot of the runoff versus the time that it rains. You should see that this plot is of little help in understanding the relationships between the various parameters.
(b) Using this plot, estimate the total runoff from 200 acres if rain falls for 3 hours at a rate of 1.2 inches per hour. Is this even possible using this plot?
(c) Using the variables in the table, complete a dimensional analysis to help you plot the data. You should obtain two dimensionless ratios. Plot these, with the ratio containing the total runoff on the ordinate. This plot should collapse the values to a single line. Draw a smooth curve through the values.
(d) Use this line to answer question (b) again.

ICA 9-9

We are interested in analyzing the velocity of a wave in water. By drawing a sketch of the wave, and labeling it, we decide that the velocity depends on the wavelength (λ), the depth of the water (H), the density of the water (ρ), and the effect of gravity (g). We have measured wave speeds in many situations; the data are given below.

Water Depth (H) [m]	Wave Length(λ) [m]	Velocity (v) [m/s]
1.0	10.0	7.4
1.0	20.0	7.7
2.0	30.0	10.8
9.0	40.0	18.7
0.2	13.0	3.5
4.0	24.0	13.6
18.0	20.0	14.0
0.3	2.6	4.0
33.0	30.0	17.1
5.0	15.0	11.9

(a) Construct a plot of wave velocity versus either wave length or water depth. You will see substantial scatter.
(b) Using your plot, estimate the wave velocity for a wave length of 25 meters in water that is 25 meters deep. Is this even possible using this plot?
(c) Perform a dimensional analysis on the parameters (v, ρ, H, g, and λ). After calculating the new dimensionless ratio values, make a dimensionless plot.
(d) Recalculate the answer to question (b).

Chapter 9 REVIEW QUESTIONS

1. Complete the following table:

Quantity	Symbol	"Derived" from	Typical SI Units	Dimensions M	L	T	Θ
(a) Dynamic viscosity	μ	Newton's law of viscosity	g/(cm s)				
(b) Mass density	ρ	$\rho = m/V$	kg/m^3				
(c) Specific heat	C_p	$Q = m\, C_p\, \Delta T$	J/(g °C)				
(d) Surface tension	σ	From theory or experiment	J/m^2				
(e) Thermal conductivity	k	Fourier's law of heat transfer	W/(m °C)				
(f) Young's modulus	E	Stress/strain	Pa				

2. The Darcy–Weisbach friction formula for pipes is used to calculate the frictional energy loss per unit mass of fluid flowing through the pipe. Examine the equations below and indicate for each if the equation is a valid or invalid equation; justify your answer for each case. In these equations,

h_L	= energy loss per unit mass	$[=]$ J/kg
f	= friction factor	$[=]$ dimensionless
L	= length of pipe	$[=]$ ft
D	= diameter of pipe	$[=]$ cm
v	= average velocity	$[=]$ cm/min
g	= acceleration of gravity	$[=]$ m/s^2

(A) $h_L = f \dfrac{L\, v}{D\, 2g}$

(B) $h_L = fL \dfrac{v^2}{2g}$

(C) $h_L = f \dfrac{L\, v^2}{D\, 2}$

(D) $h_L = f \dfrac{L\, 2D}{v\, g}$

3. We wish to analyze the velocity (v) of a fluid exiting an orifice in the side of a pressurized tank. The tank contains a fluid to a depth (H) above the orifice. The air above the fluid in the tank is pressurized to a value of (P). We realize the greater the pressure inside, the greater the velocity. We also believe the greater the depth of fluid, the greater the velocity. Examine the equations below and indicate for each if the equation is a valid or invalid equation; justify your answer for each case. In these expressions, g is the acceleration due to gravity and ρ is the fluid density.

(A) $v = \dfrac{P}{\rho} + \sqrt{2gH}$

(B) $v = \sqrt{\dfrac{P}{\rho} + 2H}$

(C) $v = \sqrt{2gH}$

(D) $v = \sqrt{\dfrac{2P}{\rho} + 2gH}$

(E) $v = \sqrt{2P + 2gH}$

4. Wind energy uses large fans to extract energy from the wind and turn it into electric power. Examine the equations below and indicate for each if the equation is a valid or invalid equation; justify your answer for each case. In these expressions, P is the power, η is the efficiency, ρ is the density of the air, A is the area swept out by the fan blades, and v is the velocity of the wind.

(A) $P = \eta\rho A^2 v^2$

(B) $P = \eta\rho A v^2$

(C) $P = \eta\rho A v^3$

(D) $P = \eta\rho^2 A v$

(E) $P = \eta\sqrt{\rho A v^3}$

5. One of the most famous experiments in physics is the Millikan oil-drop experiment. In it, very tiny drops are sprayed into a closed container by an atomizer. The drops tend to fall, but they are so small that the air slows them down. Sir George Stokes studied this part of the oil-drop experiment to see how fast the·drops would fall in the still air in the container. He found that the fall speed (v) depended on the mass of the drop (m), the acceleration of gravity (g), the radius of the drop (r), and the viscosity of the air (μ). The equation governing the motion of the drop was determined to be

$$mg - 6\pi\mu rv = 0$$

The constant (the value 6) in the second term of the equation is dimensionless. What are the dimensions of viscosity (μ)?

6. One of the most famous experiments in physics is the Millikan oil-drop experiment. In it, very tiny drops are sprayed into a closed container by an atomizer. The drops tend to fall, but they are so small that the air slows them down. Sir George Stokes studied this part of the oil-drop experiment to see how fast the drops would fall in the still air in the container. He found that the fall speed (v) depended on the mass of the drop (m), the acceleration due to gravity (g), the radius of the drop (r), and the viscosity of the air (μ). The equation governing the motion of the drop was determined to be

$$mg - 6\pi\mu rv = 0$$

What kind of quantity is the second term ($6\pi\mu rv$)? Choose from the following and prove your answer in terms of dimensions.

(A) Pressure
(B) Force
(C) Velocity
(D) Energy

7. The friction factor (f) is a dimensionless number used in fluid flow calculations. It can be related to velocity in the pipe (v) and the fluid density (ρ) by the following equation:

$$f = \dfrac{2\varphi}{\rho v^2}$$

Using the laws of dimensions in equations, determine the dimensions of the variable φ.

8. The friction factor (f) is a dimensionless number used in fluid flow calculations. It can be related to velocity in the pipe (v) and the fluid density (ρ) by the following equation:

$$f = \frac{2\varphi}{\rho v^2}$$

What kind of quantity is the variable φ? Choose from the following and prove your answer in terms of dimensions:

(A) Pressure

(B) Force

(C) Velocity

(D) Energy

9. In previous examples, we discussed quantities with fundamental dimensions of mass {M}, length {L}, time {T}, and temperature {Θ}. As we study other fields, such as electricity and magnetism, we must introduce new fundamental dimensions, such as {I}, representing electrical current, which cannot be expressed in terms of mass, length, time, or temperature. Electric power can be calculated as $P = I^2R$, where R is the resistance [ohms, Ω] and I is the electrical current [amperes, A]. Assuming that electrical power must have the same dimension as mechanical power, derive the fundamental dimension of the ohm in terms of mass {M}, length {L}, time {T}, temperature {Θ}, and electrical current {I}.

10. What are the dimensions of the constant coefficient (k) in the following equations?

   (a) Energy $= k *$ (mass) $*$ (temperature)

   (b) Energy $= k *$ (height)

   (c) Energy $= k *$ (mass) $*$ (acceleration) $*$ (length)

   (d) Force $= k *$ (pressure)

   (e) Mass flowrate $= k *$ (velocity) $*$ (area)

   (f) Pressure $= k *$ (temperature)/(volume)

   (g) Pressure $= k *$ (density) $*$ (acceleration)

   (h) Power $= k *$ (mass) $*$ (acceleration) $*$ (temperature)

   (i) Power $= k *$ (volume)/(time)

   (j) Volume of a sphere $= k *$ (diameter)^3

   (k) Volumetric flowrate $= k *$ (speed)

   (l) Work $= k *$ (volume)

11. A biodegradable fuel having a specific gravity of 0.95 and a viscosity of 0.04 grams per centimeter second is draining by gravity from the bottom of a tank. The drain line is a plastic 3-inch diameter pipe. The velocity is 5.02 meters per second. Determine the Reynolds number in the pipe for the system and indicate if the flow is laminar, in transition, or turbulent.

12. A sludge mixture having a specific gravity of 2.93 and a viscosity of 0.09 grams centimeter per second is pumped from a reactor to a holding tank. The pipe is a 2½-inch diameter pipe. The velocity is 1.8 meters per second. Determine the Reynolds number in the pipe for the system and indicate if the flow is laminar, in transition, or turbulent.

13. Water (specific gravity = 1.02; viscosity = 0.0102 grams per centimeter second) is pumped through a 0.5-meter diameter pipe. If the Reynolds number is 1,800 for the system, determine the velocity of the water in units of meters per second.

14. Water (specific gravity = 1.02; viscosity = 0.0102 grams per centimeter second) is pumped through 0.5 meter diameter pipe. If the Reynolds number is 5,800 for the system, determine the velocity of the water in units of meters per second.

15. The Peclet number is used in heat transfer in general and forced convection calculations in particular. It is a function of the two other dimensionless groups, the Reynolds number and the Prandtl number. Determine the functional form of these dimensionless groups, using Rayleigh's method. The problem depends on the following variables:

   ▪ Liquid density, ρ [=] kg/m^3

   ▪ Specific heat of liquid, C_p [=] J/(g °C)

   ▪ Liquid viscosity, μ [=] kg/(m s)

- Thermal diffusivity, α [=] m²/s
- Thermal conductivity of the plate, k [=] W/(m °C)
- Distance from edge of the plate, x [=] m
- Liquid velocity, v [=] m/s

16. When a fluid flows slowly across a flat plate and transfers heat to the plate, the following variables are important. Analyze this system using Rayleigh's method.
    - Liquid density, ρ [=] kg/m³
    - Specific heat of liquid, C_p [=] J/(g °C)
    - Liquid viscosity, μ [=] kg/(m s)
    - Thermal conductivity of the plate, k [=] W/(m °C)
    - Heat transfer coefficient, h [=] W/(m² °C)
    - Distance from edge of the plate, x [=] m
    - Liquid velocity, v [=] m/s

17. A projectile is fired with an initial velocity (v_0) at an angle (θ) with the horizontal plane. Find an expression for the range (R). The data are given in the table below. Use the data in the table to create one or more *dimensional* plots (e.g., launch speed on the abscissa and range on the ordinate). From these plots, answer the following questions.

Launch Angle (θ) [°]	Launch Speed (v_0) [m/s]	Measured Range (R) [m]
4	70	73
50	50	230
3	50	30
45	18	32
37	27	75
35	60	325
22	8	4.4
10	30	34
88	100	77
45	45	210

(a) If the launch speed is 83 meters per second and the launch angle is 64 degrees, what is the range? You will likely find it difficult to provide a good estimate of the range, but do the best you can.

(b) Complete a dimensional analysis of this situation. In this case, you would assume that the important parameters are θ, v_0, and R. Upon closer examination, however, it would seem that the range on Earth and on the moon would be different. This suggests that gravity is important, and that you should include g in the list of parameters. Finally, since it is not clear how to include θ, you could omit it and replace the velocity by v_x and v_z, where x is the distance downrange and z the height. You should use this information to determine dimensionless parameters. Also, you must decide how the lengths in R and g should appear. When you complete the analysis, you should find that these four parameters will be grouped into a single dimensionless ratio.

(c) Use the data from the table to calculate the numerical value of the ratio for each test. Note that $v_x = v \cos(\theta)$ and that you can find a similar expression for v_z. Insert these expressions into your dimensionless ratio.

(d) Assuming that you performed the dimensional analysis correctly, you should find that the ratio you obtained will always give the same value (at least nearly, within test-to-test error). Calculate the average value of the tests, and if it is nearly an integer, use the integer value.

(e) Finally, set this ratio equal to this integer, and then solve for the range R. Write your final equation for the range (i.e., R = xxxxx). Now using this equation, answer question (a) again.

18. The drag on a body moving in a fluid depends on the properties of the fluid, the size and the shape of the body, and probably most importantly, the velocity of the body. We find that for high velocities, the fluid density is important but the "stickiness" (or viscosity) of the fluid is not. The frontal area of the object is important. You might expect that there will be more drag on a double-decker bus moving at 60 miles per hour than on a sports car moving at 60 miles per hour.

The table below gives some data for tests of several spheres placed in air and in water. The terminal velocity, the point at which the velocity becomes constant when the weight is balanced by the drag, is shown.

Object	Drag (F) [lb$_f$]	Velocity (v) [ft/s]	Diameter (D) [in]	Fluid
Table tennis ball	0.005	12	1.6	Air
Bowling ball	6	60	11	Air
Baseball	0.18	41	3	Air
Cannon ball	33	174	9	Air
Table tennis ball	0.0028	0.33	1.6	Water
Bowling ball	12.4	3.1	11	Water
Baseball	0.31	1.7	3	Water
Cannon ball	31	6.2	9	Water

(a) Plot the drag on the ordinate and the velocity of the object on the abscissa for each fluid on a separate plot. Use the graphs to answer the following question: What is the drag on a baseball in gasoline (specific gravity = 0.72) at a speed of 30 feet per second? You may struggle with this, but do the best you can.

(b) Now complete a dimensional analysis of this situation and replot the data. First, recognize that the important parameters are the ball diameter (use the silhouette area of a circle), the density of the fluid, the drag, and the velocity. You will find a single dimensionless ratio that combines these parameters.

(c) Compute the value of this ratio for the eight tests. Be sure in your analysis that you use consistent units so that the final ratio is truly unitless.

(d) Use this result to help you answer question (a) again.

UMBRELLA PROJECT

BREAKEVEN ANALYSIS: SMALL PARTS

A "**widget**" is defined by the Oxford dictionary as: **An indefinite name for a gadget or mechanical contrivance, especially a small manufactured item.**

It is used when the actual product being considered is irrelevant to the discussion.

[Photo courtesy of S. Stephan]

Our engineering team has been asked by upper management to analyze the cost of upgrading an aging machine line that produces widgets. The initial information available from three different machine vendors is outlined below. Perform a breakeven analysis on all three machines and recommend a vendor for purchase.

PROJECT A SPECIFICATIONS

From the initial analysis, the following can be assumed:

- Current material cost is $0.55/widget. With a part redesign, research hopes to reduce the material cost to $0.35/widget, but purchasing is worried because the cost of raw materials may increase the material cost to $0.85/widget. Your analysis should be able to handle fluctuations in material cost. The choice of machine has no effect on the material cost.

- The current selling price per widget is $3.50. It is expected any increase in material cost will be directly passed on to the customer, so your analysis should be able to handle fluctuations in selling price.
  - The current plant operates five days per week.
  - The annual sales volume is estimated at four million parts per year.
  - Management will not consider any project length greater than two years.

Each machine vendor has supplied the following information:

Machine Company #1: WYSIWYG

Machine cost: $2,750,000

Energy cost: $0.45/widget

Labor cost: $0.25/widget

Maximum capacity per day: 5,500 widgets

Machine Company #2: Thingamabob, LLC

Machine cost: $3,250,000

Energy cost: $0.25/widget

Labor cost: $0.35/widget

Maximum capacity per day: 7,000 widgets

Machine Company #3: GizmosRUs

Machine cost: $4,500,000

Energy cost: $0.15/widget

Labor cost: $0.05/widget

Maximum capacity per day: 6,000 widgets

Special features: This machine is able to run "lights out," extending the time of operation from five to seven days per week.

PROJECT B SPECIFICATIONS

From the initial analysis, the following can be assumed:

- The current material cost is $0.75/widget. With a part redesign, research hopes to reduce the material cost to $0.65/widget, but purchasing is worried because the cost of raw materials may increase the material cost to $0.85/widget. Your analysis should be able to handle fluctuations in material cost. The choice of machine has no effect on the material cost.
- The current selling price per widget is $3.00. It is expected any increase in material cost will be directly passed on to the customer, so your analysis should be able to handle fluctuations in selling price.
  - The current plant operates five days per week.
  - The annual sales volume is estimated at five million parts per year.
  - Management will not consider any project length greater than two years.

Each machine vendor has supplied the following information:

Machine Company #1: WidgetsRUs

Machine cost: $2,500,000
Energy cost: $0.40/widget
Labor cost: $0.25/widget
Maximum capacity per day: 5,000 widgets

Machine Company #2: Widgets, Inc.

Machine cost: $3,500,000
Energy cost: $0.15/widget
Labor cost: $0.35/widget
Maximum capacity per day: 7,500 widgets

Machine Company #3: Klein Teil

Machine cost: $5,000,000
Energy cost: $0.15/widget
Labor cost: $0.05/widget
Maximum capacity per day: 6,500 widgets
Special features: This machine is able to run "lights out," extending the time of operation from five to seven days per week.

DATA ANALYSIS

Workbook

Each team must submit a final workbook, including the following components:

- A worksheet that allows an end user to change the initial vendor information and material costs and observe the effect in the graphs.
- A breakeven analysis graph, using the number of widgets produced.
- A breakeven analysis graph, using time in months.

The workbook will be graded for neatness, organization, unit consistency, and proper plots. It should be a proper workbook, containing heading information on every page.

Written Section

Each team must submit a final written communication, including the following components:

- A summary of the analysis performed, including one of the following combinations:
  - One breakeven analysis graph and one summary table
  - Two breakeven analysis graphs
- A final vendor recommendation and supporting facts to justify your recommendation.
- An explanation including supporting facts of WHY the other companies were not chosen.

For the submission format, each team may choose or may be assigned by your instructor one of the following options. The written portion will be graded on neatness, organization, spelling/grammar/mechanics, formatting of embedded graphs, and strength of conclusions.

Written Option One: Memo

A memo template, provided electronically and shown in Section 4.4 in your textbook, must be used.

Written Option Two: Short Report

A report template, provided electronically and shown in Section 4.4 in your textbook, must be used.

Written Option Three: Poster

A poster template, provided electronically and shown in Section 4.4 in your textbook, must be used.

Written Option Four: PowerPoint Presentation

A PowerPoint presentation using voice-over should be developed to address the requirements given above. Information on developing a presentation is given in your textbook in Section 4.1, and the accompanying online slides discuss voice-over.

TRENDLINE ANALYSIS: HOOKE'S LAW

When Robert Hooke first published his now famous law of elasticity in 1660, he published it in anagram form:

ceiiinossssttuv

Before patents, many scientists used anagrams to release discoveries without giving away details. He published the solution in 1678.

The designer of a museum exhibit of miniature string instruments faces a challenge that the instruments need regular tuning, but the museum budget cannot support someone with a trained ear to perform this function. You have been asked to investigate the possibility of using spring tensioners to allow an untrained tuner to be able to confirm that the string tension is correct without audible tuning. If the desired string tension of the miniature violin in the exhibit is 0.022 newtons (about one ten-thousandth of the normal violin string tension), what combination of springs can confirm this string tension yet stretch less than 1 centimeter? The idea is that a tension of 0.022 newtons will stretch the springs a known amount that can be easily measured.

PREDICTION

Prior to testing, each lab partner(s) should individually create a sketch of the force (ordinate) versus the displacement (abscissa) for the following springs:

- Spring #1: Spring constant of 1 newton per meter [N/m].
- Spring #2: Stiffer than Spring #1.
- Spring #1 and #2 in series.
- Spring #1 and #2 in parallel.

Discuss the plots of each lab partner as a group. Settle on the plot that is the "best" of the group. Each person in the group should sketch this "best" set of curves as a second set of lines on their original plot using a different line type and/or color to distinguish them.

DATA COLLECTION

Create an Excel workbook to collect the data. Place all data on a single worksheet.

Single Springs

- Connect one of the springs to an eye hook at one end.
- Measure the original distance between the bottom hook on the spring and the bottom edge of the board.

- Gently hook one mass on the bottom of the spring.
- Measure the new distance between the bottom hook of the spring and the bottom edge of the board.
- Record the displacement and the corresponding mass used in the worksheet.
- Repeat for a minimum of five different masses for this spring. Note that the masses have a hook on the top and an eyelet on the bottom so they can be easily hooked together.
- Repeat for each spring provided. Please note you do NOT need to use the same masses for each spring. Choose masses that are appropriate for the spring being tested.

For simplification, label the springs in order from the stiffest to the least stiff.

Springs in Combination

Repeat Part II for sets of two springs in parallel and then for two springs in series, forming all combinations you can with the available springs. Please note you do NOT need to use the same masses for each spring combination. Choose masses that are appropriate for the springs being tested.

With two springs you can form two combinations: one in parallel and one in series. With three springs of unique stiffness, you can form eight combinations using the following configurations:

- All three in parallel.
- All three in series.
- Two parallel springs in series with the third (three ways).
- Two series springs in parallel with the third (three ways).

DATA ANALYSIS

Workbook

Each team must submit a final workbook, including the following components:

- All data collected.
- Complete the necessary unit conversions within the worksheet. Be sure to use consistent units. Remember, mass and weight (which is a force) are NOT the same! Most spring constants are reported in units of newton per meter; complete any necessary conversions within the worksheet BEFORE creating the graph.
- Create a graph or graphs containing the data sets, with appropriate trendlines:
  - The force, position data set for the springs individually
  - The force, position data set for the springs in parallel
  - The force, position data set for the springs in series

The workbook will be graded for neatness, organization, unit consistency, and proper plots. It should be a proper workbook, containing heading information on every page.

Written Section

Each team must submit a final written communication, including the following components:

- List the spring constants in units of newton per meter for each spring and each spring combination. Sort the list in the order of stiffness, with the stiffest listed first.

- A summary of the analysis performed, including one of the following combinations:
  - One graph and one summary table
  - Two graphs

- Find a spring combination that stretches less than 1 centimeter under a force of 0.022 newtons. Note that the springs provided may not be sufficient to accomplish this task, in which case you should determine a configuration using as few springs as possible and only considering the stiffnesses provided.

For the submission format, each team may choose or may be assigned by your instructor one of the following options. The written portion will be graded on neatness, organization, spelling/grammar/mechanics, formatting of embedded graphs, and strength of conclusions.

Written Option One: Memo

A memo template, provided electronically and shown in Section 4.4 in your textbook, must be used.

Written Option Two: Short Report

A report template, provided electronically and shown in Section 4.4 in your textbook, must be used.

Written Option Three: Poster

A poster template, provided electronically and shown in Section 4.4 in your textbook, must be used.

Written Option Four: PowerPoint Presentation

A PowerPoint presentation using voice-over should be developed to address the requirements given above. Information on developing a presentation is given in your textbook in Section 4.1, and the accompanying online slides discuss voice-over.

UMBRELLA PROJECT

TRENDLINE ANALYSIS: PENDULUMS

The direction of a Foucault Pendulum's swing moves in relation to the rotation of the Earth.

It is named for Léon Foucault, a French physicist, who is credited with the experiment in 1851, the first dynamic proof of the Earth's rotation.

[Photo courtesy of E. Stephan]

You work for a clock-manufacturing company. You have been asked to explore the best combination of mass and length for a pendulum to put into a grandfather clock. If the desired pendulum swing is 30 times per minute, with the motion of the pendulum to the right and back to the left counting as one full swing, what is the best mass and length of pendulum to choose?

DATA COLLECTION

Effect of Length

Hang a 50-gram mass from the loop at the end of a long piece of fishing line. Wrap the other end of the line around a rod so the distance from the mass to the rod is about 10 inches. Carefully measure and record in a worksheet the distance from the center of the rod to the center of the mass. One person should release the pendulum and the other should use a stopwatch to time how long is required for five full swings, with the motion of the pendulum to the right and back to the left counting as one full swing. The person releasing the pendulum should pull the mass to the side about 15 degrees from the vertical, keeping the body of the mass in line with the fishing line.

After release, the student with the stopwatch should wait for at least one full swing and then start the stopwatch when the mass is at one side or the other and just beginning to reverse direction. Count five full swings and then stop the watch when the mass returns the fifth time to the point where the watch was started. Record the time in the worksheet. Keeping the length constant, repeat this procedure for a total of three trials.

Repeat the entire procedure above for lengths of approximately 15, 20, 25, and 30 inches. Remember to carefully measure and record the actual distance from the center of the rod to the center of the mass.

Effect of Mass

Hang a 200-gram mass from the loop at the end of one of the pieces of fishing line. Wrap the other end of the line around a rod so the distance from the mass to the rod is about 20 inches. One person should release the pendulum and the other should use the stopwatch to time how long is required for five full swings, with the motion of the pendulum to the right and back to the left counting as one full swing. The person releasing the pendulum should pull the mass to the side about 15 degrees from the vertical, keeping the body of the mass in line with the fishing line. After release, the student with the stopwatch should wait for at least one full swing and then start the stopwatch when the mass is at one side or the other and just beginning to reverse direction. Count five full swings and then stop the watch when the mass returns the fifth time to the point where the watch was started. Record the time in the worksheet. Keeping the mass constant, repeat this procedure for a total of three trials.

Repeat the entire procedure above for masses of 100, 50, 20, and 10 grams.

Since the masses are different sizes, you will have to adjust the length from the center of the rod to the center of the mass each time you change masses. **This length should be the same for all five masses**.

DATA ANALYSIS

Analysis Option One: Workbook

Each team must submit a final workbook, including the following components:

■ All data collected.
  • **Calculate** the average of the three times and record the "Average Time." Divide each average time by five (you timed five complete swings, not just one) to obtain the value for the period corresponding to each condition.

■ **Model for Effect of Length:**
  • Draw a proper plot of period and length.
  • Fit an appropriate trendline model.

■ **Model for Effect of Mass:**
  • Draw a proper plot of period and mass.
  • Fit an appropriate trendline model.

Do not be tempted to ascribe undue significance to small amounts of experimental error. You may see this effect in this experiment. In both trendline models, be sure to consider if the data has an offset, and include any corrections necessary.

The workbook will be graded for neatness, organization, unit consistency, and proper plots. It should be a proper workbook, containing heading information on every page.

Analysis Option Two: MATLAB

Program

Each team must write a MATLAB program that will analyze the data you collected in the lab and present your results using formatted output and plots. At a minimum, your program should:

■ **Ask** the user to enter data similar to the data collected in the lab. Be sure to give the user good instructions as to the type, format, and units of the input required for each part of the experiment.
■ For both the effect of length data and the effect of mass data, the program should **calculate** the average of the three times for each data set. Divide each average time by five (you timed five complete swings, not just one) to obtain the value for the period corresponding to each condition.
■ **Create** a set of graphs:
  • Draw a proper plot of period and length.
  • Draw a proper plot of period and mass.
  • Fit appropriate trendline models to each graph using polyfit.

All plots should appear in separate plot figures.

■ Do not be tempted to ascribe undue significance to small amounts of experimental error. You may see this effect in this experiment. In both trendline models, be sure to consider if the data has an offset, and include any corrections necessary.
■ In the command window, your program should **display using formatted output** the trendline equations for the different springs analyzed in this project; an example is shown in Tables A and B, below. All trendline values must be displayed with a reasonable number of decimal places using output from the polyfit function. For all tables, you do not need to show the table instructions "Using the trendlines . . .," the gridlines or the table headings in bold font or with a background color—you should duplicate the column format only. Note the values shown are EXAMPLES only— these are not the experimental results you will obtain.

Table A: Using the trendline on the period, length graph, for each data set, determine the type of expression shown by the trendline (linear, power, or exponential). Then, based upon the model chosen, list the value and units of the parameters m and b.

For linear:	m = slope	b = intercept
For power:	m = exponent	b = constant
For exponential:	m = exponent	b = constant

Model Type	Value and Units of "m"		Value and Units of "b"	
Linear	10	m / s	30	s

Table B: Using the trendline on the period, mass graph, for each data set, determine the type of expression shown by the trendline (linear, power, or exponential). Then, based upon the model chosen, list the value and units of the parameters m and b.

For linear:	m = slope	b = intercept
For power:	m = exponent	b = constant
For exponential:	m = exponent	b = constant

Model Type	Value and Units of "m"		Value and Units of "b"	
Linear	10	m / s	30	s

All MATLAB codes should include a proper header, including all your team member names, course/section, date, problem statement, documentation on all variables used in the program/function, and any assumptions made in the design of your algorithm. All MATLAB codes should contain an adequate number of comments throughout the code.

Written Section

Each team must submit a final written communication, including the following components:

- Which trendline type did you choose to determine the effect of each variable? Justify the choice in terms of the physical meaning of the trendline parameters, such as the physical meaning of the slope and the intercept if the trendline is linear.
- Explain why you did not choose the other trendline types in terms of their physical meaning.
- Determine the optimum mass and length of the pendulum to achieve 30 swings per minute.

For the submission format, each team may choose or may be assigned by your instructor one of the following options. The written portion will be graded on neatness, organization, spelling/grammar/mechanics, formatting of embedded graphs, and strength of conclusions.

Written Option One: Memo

A memo template, provided electronically and shown in Section 4.4 in your textbook, must be used.

Written Option Two: Short Report

A report template, provided electronically and shown in Section 4.4 in your textbook, must be used.

Written Option Three: Poster

A poster template, provided electronically and shown in Section 4.4 in your textbook, must be used.

Written Option Four: PowerPoint Presentation

A PowerPoint presentation using voice-over should be developed to address the requirements given above. Information on developing a presentation is given in your textbook in Section 4.1, and the accompanying online slides discuss voice-over.

TRENDLINE ANALYSIS: BOUNCING SPRINGS

A mass bouncing on a spring is an example of simple harmonic motion. In this process, energy is transformed between potential energy and kinetic energy.

Other examples of simple harmonic motion include pendulums and molecular vibrations.

Various devices have been designed and patented to agitate a fishing line to make lures more attractive to fish. A group of friends wants to be more successful in fishing, but does not want to go to the trouble and expense of purchasing one of these devices. They ask you as an engineer if you can design one from scrap materials.

BASIC INFORMATION

NOTE

To model the oscillating mass-spring system mathematically, differential equations are required. You will learn how to solve such equations in your future courses.

This experiment investigates the oscillation frequency of a mass suspended from a spring. When a mass is suspended from a spring and allowed to come to rest, the spring will be stretched so that the upward spring force balances the downward force (weight) of the mass. We will call the location of the mass suspended in this way the rest position.

If the mass is raised above the rest position, the spring is less stretched and the spring force on the mass is less than the weight of the mass. If the mass is then released, it will move downward due to the imbalance in the forces. When the mass reaches the location of the rest position, its velocity is not zero. In order to slow the mass to a stop, there must be an upward force exerted on the mass. As the mass descends beyond the rest position, the spring is stretched more, increasing the upward spring force so that it is greater than the force (weight) of the mass, causing the mass to decelerate (accelerate upward).

Eventually, the mass slows to a stop, but since the mass is below the rest position there is a net upward force that causes the mass to begin rising again. This continues over and over with the mass oscillating up and down with the rest position in the middle of the oscillation. Eventually, frictional forces will bring the mass back to the rest position at a complete stop.

DATA COLLECTION

Initial Setup

1. Clamp a wooden block to a table securely, with a hook on the underside of the block, and positioned so that the hook is well beyond the edge of the table.

2. Hang the spring provided from the hook.
3. Measure the distance from the underside of the block to the lowest point on the spring. Record the initial distance from the block to the bottom of the spring.
4. Read this entire step before doing it!

- For each of the three masses provided, CAREFULLY hang the mass on the bottom of the spring, and then slowly and gently lower it to the rest position.
- DO NOT simply let go of the mass or you may damage the spring.
- With each mass in the rest position, measure the distance from the underside of the block to the lowest point of the spring.
- Record the values of the masses and the corresponding distances to the rest position in an Excel workbook.

5. Repeat for each spring provided. Please note you do NOT need to use the same masses for each spring. Choose masses that are appropriate for the spring being tested.

Effect of Mass

1. Attach the smallest mass to the spring and carefully lower it to the rest position. Remeasure the rest position and verify that it agrees with the value recorded earlier.
2. Raise the mass vertically until the spring is almost, but not quite, back to the unstretched length. The distance from the underside of the block to the lowest point on the spring will be slightly more than the initial spring position. Determine the amount you raised the spring from the rest position. Record the amount raised.
3. Read this entire step before doing it!

- Reset the stopwatch.
- Carefully release the mass from the raised position so that it oscillates up and down with no horizontal motion.
- Wait for three oscillations, and then, while watching the mass, start the stopwatch when the mass reaches its lowest point.
- Count 20 full oscillations, and when the mass reaches the lowest point on the twentieth cycle, stop the watch.

4. Record the time for 20 oscillations in the table below.
5. Repeat Step 3 for the remaining masses, raising each the same amount in Step 2. Please note you do NOT need to use the same masses for each spring. Choose masses that are appropriate for the spring being tested.
6. Within the worksheet, calculate the period and frequency for each mass.

Effect of Release Position

1. Choose one spring. Attach the 50-gram mass to the spring, and carefully lower it to the rest position.
2. Raise the mass ¾ inch vertically.
3. Read this entire step before doing it!

- Reset the stopwatch.
- Carefully release the mass from the raised position so that it oscillates up and down with no horizontal motion.
- Wait for three oscillations, and then, while watching the mass, start the stopwatch when the mass reaches its lowest point.
- Count 20 full oscillations, and when the mass reaches the lowest point on the twentieth cycle, stop the watch.
- Record the time for 20 oscillations in an Excel workbook.

4. Repeat Step 3 by raising the mass a distance of 1, 1¼, 1½, and 1¾ inches. Note: If the stretch amount at rest position is less than one or more of these increments, come as close as you can without going beyond that value.
5. Within the worksheet, calculate the period and frequency for each mass.

DATA ANALYSIS

Analysis Option One: Workbook

Each team must submit a final workbook, including the following components:

- All data collected.
  - **Calculate** how much the spring was stretched by each mass (distance from block to rest position minus initial distance from block to bottom of spring) and record the spring extensions.
- **Model for Effect of Length:**
  - **Calculate** the period and frequency for each mass.
    - The period is the length of time required for one oscillation.
    - The frequency is the number of oscillations per second, which is simply the inverse of the period.
  - Draw a proper plot of period and length.
  - Fit an appropriate trendline model.
- **Model for Effect of Initial Displacement:**
  - **Calculate** the period and frequency for each mass.
    - The period is the length of time required for one oscillation.
    - The frequency is the number of oscillations per second, which is simply the inverse of the period.
  - Draw a proper plot of frequency and initial displacement.
  - Fit an appropriate trendline model.

In both models, be sure to consider if the data has an offset, and include any corrections necessary.

The workbook will be graded for neatness, organization, unit consistency, and proper plots. It should be a proper workbook, containing heading information on every page.

Analysis Option Two: MATLAB

Program

Each team must write a MATLAB program that will analyze the data you collected in the lab and present your results using formatted output and plots.

At a minimum, your program should:

- Ask the user to enter data similar to the data collected in the lab. Be sure to give the user good instructions as to the type, format, and units of the input required for each part of the experiment.
- **Calculate** how much the spring was stretched by each mass (distance from block to rest position minus initial distance from block to bottom of spring) and record the spring extensions.

- **Calculate** the period and frequency for each mass.
  - The period is the length of time required for one oscillation.
  - The frequency is the number of oscillations per second, which is simply the inverse of the period.
- **Calculate** the period and frequency for each release position.
  - The period is the length of time required for one oscillation.
  - The frequency is the number of oscillations per second, which is simply the inverse of the period.
- **Determination of Spring Constants:**
  - Using MATLAB (not by hand), determine the force applied to each spring in the Initial Setup.
  - Draw a proper plot of force (ordinate) and elongation. The graph should contain three data sets, one for each spring tested.
  - Fit an appropriate trendline model using the output from the `polyfit` function.
- **Model for Effect of Mass:**
  - Draw a proper plot of frequency (ordinate) and mass. The graph should contain three data sets, one for each spring tested.
  - Fit an appropriate trendline model using the output from the `polyfit` function.
- **Model for Effect of Initial Displacement:**
  - Draw a proper plot of frequency (ordinate) and initial displacement.
  - Fit an appropriate trendline model using the output from the `polyfit` function.

All plots should appear in separate plot figures.

- In the command window, your program should display using formatted output the trendline equations for the different springs analyzed in this project; an example is shown below. All trendline values must be displayed with a reasonable number of decimal places using output from the polyfit function. For all tables, you do not need to show the table instructions "Using the trendlines ...," the gridlines; or the table headings in bold font or with a background color—you should duplicate the column format only. Note the values shown are EXAMPLES only—these are not the experimental results you will obtain.

Table A: Using the trendlines on the force, elongation graph, determine the stiffness (k value) of each spring. As a formatted output table, list the spring name, trendline equation generated from polyfit, and the spring stiffness value and units similar to the following table.

Spring Name	Trendline Equation	Spring Stiffness (k) [value and units]
Alpha	$F = 10 \times$	10 N / m
Beta	$F = 32 \times$	32 N / m

Table B: Using the trendlines on the frequency, mass graph, for each data set, determine the type of expression shown by the trendline (linear, power, or exponential). Then, based upon the model chosen, list the value and units of the parameters m and b.

For linear:	m = slope	b = intercept
For power:	m = exponent	b = constant
For exponential:	m = exponent	b = constant

Spring Name	Model Type	Value and Units of "m"		Value and Units of "b"	
Alpha	Linear	10	m / s	30	s
Beta		25		50	

Table C: Using the trendline on the frequency, displacement graph, for the data set, determine the type of expression shown by the trendline (linear, power, or exponential). Then, based upon the model chosen, list the value and units of the parameters m and b.

For linear:	m = slope	b = intercept
For power:	m = exponent	b = constant
For exponential:	m = exponent	b = constant

Model Type	Value and Units of "m"		Value and Units of "b"	
Exponential	20	m	30	m / s

All MATLAB codes should include a proper header, including all your team member names, course/section, date, problem statement, documentation on all variables used in the program/function, and any assumptions made in the design of your algorithm. All MATLAB codes should contain an adequate number of comments throughout the code.

Written Section

Each team must submit a final written communication, including the following components:

- Which trendline type did you choose to determine the effect of each variable? Justify the choice in terms of the physical meaning of the trendline.
- Explain why you did not choose the other trendline types in terms of their physical meaning.
- Determine a mass and initial displacement required to create a complete oscillation every two seconds. Make sure the initial displacement and mass chosen will not permanently damage the spring and make sure the mass is a size commonly available. This will provide a starting point for the next phase of water testing. (This will not be part of our experiment.)

For the submission format, each team may choose or may be assigned by your instructor one of the following options. The written portion will be graded on neatness, organization, spelling/grammar/mechanics, formatting of embedded graphs, and strength of conclusions.

Written Option One: Memo

A memo template, provided electronically and shown in Section 4.4 in your textbook, must be used.

Written Option Two: Short Report

A report template, provided electronically and shown in Section 4.4 in your textbook, must be used.

Written Option Three: Poster

A poster template, provided electronically and shown in Section 4.4 in your textbook, must be used.

Written Option Four: PowerPoint Presentation

A PowerPoint presentation using voice-over should be developed to address the requirements given above. Information on developing a presentation is given in your textbook in Section 4.1, and the accompanying online slides discuss voice-over.

MATHEMATICAL MODEL ANALYSIS: CANTILEVER BEAMS AND CLEAN WATER

The New River Gorge Bridge in West Virginia, shown here, is the world's third longest single arch bridge. The bridge is 3,030 feet long, with an arch of 1,700 feet. The bridge is 876 feet above the New River, the fifth highest vehicular bridge in the world.

[Photo courtesy of E. Stephan]

Our engineering firm has been contacted by a biosystems engineering company researching a device to measure the amount of suspended sediment in rivers. The instrumentation is hanging from a long metal bar over the water. As water flows by the instruments, the resulting drag force produced makes the bar bend.

Your design team must conduct tests on the metal bar to determine a mathematical model that can be used in the field to determine the optimal instrumentation configuration.

NAE GRAND CHALLENGE FOR ENGINEERING: PROVIDE ACCESS TO CLEAN WATER

One of the 14 National Academy of Engineering Grand Challenges is **Provide Access to Clean Water.** According to the NAE website (www.engineeringchallenges.org):

> "Lack of clean water is responsible for more deaths in the world than war. About 1 out of every 6 people living today do not have adequate access to water, and more than double that number lack basic sanitation, for which water is needed. In some countries, half the population does not have access to safe drinking water, and hence is afflicted with poor health. By some estimates, each day nearly 5,000 children worldwide die from diarrhea-related diseases, a toll that would drop dramatically if sufficient water for sanitation was available."

The goal of this textbook project is to develop a model of a cantilever beam frame that will allow various water quality test instruments to be suspended over, and partially immersed in, the water below. This frame is part of a wastewater treatment facility being constructed for Engineers Without Borders (EWB), a nonprofit group that designs sustainable engineering projects for developing communities around the world. Your team must analyze the type of beam that will be used to suspend instruments over a mangrove swamp on the edge of the property set aside for the project. These instruments are especially vital during the rainy season, when runoff flows through the swamp, creating unpredictable sediment and flow conditions. You will make a recommendation as to the optimal beam configuration that allows all the instruments to be installed.

THEORY BACKGROUND

In studying springs and circuits, we established a general expression regarding how an applied force causes a change and meets with a resistance. The deflection (Δ) of a cantilever beam under a load (P) fits this same linear model.

$$P = K\Delta$$

When a "system"...	...is acted upon by a "force"...	...to change a "parameter"...	...the "system" opposes the change by a "resistance"	Equation
Physical object	External push or pull (F)	Acceleration (a)	Object mass (m)	$F = ma$
Beam	Vertical force or load (P)	Tip deflection (Δ)	Beam stiffness (K)	$P = K\Delta$

Previously, we discussed the spring stiffness (k) as a property of the spring. In reality, this one property summarizes a variety of factors that determine how the spring responds to a force. In the case of a cantilever beam, the beam stiffness (K) is a function of the beam length (L), the beam width (W), the beam thickness (T), a material property of the beam (E, the beam's modulus of elasticity or Young's modulus), and a geometrical constant (c).

We wish to study the behavior of a beam to determine the relationship between the beam stiffness and the other variables. To begin with, we assume a power relationship of the variables that make up K, but do not know the power values (m, n, p, q).

$$K = cE^m W^n T^p L^q$$

We will begin by holding several parameters constant, and varying a single parameter to determine the effect on the stiffness. For example, the beam shape (c), material (E), width (W), and thickness (T) will be kept constant. At different beam lengths (L), several masses will be applied and the resulting deflection measured.

PROJECT SPECIFICATIONS

Data Collection

Data will be collected in class according to the specific instructions provided for you by your professor, or sample data will be provided in an Excel workbook.

Model Development

The mathematical model to predict the load or deflection of a cantilever beam must be recorded on the Model Form (Appendix A, Part I). The exponent values ($m, n, p,$ and q) and corresponding graphs necessary to complete the calculations (outlined under Data Analysis) and the shape constant "c" must be completed and verified by the instructor before proceeding with the model verification.

Model Verification

Each team will test their mathematical model. To make your prediction, you must use your worksheet or your program (outlined under Data Analysis) to predict actual field conditions.

Once it has been verified your worksheet or program is calculating correctly, you will use it to complete Appendix A, Part II:

- Given the known load, predict the deflection, or
- Given the maximum deflection, predict the maximum load.

Each team will be given up to six beams at random and asked to predict the outcome of a given experimental scenario. Once the team has predicted the outcome, the team will test the actual beams or be given simulated results. The prediction and results will be compared in the final report.

Model Application

The model will be used to design a cantilever beam component of a frame that will allow various water quality test instruments to be suspended over, and partially immersed in, the water below. This frame is part of a wastewater treatment facility being constructed for Engineers Without Borders (EWB), a nonprofit group that designs sustainable engineering projects for developing communities around the world. Your team must analyze the type of beam that will be used to suspend instruments over a mangrove swamp on the edge of the property set aside for the project.

You will make a recommendation as to the optimal beam configuration that allows all the instruments to be installed, taking into consideration the following:

- Cost of the beams available, minimizing costs wherever possible. Remember that EWB operates solely on donations and funds raised by volunteers.
- More than one frame can be constructed, so more than one beam can be recommended.
- No more than three instruments can be mounted on a single beam.
- Only the support beam for the instruments must be recommended; the frame components are not considered part of the design. In order to prevent failure of the beam itself, no more than 1 inch of deflection is allowed.

Your recommendations should include a short discussion justifying the selection of the beams, summary table with the beams selected, and the instruments to be mounted on each one.

Table 1 contains a list of the instruments to be installed. A portion of each one will be suspended below the water line, creating a drag force. The table includes the estimated drag force of each instrument. Assume all instruments are mounted at the end of the beam, and that up to three instruments can be mounted at the same location using specially designed mounting brackets.

Table 2 contains the beams available for use. All beams must be clamped at the top of the support frame with no beam length extending above the top of the frame. The beams may not be cut or made shorter than the length shown in the table. Your team only needs to recommend the beams to be used to mount the instruments, not the entire support frame. Only one beam of each type is available.

Table 1 Instruments used to test water quality and estimated forces each will apply when mounted in slow-moving water

Instrument	Estimated Drag Force [pound-force]
Turbidity meter	3
Portable sampler	1
Velocity flow meter	4
Nutrient meter (ammonium and orthophosphate)	2
pH electrode	0.5

Table 2 List of materials available to construct the cantilever beam segments of the frames that will support water quality test instruments

Beam Type	Cross Section [in × in]	Length [in]	Cost
Aluminum	0.5 × 0.25	18	$10
Aluminum	0.25 × 0.25	30	$4
Aluminum	1.0 × 0.125	18	$13
Stainless steel	0.5 × 0.125	24	$15
Stainless steel	0.5 × 0.25	24	$20
Stainless steel	0.25 × 0.25	18	$10

Figure 1 View from the side of a support frame with cantilever beam and mounted water quality test instrument. Drag forces will push the beam perpendicular to the bank of the swamp, in the direction of the water flow. Figure 1A: View from above—the frame, beam, and instrument.

DATA ANALYSIS

Analysis Option One: Workbook

Examine the data taken in the lab. You should reorder your data into the following groups. Note that some beams may appear in more than one group . . . and one beam should appear in EVERY group.

- Length data, testing 1 inch wide by ⅛ inch thick aluminum beams.
- Width data, testing ⅛ inch thick by 18 inches long aluminum beams.
- Thickness data, testing 1 inch wide by 18 inches long aluminum beams.
- Modulus of elasticity data, testing 1 inch wide by 18 inches long by ⅛ inch thick beams.

Create two graphs for each parameter (eight total), using the data above to determine the relationship between the stiffness and the parameter. Each graph should be displayed as an independent worksheet and not embedded within a worksheet.

- Length: (A) force versus deflection and   (B) stiffness versus L
- Width: (A) force versus deflection and   (B) stiffness versus W
- Thickness: (A) force versus deflection and   (B) stiffness versus T
- Modulus: (A) force versus deflection and   (B) stiffness versus E

For parameters that are not linear, a graph must be included using semilog or log–log coordinates making the data appear linear. For all graphs, the appropriate trendline equation and R^2 value must be given.

Create one worksheet showing the determination of shape constant "c" for each stiffness trendline generated (four total), the average value for "c," the standard deviation, and units where appropriate.

Create one worksheet, allowing the user to predict actual field conditions according to the following specifications:

- Use Conditional Statements, Data Validation, and LOOKUP functions to:
  - Create a list to allow the user to choose the input calculation units (AES, Metric, English).
    - AES units should ask for calculations in units of inches, pounds-mass, pounds-force, and pound-force per square inch.
    - Metric units should ask for calculations in units of centimeters, grams, newtons, and pascals.
    - English units should ask for calculations in units of feet, slugs, pounds-force, and pound-force per square foot.
  - Create a list to allow the user to choose the beam material.
  - Request correct input parameters in the selected unit system from the user.
  - Create an error message if the data entered are outside the allowable range for the parameters as tested during the experiment. If the input parameters are outside the range of those tested—for example, if the user enters a beam length of 50 feet—a warning should appear to tell the user the parameters exceed the acceptable range.
- The user should be able to choose to enter the load or deflection. Then:
  - If the load is entered, the program will predict the deflection.
  - If the maximum deflection is entered, the program will predict the maximum load.

The workbook will be graded for neatness, organization, unit consistency, and proper plots. It should be a proper workbook, containing heading information on every page.

Analysis Option Two: MATLAB

MATLAB Code and Excel Workbook

Examine the data taken in the lab in the Excel workbook. You should reorder your data into the following groups. You may reorder this data manually in Excel, or within your code after importing the data. Note that some beams may appear in more than one group . . . and one beam should appear in EVERY group.

- Length data, testing 1 inch wide by ⅛ inch thick aluminum beams.
- Width data, testing ⅛ inch thick by 18 inches long aluminum beams.
- Thickness data, testing 1 inch wide by 18 inches long aluminum beams.
- Modulus of elasticity data, testing 1 inch wide by 18 inches long by ⅛ inch thick beams.

Import the data into MATLAB using `xlsread`. Create `polyfit` solutions for each parameter, using the data to determine the relationship between the stiffness and the parameter.

- Length: (A) force versus deflection and   (B) stiffness versus L
- Width: (A) force versus deflection and   (B) stiffness versus W
- Thickness: (A) force versus deflection and   (B) stiffness versus T
- Modulus: (A) force versus deflection and   (B) stiffness versus E

A menu should ask the user to choose one parameter to display graphically. The chosen parameter should have two corresponding graphs appear, listed as (A) and (B) above. The graphs should be proper plots, and show both experimental data and the appropriate trendline(s). Once displayed, the program should ask the user if they wish to see another parameter displayed.

The code should determine the shape constant "c" for each beam parameter (four total) and then determine the average value for "c."

The code should create a GUI, allowing the user to predict actual field conditions.

- Create a list to allow the user to choose the input calculation units (AES, Metric, English) as a pop-up menu:
  - AES units should ask for calculations in units of inches, pounds-mass, pounds-force, and pound-force per square inch.
  - Metric units should ask for calculations in units of centimeters, grams, newtons, and pascals.
  - English units should ask for calculations in units of feet, slugs, pounds-force, and pound-force per square foot.
- Create a list to allow the user to choose the beam material as a pop-up menu.
- Request correct input parameters in the selected unit system from the user as edit text boxes.
- Create an error message if the data entered are outside the allowable range. (If the input parameters are outside the range of those tested—for example, if the user enters a beam length of 50 feet—a warning should appear to tell the user the parameters exceed the acceptable range.)
- The user should be able to choose to enter the load or deflection as a pop-up menu. Then:
  - If the load is entered, the program will predict the deflection.
  - If the maximum deflection is entered, the program will predict the maximum load.

It is suggested, for efficiency, you examine ways to use functions throughout your code.

Written Section

Each team must submit a final written communication, including the following components:

- Discussion of the method used to determine the mathematical model:

$$K = cE^m W^n T^p L^q$$

including a set of sample figures to illustrate the method used to determine the exponent for one parameter (one plot of force, deflection; one plot of stiffness, chosen parameter illustrating logarithmic axis).
- Table showing the resulting exponents m, n, p, and q, and the shape constant c.
- A summary table that compares predicted load or deflection, actual results, and error calculation.
- Recommendation as to the optimal beam configuration and total cost that allows all the instruments to be installed for the EWB project. Be sure to justify your selection and explain WHY other choices are not better.

For the submission format, each team may choose or may be assigned by your instructor one of the following options. The written portion will be graded on neatness, organization, spelling/grammar/mechanics, formatting of embedded graphs, and strength of conclusions.

Written Option One: Short Report

A report template, provided electronically and shown in Section 4.4 in your textbook, must be used.

Written Option Two: Poster

A poster template, provided electronically and shown in Section 4.4 in your textbook, must be used.

Written Option Three: PowerPoint Presentation

A PowerPoint presentation using voice-over should be developed to address the requirements given above. Information on developing a presentation is given in your textbook in Section 4.1, and the accompanying online slides discuss voice-over.

APPENDIX A

Part I: Model Development

Model: The model should take the form of $K = cE^m W^n T^p L^q$

Model Parameter	Value	Verified by/on
Exponent m on (E) parameter		
Exponent n on (W) parameter		
Exponent p on (T) parameter		
Exponent q on (L) parameter		
Value and units of constant c		

Part II: Model Verification

Testing Results: Fill in the chart below during actual testing. You will be given a maximum of six beams, forming a combination of beams to test under various loading conditions and beams to test under various deflection conditions.

Test	Beam Parameters			Deflection Achieved	
Load Applied	Length	Width	Thickness	Prediction	Actual
1					
2					
3					

Test	Beam Parameters			Load Required	
Deflection	Length	Width	Thickness	Prediction	Actual
1					
2					
3					

Prediction Verified by: _____

Actual Results Verified by: _____

STATISTICAL ANALYSIS: CONFIGURATION MATTERS

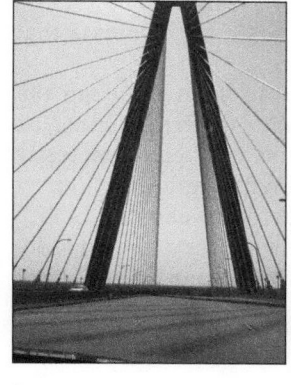

The Cooper River Bridge connects Charleston and Mount Pleasant, SC. The cable-stayed bridge has a main span of 1,546 feet, the second longest cable stay bridge in the Western Hemisphere.

[Photos courtesy of E. Stephan]

Our engineering firm has been contacted to test prototypes of bridge struts that will be part of a new bridge design. The design utilizes prefabricated metal–carbon composite struts that are bonded into the desired design configuration on site. The goal of this project is to test three different configurations and recommend a design for a new bridge.

GRAND CHALLENGE FOR ENGINEERING: RESTORE AND IMPROVE URBAN INFRASTRUCTURE

One of the 14 National Academy of Engineering Grand Challenges is **Restore and Improve Urban Infrastructure.** According to the NAE website (www.engineeringchallenges.org):

> "It is no secret that America's infrastructure, along with those of many other countries, is aging and failing, and that funding has been insufficient to repair and replace it. Engineers of the 21st century face the formidable challenge of modernizing the fundamental structures that support civilization.
>
> The problem is particularly acute in urban areas, where growing populations stress society's support systems, and natural disasters, accidents, and terrorist attacks threaten infrastructure safety and security . . . solutions to these problems must be designed for sustainability, giving proper attention to environmental and energy-use considerations . . . along with concern for the aesthetic elements that contribute to the quality of life."
>
> "Rebuilding and enhancing urban infrastructure faces problems beyond the search for engineering solutions. Various policies and political barriers must be addressed and overcome. Funding for infrastructure projects has been hopelessly inadequate in many areas, as the American Society of Civil Engineers' "report card" documented. And the practice of letting infrastructure wear out before replacing it, rather than incorporating technological improvements during its lifetime, only exacerbates the problems."

The goal of this textbook project is to test three different configurations, and recommend a design for a new bridge.

STRUT DESIGN AND CONSTRUCTION

Data will be collected in class according to the specific instructions provided for you by your professor, or sample data will be provided in an Excel workbook.

All prototypes of the bridge struts must be constructed utilizing the following specifications:

- Only the glue provided may be used. No additional materials, such as adhesive, tape, and caulk may be used.
- Five prototypes of three different bridge strut designs are to be built according to the designs shown below. Other strut design prototypes will not be included.
- The bridge strut spans an open distance of 1 foot; the total length of the bridge strut may not be less than 1 foot, 6 inches, and may not exceed 2 feet.
- The bridge strut ends will be clamped to the supporting surfaces.
- The prototypes should be allowed to dry for at least 48 hours prior to testing.
- The bridge must accommodate a bucket with a wire handle for testing.

The bridge strut prototypes utilize the following testing method:

- The magnitude of applied load at failure will be determined by measuring the mass in the container hung on the bridge, using a scale, recorded in units of grams.
- A strut will be considered to fail when its deflection from horizontal reaches 1 inch or when the strut cracks or breaks.

Flush: Staggered:

Stacked:

DATA ANALYSIS

Workbook

Each team must submit a final workbook, including the following components:

- Data analysis on each design compiled for all given data for all three designs:
  - Raw data for each trial
  - Average
  - Median
  - Standard deviation
  - Minimum and maximum

- Determine the maximum and minimum values that define the range of two and three standard deviations from the average (plus and minus).
- Use unique conditional formatting on all three designs for the following conditions:
  - For cells outside of two but less than three standard deviations on the low side of the average.
  - For cells outside of two but less than three standard deviations on the high side of the average.
  - For cells outside of three standard deviations on either side of the average.

- For each design, write a conditional statement that determines the following:
  - If the average for the team is within two standard deviations on either side of the mean, leave the cell blank.
  - If the average for the team is outside of two but less than three standard deviations on the low side of the average, show the word "Low."
  - If the average for the team is outside of but less than three standard deviations on the high side of the average, show the word "High."
  - If the average for the team is outside of three standard deviations on either side of the average, show the words "WAY OFF!"

- Three separate worksheets, one for each design, of the compiled data shown as a:
  - Histogram
  - Cumulative Distribution Function (CDF)

The workbook will be graded for neatness, organization, unit consistency, and proper plots. It should be a proper workbook, containing heading information on every page.

Written Section

Each team must submit a final written communication, including the following components:

- A discussion of:
  - Any outliers (two standard deviations away from the average).
  - The upper load limit for each design.
  - Stick count per bridge and cost comparison; assume each stick represents a strut made of metal-carbon composite, costing $500 each, and the cost of the glue, which represents the bonding agent for the composite struts, is negligible.
  - Final design choice and justification.
- Determine the optimal strut design to recommend, answering the following questions:
  - What is the recommended maximum load for each design?
  - Which designs can withstand a load imposed by a mass of 4 pounds-mass 90% of the time?
  - At what load would you expect 20% of the bridge struts for each design to fail?
  - Which design has the highest load to cost ratio?

For the submission format, each team may choose or may be assigned by your instructor one of the following options. The written portion will be graded on neatness, organization, spelling/grammar/mechanics, formatting of embedded graphs, and strength of conclusions.

Written Option One: Short Report

A report template, provided electronically and shown in Section 4.4 in your textbook, must be used.

Written Option Two: Poster

A poster template, provided electronically and shown in Section 4.4 in your textbook, must be used.

Written Option Three: PowerPoint Presentation

A PowerPoint presentation using voice-over should be developed to address the requirements given above. Information on developing a presentation is given in your textbook in Section 4.1, and the accompanying online slides discuss voice-over.

MATLAB MINI-PROJECT: ADVANCED PERSONALIZED LEARNING

Many textbooks used in engineering disciplines use online assessment tools—including those produced by our publisher, Pearson, that have research-backed data that show that students perform better on examinations, work more efficiently, have better evidence of problem solving transfer—and even cheat less on their homework—when using online systems for completing algorithmic homework and assignments that provide rich, interactive feedback to students.

[Photo courtesy of E. Stephan]

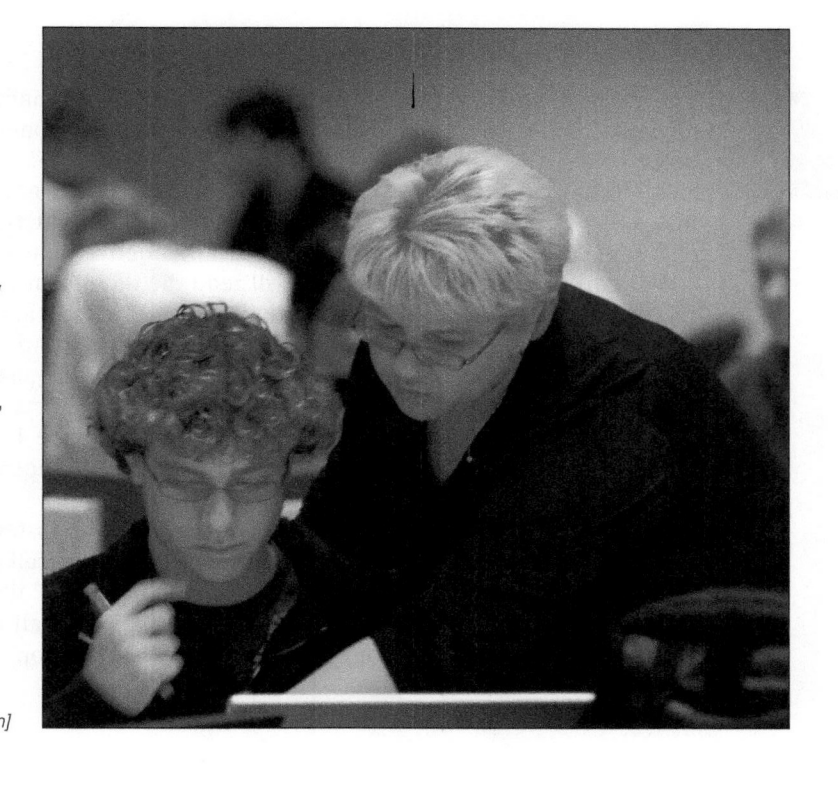

One of the Grand Challenges for Engineering, according to the National Academy of Engineering, is **Advance Personalized Learning.** According to a study published by the American Society for Engineering Education, undergraduate enrollment in engineering programs has increased 14% in the last 10 years. However, with more students interested in engineering, many engineering departments and programs that serve those students have not grown proportionally, so class sizes and student-to-faculty ratios have both increased. In addition, research on education has shown that even in a single classroom, many students have different learning styles, so the traditional one-size-fits-all approach to teaching and learning is quickly being replaced with more "personalized" learning systems. Multidisciplinary research in fields like neuroscience, intelligent systems, and education will help steer the future of developing future personalized learning systems.

PROBLEM STATEMENT

In this project, you will build a program to provide personalized feedback based on student performance and participation on different components in a first-year engineering course. In the provided Microsoft Excel workbook, there are two different sheets—"Students" contains a list of all students and their grades on different assignments, and "Assignments" contains a list of each assignment, the textbook section that assignment covered, as well as a list of recommended activities for the student.

We want to write a program that will read the data from the Excel workbook and allow the instructor to provide personalized feedback by analyzing their responses. There should be two modes of operation. First, your program should give the user the menu option to look up a specific student by typing their username as a string and displaying their personalized feedback in MATLAB's Command Window, or reporting an error message if the student is not found in the grade book. In addition to the Personalized Feedback Criteria listed below, the report should also contain the students' name, username, and overall grade.

The second menu option is to process the entire class roster and write a new Excel file that contains only students who have a calculated overall grade less than 70. The Excel workbook should contain a sheet, "Flagged Students," that has three columns of information: the students' name, username, and their overall numerical grade so far. Sample output and a screenshot of the resulting "intervention" file are included below.

Personalized Feedback Criteria:

- **Participation:** If the student has missed more than three days of class, your program should display something in the command window that recommends they attend class more often. Note that the attendance information is stored in columns labeled Day 1–Day 26 and absences are marked with 0's; any number greater than 0 is considered present or excused.
- **Assignment Performance:** If any score on an assignment is less than 70, your code should look up the section coverage and display a recommendation for review for every assignment completed that meets the criteria. Note that assignment grades are located in columns labeled A1–A13.
- **Exam Performance:** For the first exam in the course, the scores on each individual question are recorded in columns EQ1–EQ16, where EQ1 corresponds to Exam Question 1, EQ2 corresponds to Exam Question 2, etc. The overall weighted exam score is in the "Exam Grade" column. If the student missed more than half of the

points available on each question, your program should look up and display the recommended items for review.

Questions 1–8, 12–13, and 15 were worth 5 points each; all remaining questions were worth 20 points each.

■ **Overall Grade:** The overall grade should be determined using the following rubric, and scaled out of the current points possible:

- Assignments are worth 1% each
- Exams are worth 25% each

For example, if 5 assignments and one exam had been completed, the grade would be the total points earned divided by 30, displayed as a percentage.

HELPFUL FUNCTIONS

Comparing Strings: `strcmp` and `strcmpi`

In order to compare strings, you will need to use the string comparison function, `strcmp`, or the case-insensitive (e.g., dbowman and DBOWMAN are equivalent) string comparison function `strcmpi`. The syntax is simple:

```
A='dbowman'; B='DBOWMAN';
if strcmp(A,B)==1
% this is FALSE
        fprintf('These variables are equivalent')
end
```

```
A='dbowman'; B='DBOWMAN';
if strcmpi(A,B)==1
% this is TRUE
        fprintf('These variables are equivalent')
end
```

For more information: http://www.mathworks.com/help/techdoc/ref/strcmp.html.

All MATLAB codes should include a proper header, including your name, course/section, date, problem statement, documentation on all variables used in the program/function, and any assumptions made in the design of your algorithm. All MATLAB codes should contain an adequate number of comments throughout the code.

SAMPLE OUTPUT

The results shown below are a SAMPLE ONLY and are not necessarily the result you will achieve by correctly conducting the analysis.

```
Type the student's username: custu1

Student Name:  LAST1 FIRST1
Student Username:  CUSTU1

Days Missed:
Total Absences:  0
```

```
Recommended review exam question 8:  Grade: 0 out of 5 points
- Ch 18.1 - 18.2:                     Read: pages 519 - 523
- Ch 18.1 - 18.2:                     Watch: online materials for 18.1 - 18.2
- Ch 18.1 - 18.2:                     Recommend: p. 567: 14, 15

Recommended review exam question 13:  Grade: 0 out of 5 points
- Ch 18.1 - 18.2:                     Read: pages 519 - 523
- Ch 18.1 - 18.2:                     Watch: online materials for 18.1 - 18.2
- Ch 18.1 - 18.2:                     Recommend: p. 567: 14, 15
** OVERALL GRADE:                     91.3
```

UMBRELLA PROJECT

MATLAB MINI-PROJECT: SECURING CYBERSPACE

Creating secure cyber systems is essential since so much of our critical utilities, finances, and even entertainment relies on secure networks. In 2011, Sony's PlayStation Network, a gaming and digital media service used by devices like the PlayStation 3 and other Sony media devices, suffered a long-term outage due to an illegal intrusion by hackers who gained access to personal information of Sony's customers, impacting over 77 million registered accounts—the largest security breach in history. According to Sony, the cost of the security breach and network outage was over $171 million dollars.

BACKGROUND

One of the 14 NAE Grand Challenges is **Advance Health Informatics**. Medical records today are plagued by mixtures of old technologies like paper and new technologies like computers and Tablet PCs. Computerized records are often incompatible, using different programs for different kinds of data, even within the same hospital! Sharing information over networks complicates things even further because of differences in computer systems, data recording rules, and network security concerns for protecting patient privacy.

In addition to Advancing Health Informatics, another one of the 14 NAE Grand Challenges is **Secure Cyberspace**. Modern communication devices like smartphones and computers, as well as communication protocols like web, phone, text messaging, e-mail, and instant messaging are all heavily used by the average consumer to do work and keep in touch with friends and family—every day. In addition, many companies and government agencies rely on these cyber utilities to conduct everyday work, so protection of cyberspace will prevent or reduce disruptions of essential services and minimize problems with stolen data like identity theft.

With secure networks and standards for electronic medical records, work to address these two Grand Challenges will greatly advance the practice of medicine globally and will help to improve the quality of living for everyone.

PROJECT A: ROTATION ENCODING AND DECODING

The purpose of encoding data is to hide the words from plain text by shifting the letters by a certain number of characters. This type of encoding is known as a Caesar cipher, named after Julius Caesar who used this trick to communicate coded information to his generals. For example, if we shifted (or sometimes called rotated) the characters up by three in the word "dog," the "d" would become "g," "o" would become "r," and "g" would become "j," or "grj." Once a character hits the end of the alphabet, it will wrap around to the beginning of the sequence—for example, "hazy" with a rotation of three would be "kdcb." To decode a word coded with a Ceasar cypher, you need to rotate the opposite direction. For example, "wljhu" decoded with a rotation of three would be "tiger."

For this assignment, your encoder and decoder functions must accept two arguments—the string and the rotation number, and return the encoded or decoded string. For storing encoded data in an Excel workbook, you might want to consider storing the encoded text and the rotation number in separate cells.

PROJECT B: STEGANOGRAPHIC ENCRYPTION AND DECRYPTION

Steganography is the practice of hiding messages in such a way that no one can detect the original message apart from the original sender and the intended recipient and requires some "key" to interpret the original message. Many different forms of steganography have existed before computers, including concealing messages in Morse code on knitting yarn during World War II in order to pass secret messages without being detected by enemies. Many movies, including *The Da Vinci Code*, have referenced the act of hiding encrypted information within different mediums, including painted pictures. Steganography is one of the original ideas for implementing secure text transfer and storage between computers. Assume we want to encrypt the word "tiger" using a steganographic encryption scheme—the result is one of many possibilities:

Encrypted Text: T3gctkWwb4iV846gsBoe99yr

Key: [5 11 16 20 24]

Note that the 5th, 11th, 16th, 20th, and 24th character in the encrypted text spell the word "tiger" and that there would be no possible way to know that information without the key to unlock the text.

Consider the following:

Encrypted Text: bm2dUo61Lo1L52sb9KSe

Key: [2 6 10 15 20]

If you pull out the 2nd, 6th, 10th, 15th, and 20th characters, you will discover the hidden word is "moose".

Here is another example:

Encrypted Text: 26Hy2t52x9bi77rSHgVeYLu2rr7R DypTcs9uEWVb

Key: [6 12 18 20 25 29 34 37 41]

This encrypted text contains the words "tiger cub." Note that between each character there are between 1 and 10 random uppercase, lowercase, or numbers separating the important text. The space between tiger and cub is given as the space character in the encrypted text, and other special characters (like dashes or commas) should be included in the same way.

For this assignment, your encryption function must accept one argument—the string to be hidden, and return two arguments—the encrypted text and the "key" for the text—for each line of text required. For example, for this assignment, there would be six encoded strings (for the name, gender, etc.) and six keys, so you would need to call the encryption function six times to generate both. For the decryption function, your function must accept two arguments—the encrypted text and the "key," and return one argument—the decoded text. For storing encrypted data in an Excel workbook, you might want to consider storing the encrypted text and the key in two or more cells in the worksheet.

PROBLEM STATEMENT

You work for a biomedical technology firm developing a standardized suite of software for use at every hospital across the world. As part of the software suite, your job is to develop the interface and secure file format in order to store medical information in an efficient, but safe manner.

To do this, your team is required to develop a program to store or read medical data in a Microsoft Excel workbook. Each patient must have their medical data stored as a row in a single Microsoft Excel worksheet within the workbook and all of the data must be stored in a "secure" fashion. Your team must also write functions to (a) encode or (b) encrypt the medical data before storing in the workbook, as well as functions to (a) decode or (b) decrypt the medical data to display the patient information when queried by the user. You will be assigned by your professor to complete either Project A (the creation of an encoder and decoder) or Project B (encrypter and decrypter).

DESIGN CRITERIA

Code

Each team must create the following programs/functions in MATLAB:

PGM_TEAM.m—the main interface (program) to allow the user to choose to create a new patient in the command window or read patient information from a Microsoft Excel workbook. The resulting data, from either method, should display in the command window using formatted output. Finally, the program should create a workbook that contains (as (a) encoded or (b) encrypted data):

- Patient name (text)
- Patient gender (text)
- Patients data of birth (YYYY-MM-DD) (text)
- Number of children (number)
- List of allergies (text)
- List of drug prescriptions (text)

- For Project A: Encode/Decode:
  - **Encoder_TEAM.m:** A function that implements a simple character rotation encoding scheme.
  - **Decoder_TEAM.m:** A function that implements a simple character rotation decoding scheme.
- For Project B: Encrypt/Decrypt:
  - **Encrypt_TEAM.m:** A function that implements a simple steganographic encryption algorithm.
  - **Decrypt_TEAM.m:** A function that will decrypt the encrypted text created by the Encrypt_TEAM function.

In all program names, the TEAM stands for your team identifier, as given by your instructor. All MATLAB codes should include a proper header, including all your team member names, course/section, date, problem statement, documentation on all variables used in the program/function, and any assumptions made in the design of your algorithm. All MATLAB codes should contain an adequate number of comments throughout the code.

Microsoft Excel Workbook

In addition to the MATLAB code, your team should design a Microsoft Excel workbook to contain the information required by the program, as well as any other information your code might need to display the user information. Before you submit your code, the workbook your team submits should contain the following patients:

Patient: LUKE SKYWALKER	Patient: LEIA ORGANA	Patient: HAN SOLO
Gender: Male	Gender: Female	Gender: Male
DOB: 1965-11-05	DOB: 1973-10-13	DOB: 1965-12-15
Children: 2	Children: 0	Children: 1
Allergies: Grass, Mold	Allergies: *none*	Allergies: Carbonite, Wookie dander
Prescriptions: Zocor®, Daforce	Prescriptions: *none*	Prescriptions: Cymbalta®

ASCII CHARACTERS

All text and characters stored in MATLAB and other computer programming languages are represented as ASCII (American Standard Code for Information Exchange) characters. Consider the following assignment statement:

```
m='dog'
```

You might have noticed that if you accidentally use a %f control character in an fprintf statement when you are trying to display a string, you might see something like this:

```
>>fprintf('The animal is a %.0f\n',m)
The animal is a 100
The animal is a 111
The animal is a 103
```

The reason for this strange output is due to the fact that MATLAB interprets the characters as their ASCII decimal values, rather than their intended character representation:

```
>> fprintf('The animal is a %s\n',m)
The animal is a dog
```

The table below shows each ASCII character and the corresponding decimal value for each letter or number. Note that there are many more characters available in the full set of ASCII values (http://www.asciitable.com/) but for the encoder, we only need to worry about uppercase, lowercase, and numerical values.

Character	A	B	C	D	E	F	G	H	I	J	K	L	M
Value	65	66	67	68	69	70	71	72	73	74	75	76	77

Character	N	O	P	Q	R	S	T	U	V	W	X	Y	Z
Value	78	79	80	81	82	83	84	85	86	87	88	89	90

Character	a	b	c	d	e	f	g	h	i	j	k	l	m
Value	97	98	99	100	101	102	103	104	105	106	107	108	109

Character	n	o	p	q	r	s	t	u	v	w	x	y	z
Value	110	111	112	113	114	115	116	117	118	119	120	121	122

Character	0	1	2	3	4	5	6	7	8	9
Value	48	49	50	51	52	53	54	55	56	57

Note that we actually change a string by adding or replacing values in a string by treating a string character like a vector of numbers. For example, if we want to shift the "o" in the word "dog" stored in variable "m" to create the word "dug":

```
m(2)=m(2)+6
```

Likewise, we could replace a character in a string by typing an ASCII value directly, so if we want to change the current value in "m" to display the word "dig," we could type:

```
m(2)=105
```

HELPFUL FUNCTIONS

■ **char:** If you want to convert a decimal value to a corresponding ASCII character, you will want to use the char function. For example:

```
X=[char(97),char(103),char(101)]
```

will store the string "age" in the variable X.

■ **randi(x):** If you want to generate a random positive whole/integer number, the randi function will generate a number between 1 and x, the input argument. For example, if you call randi(5), you will randomly generate a 1, 2, 3, 4, or 5. This function might be useful in the encryption function for generating random uppercase, lowercase, or numerical characters.

MATLAB MINI-PROJECT: DO YOU WANT TO PLAY A GAME?

Video games have existed in some capacity since 1947 when Thomas T. Goldsmith Jr. and Estle Ray Mann designed a "Cathode Ray Tube Amusement Device" that allowed the player to control a dot on the screen of a television.

[Photo courtesy of E. Stephan]

BACKGROUND

While not directly addressing a specific engineering Grand Challenge, video games actually have some positive effects on video game players, including better hand-eye coordination and visuomotor skills. Video games are often exploited as a tool for education, especially simulation-based games like Sim City, which has been shown to improve strategic thinking and planning skills.

Card games, on the other hand, have existed as early as the ninth century during the Tang Dynasty, where games were played using different leaves. The modern card game with four suits originated in France in approximately 1480, and the contents of the deck of cards have only had a few changes since then, including the addition of the "Ace" and "Joker" cards.

DESIGN CRITERIA

For this project, your team is required to implement any card game using MATLAB.

- All selections ("Hit," "Stand," "Do you want to play again?," etc.) should be done using the menu function. Any numerical or text input may be done with input functions. All inputs (using either menu or input functions) must be validated using `while` loops.
- Your game must implement a real card game. You may choose any **reasonable** card game except overly trivial games like **War** or **52 pick-up**. Acceptable games allow the player to discard and/or draw cards from the deck. For a comprehensive list of card games, visit http://www.pagat.com/alpha.html. Your code should clearly explain to the player which game is being played and any special "house" rules that apply.
- Your card game should only involve one human player. The person running your code may play against computer players, generated by your code. Your instructor will require one or more of the following options required for your project:
  - **Option 1:** Your game does NOT need to display cards graphically (output to the Command Window is fine—e.g., "You drew the Queen of Hearts. Cards in your hand: three of Spades, Queen of Hearts, Ace of Clubs"), but you will earn bonus points if you figure out a way to allow the user to select/see their cards graphically.
  - **Option 2:** Your game should include a GUI to allow the user to press cards to select/discard/etc. The following link contains card images that are free for you to use in your code: http://www.jfitz.com/cards/
- As soon as the game is over, the user must be able to select whether they want to play again using a menu. If the player chooses to play again, the Command Window should clear and the game should start again.
- *Hint*: If you need to generate a random number in your program, look up the `randi` built-in function.

Code

Each team must create the following programs/functions in MATLAB:

- **MP3_TEAM.m**—the main interface (program) to allow the user to play your card game, where TEAM is your team identifier as assigned by your instructor.

You may create any additional functions, but you must include your TEAM identifier in each function name.

All MATLAB codes should include a proper header, including all your team member names, course/section, date, problem statement, documentation on all variables used in the program/function, and any assumptions. All MATLAB codes should contain an adequate number of comments throughout the code.

Grade Scaling

The difficulty of the game your team attempts will be accounted for in the grading of your project.

- 1.0 multiplier: Straightforward games that calculate scores based on card faces like Blackjack.
- 1.1 multiplier: Games that require your code to calculate hands for two or more "computer" players like Euchre.
- 1.2 multiplier: Games that require calculating scores using hand ranking like Poker (flush, straight, pairs, three of a kind, etc.).

This multiplier will be weighted on your final project grade — if your calculated score is 80 and you implemented a Poker game, your overall score would be 80*1.2 = 96.

UMBRELLA PROJECT

MATLAB PROJECT: IMAGE PROCESSING

Image-processing applications have enabled computers to recognize differences and segments in images, websites like Facebook to recognize people in pictures, and cell phones to be able to serve as bar code or QR scanners. While some of these actions seem trivial to the human eye, there's a significant amount of computations required in the background for these simple actions to occur.

[Photo courtesy of E. Stephan]

Your firm has been contacted by a fastener company that needs a device to count the number of nuts and bolts on an assembly line. Cameras are located above the assembly line and take pictures periodically of the contents within the view of the camera.

PROBLEM STATEMENT

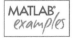

Develop a MATLAB function to count the number of nuts and bolts within the current view of a camera on an assembly line. You are given test images to use for the development of your function.

- You must create four MATLAB functions to count the number of nuts and bolts using:
  - Function 1: MATLAB built-in functions
  - Function 2: No built-in function to perform image erosion
  - Function 3: No built-in function to perform image thresholding
  - Function 4: No built-in function to perform image erosion or thresholding
- Using the four functions, determine which function performs best on a single laptop. Record the time it takes for each function to execute.
- Choose the best performing function and execute it on each team member's laptop to determine the best performing laptop. Record the execution time, laptop model, processor information, and RAM size for each test.
- Choose the best performing laptop. Using the best performing function on the best performing laptop, record the execution time for the following:
  - Different resolution images (three images)
  - Different nut/bolt arrangements (three images)
- Propose a solution to the customer based on efficiency of the software and the company's design specification.

DESIGN CRITERIA

Code

Save each image-processing function as a separate file with the following naming scheme:

- Using MATLAB built-in functions (saved as nutsbolts_TEAM.m)
- No built-in function to perform image erosion (saved as nutsbolts_no_e_TEAM.m)
- No built-in function to perform image thresholding (saved as nutsbolts_no_t_ TEAM.m)
- No built-in function to perform image erosion or thresholding (saved as nutsbolts_ no_e_or_t_TEAM.m)

where TEAM is your team identifier as assigned by your instructor.

Written Section

Each team must submit a final written communication, including the following components:

- Discussion of determination of the most efficient function and hardware configuration.
- Sample figures to illustrate the method used to determine the optimum configuration.
- Total cost analysis for each function developed for the client.
- Discussion of the performance of your function as more nuts and bolts are within the view of the camera, including a proper plot of the relationship between execution time the number of nuts and bolts in the image.
- Discussion of the performance of your function using an image with a higher resolution including a proper plot of the relationship between the execution time and the total number of pixels in an image.
- Discussion of the algorithm developed to determine whether an object is a nut or bolt.
- Your instructor will provide a list of speed and cost requirements. You will recommend the best configurations to meet the specifications required.
- Function cost and performance analysis.
- Computer performance analysis.

For the submission format each team may choose or may be assigned by your instructor one of the following options. The written portion will be graded on neatness, organization, spelling/grammar/mechanics, formatting of embedded graphs, and strength of conclusions.

Written Option One: Short Report

A report template, provided electronically and shown in Section 4.4 in your textbook, must be used.

Written Option Two: Poster

A poster template, provided electronically and shown in Section 4.4 in your textbook, must be used.

Written Option Three: PowerPoint Presentation

A PowerPoint presentation using voice-over should be developed to address the requirements given above. Information on developing a presentation is given in your textbook in Section 4.1, and the accompanying online slides discuss voice-over.

Project Website

Each team must develop and maintain a project website that contains pages dedicated to:

- **A "home" page:** includes a short blurb about the project.
- **Project definition:** a description of your project and the charge your team must accomplish.
- **Team information:** an introduction of each team member (personal) and description of their role within your team (professional).
- **To do list:** a continually updated list that includes an owner, description of the item, due date, and status of whether that item is complete or incomplete.
- **"Daily" updates:** a "blog" update posted (M, W, F) by **ONE** member of the team that documents the events of meetings, who, what, and when every item on the "to do" list is being developed.
- **Weekly updates:** a "blog" update of the big picture of your project development. **These should be INDIVIDUALLY posted by EVERY member of the team by Fridays at 5:00 p.m.** Each team member is required to post a weekly update answering the following questions:

  - What were the major accomplishments for your team last week?
  - What does your team plan to accomplish by this Friday?
  - What were the "road bumps" encountered by your team last week and how did you solve these problems?
  - What problems do you anticipate this week?

- **Calendar:** an embedded calendar of relevant due dates for the project, to-do items, and group meetings.

Each team may use the Google Site Project template or develop your own page from scratch. The site must be secure (only your team + your instructor should have access to your project site) and editable by any member of your team. This security is built in to Google Sites, but you are free to explore alternatives. For more information on how to set up, use, or share Google Sites or use Templates with Google Sites, please refer to the following link: http://sites.google.com/site/projectwikitemplate_en/.

UMBRELLA PROJECT

MATLAB PROJECT: DMV LINES

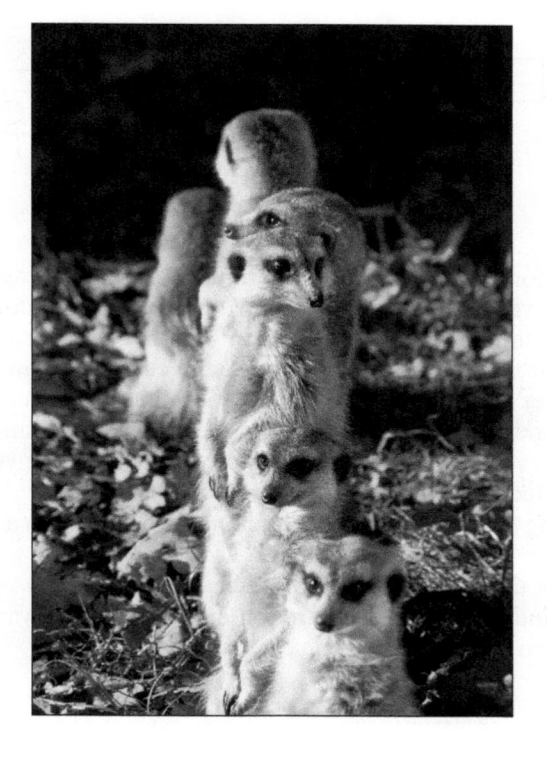

Queuing research occurs in diverse fields like computer networking to make digital communication faster, traffic routing to help people move around faster, all the way to the design of theme parks to allow customers to move around the park without standing in too many long lines.

Your firm has been contacted by the Department of Motor Vehicles (DMV) to conduct an analysis of their current customer service performance and recommend changes that would benefit the service time of each customer. To perform the analysis, your team is provided with a list of arrivals to the DMV over the span of three days. Your team must determine the ideal arrangement of the DMV in order to guarantee the smallest average waiting time for each customer.

PROBLEM STATEMENT

You must conduct six analyses of different first come, first serve queuing schemes:

- Two lines, each capable of holding eight people;
- Four lines, each capable of holding four people;
- Eight lines, each capable of holding two people;
- Two lines, each separated by length of service time, holding eight people each;
- Four lines, each separated by length of service time, holding four people each;
- Eight lines, each separated by length of service time, holding two people each.

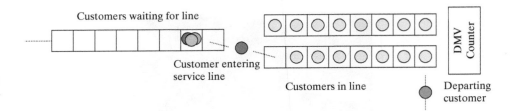

Figure 1 Example of "two lines, each capable of holding eight people."

- The best performing queuing scheme minimizes the average wait time of the customer and serves the most customers. We define wait time of a customer as the sum of the service times of the people in front of that customer when they first enter the line. Note that wait time does not include the customer's own service time.
- If the customer arrives at the DMV and every line is full, the time the customer waits for a line to open up must be included in the total waiting time for that customer. The DMV closes every day at 5:00 p.m., so any customers not yet in one of the queues will be "rejected."
- After selecting the best performing queuing scheme, design a system that can be used at the entrance of the DMV to "ticket" each customer.
- In the service time separated queuing schemes your team will want to try different designs for finding the ideal separation criteria (e.g., all waiting times greater than five minutes go in line 1, everyone else in line 2).

DESIGN CRITERIA

Code

Save each queuing scenario as a separate file with the following naming scheme:

- Two lines, each capable of holding eight people—Save as Lines2_8_TEAM.m
- Four lines, each capable of holding four people—Save as Lines4_4_TEAM.m
- Eight lines, each capable of holding two people—Save as Lines8_2_TEAM.m
- Two lines, each separated by service time—Save as SLines2_8_TEAM.m
- Four lines, each separated by service time—Save as SLines4_4_TEAM.m
- Eight lines, each separated by service time—Save as SLines8_2_TEAM.m
- Ticketing system—Save as Ticketing_TEAM.m

where TEAM is your team identifier as assigned by your instructor.

Written Section

Each team must submit a final written communication, including the following components:

- A summary of the project, procedure, and results.
- Discussion of the algorithm designed to separate appointments based on service time.
- Discussion of determination of the most efficient queuing scheme.
- Discussion and a graph (as a proper plot) to illustrate the relationship between the number of lines and the average waiting time.
- Discussion and a graph (as a proper plot) to illustrate the relationship between the different queuing schemes and the average waiting time.
- Questions answered:

  - If it were necessary to make budget cuts, which queuing scheme would be best to ensure that each line is fully utilized, while providing a small waiting time to the customer?
  - If we double the length of each line (in Lines2_8, Lines4_4, and Lines8_2) but retain the original number of lines, would the average waiting time increase, decrease, or stay the same?
  - If we double the length of each line (in SLines2_8, SLines4_4, and SLines8_2) but retain the original number of lines, would the average waiting time increase, decrease, or stay the same?
  - If we double the number of lines (in Lines2_8, Lines4_4, and Lines8_2) but retain the original line capacity, would the average waiting time increase, decrease, or stay the same?
  - If we double the number of lines (in ServiceLines2_8, ServiceLines4_4, and ServiceLines8_2) but retain the original line capacity, would the average waiting time increase, decrease, or stay the same?

For the submission format, each team may choose or may be assigned by your instructor one of the following options. The written portion will be graded on neatness, organization, spelling/grammar/mechanics, formatting of embedded graphs, and strength of conclusions.

Written Option One: Short Report

A report template, provided electronically and shown in Section 4.4 in your textbook, must be used.

Written Option Two: Poster

A poster template, provided electronically and shown in Section 4.4 in your textbook, must be used.

Written Option Three: PowerPoint Presentation

A PowerPoint presentation using voice-over should be developed to address the requirements given above. Information on developing a presentation is given in your textbook in Section 4.1, and the accompanying online slides discuss voice-over.

Project Website

Each team must develop and maintain a project website that contains pages dedicated to:

- **A "home" page:** includes a short blurb about the project.
- **Project definition:** a description of your project and the charge your team must accomplish.
- **Team information:** an introduction of each team member (personal) and description of their role within your team (professional).
- **To do list:** a continually updated list that includes an owner, description of the item, due date, and status of whether that item is complete or incomplete.
- **"Daily" updates:** a "blog" update posted (M, W, F) by **ONE** member of the team that documents the events of meetings, who, what, and when every item on the "to do" list is being developed.
- **Weekly updates:** a "blog" update of the big picture of your project development. **These should be INDIVIDUALLY posted by EVERY member of the team by Fridays at 5:00 p.m.** Each team member is required to post a weekly update answering the following questions:
  - What were the major accomplishments for your team last week?
  - What does your team plan to accomplish by this Friday?
  - What were the "road bumps" encountered by your team last week and how did you solve these problems?
  - What problems do you anticipate this week?
- **Calendar:** an embedded calendar of relevant due dates for the project, to-do items, and group meetings.

Each team may use the Google Site Project template or develop your own page from scratch. The site must be secure (only your team + your instructor should have access to your project site) and editable by any member of your team. This security is built in to Google Sites, but you are free to explore alternatives. For more information on how to set up, use, or share Google Sites or use Templates with Google Sites, please refer to the following link: http://sites.google.com/site/projectwikitemplate_en/.

UMBRELLA PROJECT

MATLAB PROJECT: DESIGNING A BETTER VACUUM

Robotic vacuums and other small electronics often rely on embedded systems that are designed to do only a few different tasks. Hardware on embedded systems is usually designed in a manner that reduces the energy usage requirements of the device, but may suffer operational or speed restrictions as a result.

[Photo courtesy of E. Stephan]

Your team is doing consulting work for an electronics manufacturer that is designing a new line of automatic vacuum robots. These robots are unique because they contain sensing capabilities that can map out the floor plan of a room before they begin cleaning. Your team has been charged with developing the algorithms that will control the different models of robotic vacuums.

PROBLEM STATEMENT

■ The manufacturer plans to develop three models of robotic vacuums:

- The economy robot. This robot should clean 100% of the floor in a floor plan, even if the surface has been detected to be clean. The battery life of the economy robot is poor. A robot with "poor" battery life will be able to clean 250 square feet before recharging.
- The regular robot. This robot should clean 100% of the floor in a floor plan, even if the surface has been detected to be clean. The battery life of the regular robot is average. A robot with "average" battery life will be able to clean 350 square feet before recharging.
- The high-end "intelligent" robot. This robot should only clean the dirty parts of the floor. The battery life of the high-end robot is poor. A robot with "poor" battery life will be able to clean 250 square feet before recharging.

You may assume that it takes every robot 60 seconds to recharge. When the robot's battery is empty, it will travel back to the charge station at a rate of 1 pixel per second. After it is fully charged, it will return to where it left off at a rate of 1 pixel per second (without cleaning on the return path).

■ The "sensing capabilities" of the robot will generate a matrix. You may assume that the manufacturer has a separate interface to generate the matrix, so you will not need to develop the sensor—instead, you will write your code assuming that the matrix is provided by some separate mechanism. Test matrices are provided by the manufacturer in a Microsoft Excel workbook. In addition, a blank floor plan is provided in the workbook for creating your own custom floor plan.

■ Your team will need to export movies of your robot cleaning each of the provided floor plans. The provided Microsoft Excel file with floor plan matrices also contains a blank floor plan so that you can create your own custom floor plan for testing. Upon completion, you should have 12 total movies of your three vacuums cleaning the four different floor plans, all due at the same time as the source code.

FLOOR PLAN MATRIX

The manufacturer has developed a sensing mechanism that will generate a 30×25 matrix of values that represent different values, as defined below. The algorithms developed should use this matrix as the input to clean the floor.

Floor Plan Matrix Values:

- ■ 0   A wall, couch, or any other surface where the vacuum cannot travel
- ■ 4   Clean floor
- ■ 3   Dirty floor
- ■ 2   Charging station
- ■ 1   The current location of the robot in the image

You may assume that the matrix will always be bordered by a wall and the charging station is always in the same location.

DESIGN CRITERIA

Code

It is suggested, for efficiency that you examine ways to use functions throughout your code.

Save each image-processing function as a separate file with the following naming scheme:

- The economy model (saved as economy_TEAM.m).
- The regular model (saved as regular_TEAM.m).
- The high end model (saved as highend_TEAM.m).

You should create a main GUI that will allow the user to select the model, the floor plan to use, and whether or not the code should export a floor plan movie after your vacuum finishes cleaning the floor plan. Save this program as VacuumProject_TEAM.m, where TEAM is your team identifier as assigned by your instructor.

Each robot should display a summary in the command window (after cleaning a floor plan), including the following:

- The ratio of clean floor to dirty floor. For example, "36% of the floor was covered with dirt."
- The area of the floor plan. You may assume that each "pixel" represents a 1 foot × 1 foot tile. "Floor plan surface area: 1,200 square feet."
- The amount of time it took the robot to clean the floor. You may assume that it takes five seconds to clean a single dirty "pixel" on the floor.
- The number of times the robot had to recharge. "The robot had to recharge five times."

PowerPoint Presentation/Video

A PowerPoint presentation using voice-over should be developed to address the requirements given above. Information on developing a presentation is given in your textbook in Section 4.1, and the accompanying online slides discuss voice-over.

Each team must submit a final presentation, including the following components:

- Introduction and background on the project.
- Discussion of the algorithm your team designed for each vacuum model.
- Sample figures to illustrate the performance difference in each model.
- Discussion about who should buy each robot-consider housing size (house, apartment, townhome, dorm), power efficiency (how much power does the robot consume relative to the size of each home?), and time (how long will the robot run in each housing unit?).

The presentation will be graded for neatness, organization, presentation quality, formatting of embedded graphs, and strength of conclusions. As an alternative, your team can create a narrated video and submit it in a common video format (AVI, MOV, etc.)—ask your instructor before using a different format. This narrated PowerPoint should last no longer than five minutes.

Project Website

Each team must develop and maintain a project website that contains pages dedicated to:

- **A "home" page:** includes a short blurb about the project.
- **Project definition:** a description of your project and the charge your team must accomplish.
- **Team information:** an introduction of each team member (personal) and description of their role within your team (professional).
- **To do list:** a continually updated list that includes an owner, description of the item, due date, and status of whether that item is complete or incomplete.
- **"Daily" updates:** a "blog" update posted (M, W, F) by **ONE** member of the team that documents the events of meetings, who, what, and when every item on the "to do" list is being developed.
- **Weekly updates:** a "blog" update of the big picture of your project development. **These should be INDIVIDUALLY posted by EVERY member of the team by Fridays at 5:00 p.m.** Each team member is required to post a weekly update answering the following questions:
  - What were the major accomplishments for your team last week?
  - What does your team plan to accomplish by this Friday?
  - What were the "road bumps" encountered by your team last week and how did you solve these problems?
  - What problems do you anticipate this week?
- **Calendar:** an embedded calendar of relevant due dates for the project, to do items, and group meetings.

Each team may use the Google Site Project template or develop your own page from scratch. The site must be secure (only your team + your instructor should have access to your project site) and editable by any member of your team. This security is built in to Google Sites, but you are free to explore alternatives. For more information on how to set up, use, or share Google Sites or use Templates with Google Sites, please refer to the following link: http://sites.google.com/site/projectwikitemplate_en/.

CREATING IMAGES AND VIDEO IN MATLAB

Assume we read in the first floor plan to a matrix A. In an image, we will refer to the "values" in a matrix as pixels.

To plot the matrix A as an image:

```
imagesc(A)        % display the contents of matrix A
colormap(gray)    % convert the image to a scaled grayscale image.
axis('image')     % resize the plot in the figure to the aspect

                  % ratio of the matrix
axis off          % turn off the axis labels
```

The above segment of MATLAB code will create the image shown in the following page. Note that the wall pixels are black, the shades of gray represent the dirt and the charging station, and white represents the floor. *The shades of gray will differ in your image since you will also be drawing the current location of the robot.*

Image of a floor plan showing the walls, dirt, floor, and charging station (top left) without a robot.

Videos in MATLAB

To follow the path of your robot, you will need to use a couple of MATLAB functions to capture each plot and generate the movie.

getframe

getframe will capture the image currently drawn on the figure and store it into a variable in MATLAB's workspace. Typically, this function is used within a for-loop to capture multiple frames.

```
for i = 1:1:30
    % ...
    imagesc(A);      % display the image
    M(i)=getframe;   % capture the figure
    % ...
end
```

movie

The movie function will allow you to play back the frames stored in the workspace. In the example above, the frames are stored in the variable M.

```
movie(M)
```

To control the speed of the video, you can change the frame rate of the video.

```
movie(M,1,30)
```

The above line of code will play the movie M one time (second argument: 1) at a rate of 30 frames per second (third argument: 30).

movie2avi

movie2avi will allow you to export the video stored in MATLAB's workspace to an AVI video file. AVI files can be embedded in PowerPoint presentations and played on computers without any additional software.

```
movie2avi(M,'MyMovie.avi','fps',30)
```

As an example, the above line of code will export the MATLAB video to a file named "MyMovie.avi" with a frame rate of 30 frames per second.

In order to determine the proper frame rate, you should try to make each video between 45 and 60 seconds long.

COMPREHENSION CHECK ANSWERS

CHAPTER 3

CC 3-1

Product	Computer	Automobile	Bookshelf
Inexpensive	Less than $300	Less than 1/5 the median annual U.S. family income	Less than $30
Small	Folds to the size of a DVD case	Two can fit in a standard parking space	Collapses to the size of a briefcase
Easy to assemble	No assembly; just turn on	All parts easily replaceable	Requires only a screwdriver
Aesthetically pleasing	Body color options available	Looks like the Batmobile©	Blends well with any décor
Lightweight	Less than one pound	Less than one ton	Less than 5% of the weight of the books it can hold
Safe	Immune to malware	Receives 5 star rating in NCAP crash tests	Stable even if top-loaded
Durable	Survives the "Frisbee® test"	200,000 mile warranty	Immune to cat claws
Environmentally friendly	Contains no heavy metals	Has an estimated MPG of at least 50	Made from recycled materials Low VOC finish

CC 3-2

- Decrease aerodynamic drag
  - Remove unnecessary protrusions
  - Redesign body based on wind-tunnel testing
- Decrease weight
  - Use carbon-composite materials
  - Remove unnecessary material
- Increase engine efficiency
  - Use ceramic parts (e.g., valves and pistons) so engine can run hotter, thus more efficiently
  - Change to hybrid design with regenerative braking
  - Limit maximum acceleration if consistent with safety
- Manage friction
  - Improved bearings in wheels, engine, etc.
  - Redesign tires for less slippage on road surface
- Encourage fuel-efficient driving
  - Include displays for real-time and cumulative fuel usage (MPG)

CC 3-3

PAT

Hindrance: Tended to slow the team down due to difficulty understanding things.

Helpful: Always available and willing to do assigned tasks. The individuals who helped explain things to Pat probably developed a deeper understanding of the material in the process, thus this was helpful to them personally, though not to the team directly. Probably the second most useful team member.

CHRIS

Hindrance: Often absent, seldom prepared, seldom contributes, offers excuses for poor performance. Definitely the worst team member.

Helpful: Teaches the other team members about the real world, and how to deal with slackards.

TERRY

Hindrance: Not a team player, impatient, not encouraging to others, wants to dominate the team. Despite cleverness, probably the second worst team member.

Helpful: Solves problems quickly.

ROBIN

Hindrance: No obvious hindrance.

Helpful: The real leader of the group, kept things going, encouraging to weaker members. The most useful team member.

CHAPTER 5

CC 5-1

(a)	Significant figures: 2	Decimal places: 4
(b)	Significant figures: 4	Decimal places: 0
(c)	Significant figures: 3	Decimal places: 2
(d)	Significant figures: 3	Decimal places: 0
(e)	Significant figures: 2	Decimal places: 0 or 3
(f)	Significant figures: 5	Decimal places: 0
(g)	Significant figures: 7	Decimal places: 0
(h)	Significant figures: 5	Decimal places: 3

CC 5-2

- **(a)** −58.9
- **(b)** 247
- **(c)** 2.47
- **(d)** 0.497

CC 5-3

- **(a)** Elevator capacity may require a conservative estimate of 180 pounds.
- **(b)** Serving sizes are usually measured in integer cups, so estimate at 1 cup; but to make sure the bowl is full, round up to 1.3 cups.
- **(c)** If recording, conservative might be to round up to 33 seconds. If it doesn't matter, 30 seconds is fine.

CC 5-4

	Scientific notation:	Engineering notation:
(a)	5.809×10^7	58.083×10^6
(b)	4.581×10^{-3}	4.581×10^{-3}
(c)	4.268×10^7	42.677×10^6

CHAPTER 6

CC 6-1

$H = 15$ ft
$W = 18.5$ ft
$L = 25$ ft

CC 6-2

Objective:

Determine the mass of the gravel in units of kilograms.

Observations:

- Assume the container is full, thus the height of the gravel is 15 feet.
- Assume the gravel is flat on the top and not mounded up.
- Neglect the space between the gravel pieces.

CC 6-3

List of variables and constants:

- ρ = density   [=] lb_m/ft^3 = 97 lb_m/ft^3 —given
- V = volume of container [=] ft^3
- m = mass of gravel   [=] kg
- L = length   [=] ft   = 25 ft—given
- W = width   [=] ft   = 18.5 ft—given
- H = height   [=] ft   = 15 ft—assumed

CC 6-4

Equations:

1. Density in terms of
   mass and volume: $\rho = m/V$
2. Volume of a rectangle: $V = L \times W \times H$
3. Unit conversion: 1 kg $= 2.205$ lb_m

CC 6-5

- First, find the volume of the container; use equation (2)
  $V = L \times W \times H$
- Substituting L, W, and H:
  $V = (25$ ft$)(18.5$ ft$)(15$ ft$) = 6937.5$ ft^3
- Second, find the mass of gravel; use equation (1)
  $\rho = m/V$
- Substituting the density and the volume:
  $(97$ bm$/ft^3) = m$ $(6937.5$ ft$^3)$ $m = 672937.5$ lb_m
- Convert from pound-mass to kilograms:

$$\frac{672{,}937.5\,lb_m}{} \left| \frac{1\,kg}{2.205\,lb_m} \right. = 305{,}881\,kg \cong 306{,}000\,kg$$

CHAPTER 7

CC 7-1

(a) $5 = 10^{-9}$ picoliters
(b) $8 = 10^{-14}$ microliters
(c) $3 = 10^{-19}$ liters

CC 7-2

(a) Incorrect: 5 s
(b) Incorrect: 60 mm
(c) Incorrect: 3,800 mL OR 3.8 L

CC 7-3

5.5 mi

CC 7-4

451 in

CC 7-5

328 ft

CC 7-6

2 km/min

CC 7-7

26 flushes

CC 7-8

84 ft^3

CC 7-9

0.16 m^3

CC 7-10

1042 L

CC 7-11

		Exponents			
Quantity	Units	M	L	T	Θ
Geometric quantities					
Area	ft^2	0	2	0	0
Volume	gal	0	3	0	0
	L	0	3	0	0
Rate quantities					
Flowrate	gal/min	0	3	−1	0
Evaporation	kg/h	1	0	−1	0

CC 7-12

$$1\ \Omega = 1\ \frac{\mathrm{kg\,m^2}}{\mathrm{s^3 A^2}}$$

CC 7-13

$cm^{3/2}$

CC 7-14

(a) 210 Tm
(b) 1.3×10^{11} mi
(c) 1,400 AU
(d) 0.022 light years

CC 7-15

2.72 gal

CHAPTER 8

CC 8-1

13.3 N

CC 8-2

2.2 N

CC 8-3

11 lb$_f$

CC 8-4

$3122\ \dfrac{\mathrm{lb_m}}{\mathrm{ft^2}}$

CC 8-5

1.53

CC 8-6

194.5 K

CC 8-7

$0.000357\ \dfrac{\mathrm{BTU}}{\mathrm{g\,K}}$

CC 8-8

221 in Hg

CC 8-9

1.22 atmW

CC 8-10

220 kPa

CC 8-11

2.4 L

CC 8-12

16.9 m

CC 8-13

20 K

CC 8-14

0.83 hr

CC 8-15

61.3 W

INDEX